Everyday Mathematics®

Teacher's Guide to Games

Grades Pre-K to 6

McGraw Hill Wright Group

The McGraw·Hill Companies

Photo Credits
Phil Martin

Illustration Credits
Yoshi Miyake

Cover Credits
© Chad Baker/Photodisc/Getty Images

www.WrightGroup.com

 **Wright Group**

Copyright © 2010 by The McGraw-Hill Companies, Inc.

Printed in the United States of America.

Send all inquiries to:
Wright Group/McGraw-Hill
P.O. Box 812960
Chicago, IL 60681

ISBN 978-0-07-622014-4
MHID 0-07-622014-1

5 6 7 8 9 QDB 15 14 13 12 11

Contents

PART 1 Using the Games

PART 2 Game Directions

You can use this chart to help you choose games for your students. The **Grades** listed tell where the game appears in the core program. (For differentiation, you may want to look at games designed to be played one or two grades above or below your students' grade.) The **Skills** that students practice in each game are listed. The 🖥 icon indicates games that will be available online and on CD in January 2010.

Game Title	Grade(s)	Skill(s)	Page
Addition Card Draw	2	Adding 3 numbers	2
Addition Spin	1–2	Mental addition	3
Addition Top-It 🖥	K–5	Adding; comparing sums	4
Algebra Election	5–6	Variable substitution; solving equations	6
Angle Race 🖥	3	Recognizing angle measures	8
Angle Tangle	4–6	Estimating and measuring angle size	10
Animal Weight Top-It	1	Adding, subtracting, and comparing 2-digit numbers	11
Array Bingo	2–3	Multiplication with arrays	13
Attribute Spinner Game	K	Choosing blocks based on attributes (color, shape, and size)	15
Attribute Train Game	K–1	Identifying blocks that differ by just one attribute (shape, size, or color)	16
Base-10 Exchange Games 🖥	1–4	Place-value concepts; counting and exchanging blocks	17
Baseball Multiplication 🖥	3–5	Multiplication	19

PART 3 Game Masters

PART 1 Using the Games

Introduction

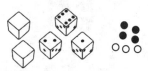

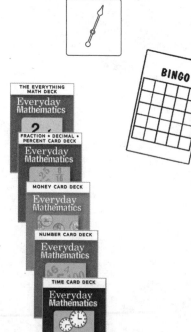

Welcome to *Everyday Mathematics!* Games are an integral part of the *Everyday Mathematics* curriculum, and this *Teacher's Guide to Games* provides all of the information you need to successfully use the *Everyday Mathematics* games in your classroom.

The *Everyday Mathematics* Games Kits provide the materials your students need to play the games. Each kit includes enough materials so that any game that has a gameboard can be played simultaneously by five groups of students.

◆ New Features

- ◆ Each kit includes both new and redesigned gameboards.

- ◆ Separate kits are available for each of Grades 1–6. The Early Childhood kit now addresses both Pre-K and Kindergarten needs.

- ◆ The *Teacher's Guide to Games* now includes directions and Game Masters for all *Everyday Mathematics* 3rd-edition games from Pre-K through Grade 6.

- ◆ All games are aligned to the *Everyday Mathematics* Program Goals for Pre-K through Grade 6. (See page xxx.)

- ◆ Differentiation Options—suggestions for Reteaching, Enrichment, and ELL Support—are included to meet the diverse needs of your students.

- ◆ Online features include:
  - gameboards to use for demonstration
  - access to the *Teacher's Guide to Games*

- ◆ All materials for each kit are now packaged in a durable, reusable plastic tub.

- ◆ Spanish-language gameboards are available separately.

Playing and Managing the Games

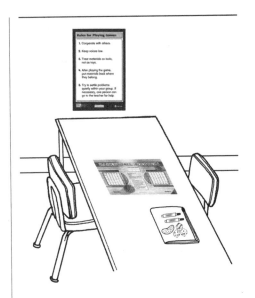

Organizing the Games

- Establish a routine that encourages playing games at least 2 or 3 times per week. Make sure all students have a chance to play.

- Set up game stations where students can rotate to a new station about every 10 minutes. Station time can occur at the beginning or the end of a lesson, during mathematics time, or when a substitute teacher is in the classroom.

- Organize game materials by type in a designated area of the room, or put the materials each group will need in a bag labeled with the name of the game.

Choosing a Game

- To choose a game that meets your students' learning needs, use the Program Goals chart starting on page xxx. You can also refer to the Table of Contents, which lists the skills and the grade levels for which each game is part of the core program.

- Before introducing a new game, read the Readiness notes to see whether there are important prerequisite skills you may need to review. The Readiness notes also describe basic variations that can help your students access the game.

Demonstrating and Monitoring Play

- Demonstrate each new game with the help of volunteers as you or a student reads the directions aloud. Model the use of any Record Sheets, and make sure students understand the object of the game.

- Ask students to consider whether there are any tools they might need to help them play the game. Students who are just beginning to learn multiplication, for example, may need to refer to a Facts Table when they play multiplication games.

- Talk about how students will resolve any disagreements. Consider assigning one student in each group to take charge of the Student Reference Book and to refer to it as needed to clarify rules or to assist with mathematical questions.

- Use the Differentiation Options for Readiness, Enrichment, and ELL Support to modify or adapt the games to your students' needs. Also encourage students to modify the games for a greater challenge, to practice different skills, or simply to have more fun.

Games Kits

There are seven different Games Kits—one for Early Childhood (Pre-Kindergarten and Kindergarten) and one for each of Grades 1–6. Each kit contains a *Teacher's Guide to Games* that includes all of the games in the entire *Everyday Mathematics* curriculum. Each kit has the materials needed for the games in that kit, including card decks, dice, and gameboards for the most popular games. A complete list of the items in each Games Kit follows.

◆ Games Kit Components

Early Childhood Components

- ◆ 1 *Teacher's Guide to Games*
- ◆ 5 copies each of 6 two-sided gameboards
- ◆ 6 gameboard dividers
- ◆ 12 dot-dice
- ◆ 48 blank dice
- ◆ 10 inch cubes
- ◆ 450 counters
- ◆ 5 sets of play money coins
- ◆ 4 sets of play money bills
- ◆ 5 transparent spinners
- ◆ 5 Number Card Decks
- ◆ cardstock dominoes for *Domino Concentration*
- ◆ cardstock monsters for *Monster Squeeze*
- ◆ cardstock cars for *Racing Cars*
- ◆ 1 poster
- ◆ 5 write-on/wipe-off sleeves

Grade 1 Components

- ◆ 1 *Teacher's Guide to Games*
- ◆ 5 copies each of 8 two-sided gameboards
- ◆ 8 gameboard dividers
- ◆ 24 dot-dice
- ◆ 16 blank dice
- ◆ 450 counters
- ◆ 5 sets of play money coins
- ◆ 4 sets of play money bills
- ◆ 5 transparent spinners
- ◆ 5 Everything Math Decks
- ◆ 5 Time Card Decks
- ◆ 5 Money Card Decks
- ◆ cardstock bunnies for *Bunny Hop*
- ◆ cardstock dominoes for *Domino Concentration*
- ◆ cardstock monsters for *Monster Squeeze*
- ◆ 1 poster
- ◆ 5 write-on/wipe-off sleeves

NOTE: To avoid duplication of materials, any manipulatives that are provided with the *Everyday Mathematics* grade-level manipulative kits are not included in the Games Kits (except the Everything Math Deck, dot-dice, and blank dice.)

Grade 2 Components

- 1 *Teacher's Guide to Games*
- 5 copies each of 8 two-sided gameboards
- 8 gameboard dividers
- 24 dot-dice
- 16 blank dice
- 450 counters
- 5 sets of play money coins
- 4 sets of play money bills
- 5 transparent spinners
- 5 Everything Math Decks
- 5 Time Card Decks
- 5 Money Card Decks
- cardstock game cards for *Array Bingo*
- 1 poster
- 5 write-on/wipe-off sleeves

Grade 3 Components

- 1 *Teacher's Guide to Games*
- 5 copies each of 8 two-sided gameboards
- 8 gameboard dividers
- 24 dot-dice
- 16 blank dice
- 450 counters
- 5 sets of play money coins
- 4 sets of play money bills
- 5 transparent spinners
- 5 Everything Math Decks
- 5 Time Card Decks
- 5 Money Card Decks
- cardstock game cards for *Angle Race*
- cardstock game cards for *Array Bingo*
- 5 Bingo Pads
- 1 poster
- 5 write-on/wipe-off sleeves

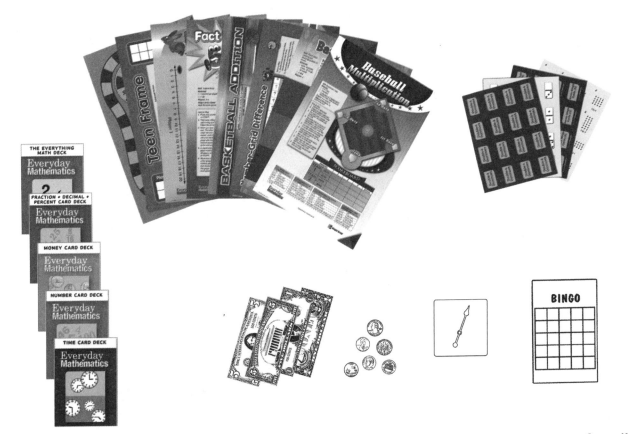

Grade 4 Components

- 1 *Teacher's Guide to Games*
- 5 copies each of 8 two-sided gameboards
- 8 gameboard dividers
- 24 dot-dice
- 16 blank dice
- 450 counters
- 5 transparent spinners
- 5 Everything Math Decks
- 5 Fraction/Decimal/Percent Card Decks
- cardstock game cards for:
  - *Chances Are*
  - *Fraction Of*
  - *Grab Bag*
  - *Polygon Pair-Up*
  - *Rugs and Fences*
- 5 Bingo Pads
- 1 poster
- 5 write-on/wipe-off sleeves

Grade 5 Components

- 1 *Teacher's Guide to Games*
- 5 copies each of 8 two-sided gameboards
- 8 gameboard dividers
- 24 dot-dice
- 16 blank dice
- 450 counters
- 5 transparent spinners
- 5 Everything Math Decks
- 5 Fraction/Decimal/Percent Card Decks
- cardstock game cards for:
  - *Algebra Election*
  - *Build-It*
  - *First to 100*
  - *Fraction Of*
  - *Fraction Action, Fraction Friction*
  - *Polygon Capture*
  - *Spoon Scramble*
  - *3-D Shape Sort*
- 5 Bingo Pads
- 5 Four-Quadrant Coordinate Grid Pads
- 1 poster
- 5 write-on/wipe-off sleeves

Grade 6 Components

◆ 1 *Teacher's Guide to Games*
◆ 5 copies each of 8 two-sided gameboards
◆ 8 gameboard dividers
◆ 24 dot-dice
◆ 16 blank dice
◆ 450 counters
◆ 5 transparent spinners
◆ 5 Everything Math Decks
◆ 5 Fraction/Decimal/Percent Card Decks
◆ cardstock game cards for:
  • *Algebra Election*
  • *Build-It*
  • *First to 100*
  • *Fraction Action, Fraction Friction*
  • *Landmark Shark*
  • *Polygon Capture*
  • *Solution Search*
  • *Spoon Scramble*
  • *3-D Shape Sort*
◆ 5 Four-Quadrant Coordinate Grid Pads
◆ 1 poster
◆ 5 write-on/wipe-off sleeves

Rules for Playing Games

1. Cooperate with others.
2. Keep voices low.
3. Treat materials as tools, not as toys.
4. After playing the game, put materials back where they belong.
5. Try to settle problems quietly within your group. If necessary, one person can go to the teacher for help.

BINGO

◆ The *Teacher's Guide to Games*

Sections

Part 1: Tips for managing games, descriptions of materials, information about skills and Program Goals addressed by each game.

▼

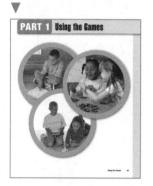

PART 1 Using the Games

PART 2 Game Directions

▲

Part 2: Game directions in alphabetical order for all of the *Everyday Mathematics* games.

Part 3: Game Masters in the order in which the games are listed in Part 2.

▼

PART 3 Game Masters

Features

Grade levels: where the game is played in the Core Program.

Games Across the Grades: suggested grade-level uses for each game.

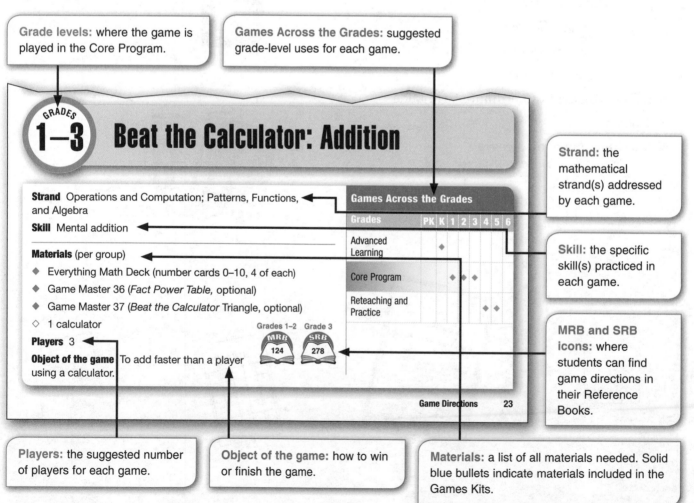

GRADES

1–3

Beat the Calculator: Addition

Strand Operations and Computation; Patterns, Functions, and Algebra

Skill Mental addition

Materials (per group)

◆ Everything Math Deck (number cards 0–10, 4 of each)

◆ Game Master 36 (*Fact Power Table,* optional)

◆ Game Master 37 (*Beat the Calculator* Triangle, optional)

◇ 1 calculator

Players 3

Object of the game To add faster than a player using a calculator.

Games Across the Grades

Grades	PK	K	1	2	3	4	5	6
Advanced Learning		◆						
Core Program			◆	◆	◆			
Reteaching and Practice						◆	◆	

Grades 1–2 Grade 3

MRB 124   **SRB** 278

Game Directions 23

Strand: the mathematical strand(s) addressed by each game.

Skill: the specific skill(s) practiced in each game.

MRB and SRB icons: where students can find game directions in their Reference Books.

Players: the suggested number of players for each game.

Object of the game: how to win or finish the game.

Materials: a list of all materials needed. Solid blue bullets indicate materials included in the Games Kits.

Reduced versions of Game Masters and gameboards are pictured for easy identification.

Directions: numbered steps for playing the game.

Advanced Version: a more challenging version of the game. Some games include **Another Way to Play,** a way to vary the game without changing its difficulty.

Differentiation Options: optional activities that help you modify the game to meet students' individual needs.

Readiness suggestions begin with a list of prerequisite skills that students need to have mastered before playing. Use this information to determine whether your students are ready for the game and to guide your introduction of the game.
Use the bulleted game modifications to help students access the game at a more basic level.

Enrichment suggestions provide ideas for extending all students' understanding of the skills.

ELL Support suggestions provide support for language development for all students, especially English language learners.

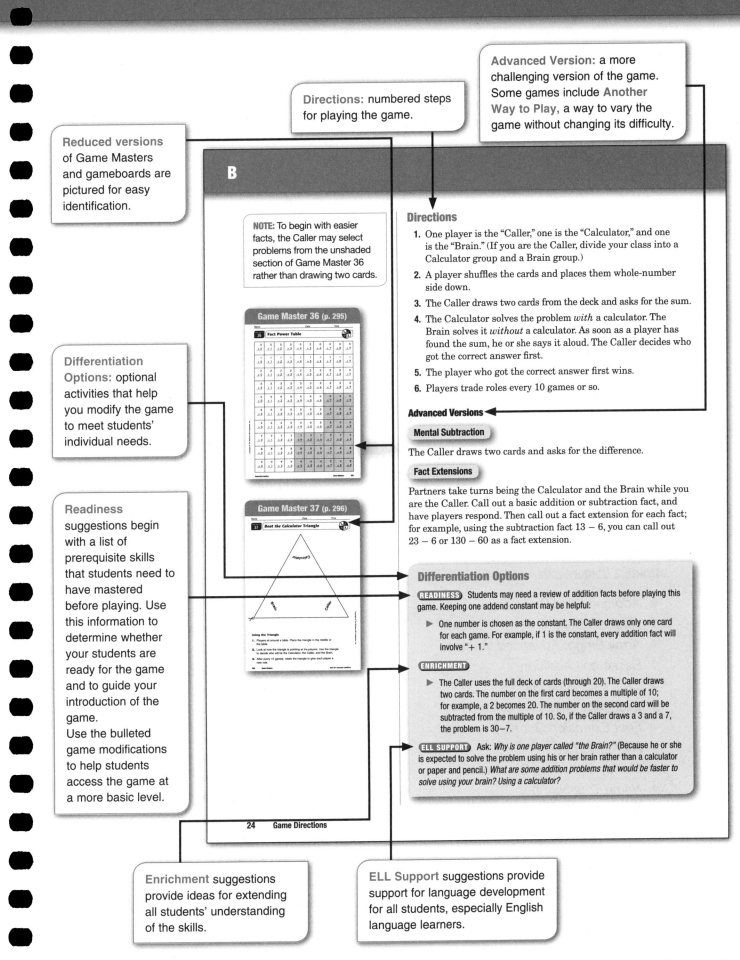

B

NOTE: To begin with easier facts, the Caller may select problems from the unshaded section of Game Master 36 rather than drawing two cards.

Game Master 36 (p. 295)

36 Fact Power Table

Game Master 37 (p. 296)

37 Beat the Calculator Triangle

Using the Triangle
1. Players sit around a table. Place the triangle in the middle of the table.
2. Look at how the triangle is pointing at the players. Use the triangle to decide who will be the Calculator, the Caller, and the Brain.
3. After every 10 games, rotate the triangle to give each player a new role.

24   Game Directions

Directions

1. One player is the "Caller," one is the "Calculator," and one is the "Brain." (If you are the Caller, divide your class into a Calculator group and a Brain group.)
2. A player shuffles the cards and places them whole-number side down.
3. The Caller draws two cards from the deck and asks for the sum.
4. The Calculator solves the problem *with* a calculator. The Brain solves it *without* a calculator. As soon as a player has found the sum, he or she says it aloud. The Caller decides who got the correct answer first.
5. The player who got the correct answer first wins.
6. Players trade roles every 10 games or so.

Advanced Versions

Mental Subtraction

The Caller draws two cards and asks for the difference.

Fact Extensions

Partners take turns being the Calculator and the Brain while you are the Caller. Call out a basic addition or subtraction fact, and have players respond. Then call out a fact extension for each fact; for example, using the subtraction fact $13 - 6$, you can call out $23 - 6$ or $130 - 60$ as a fact extension.

Differentiation Options

READINESS Students may need a review of addition facts before playing this game. Keeping one addend constant may be helpful:

▶ One number is chosen as the constant. The Caller draws only one card for each game. For example, if 1 is the constant, every addition fact will involve "+ 1."

ENRICHMENT

▶ The Caller uses the full deck of cards (through 20). The Caller draws two cards. The number on the first card becomes a multiple of 10; for example, a 2 becomes 20. The number on the second card will be subtracted from the multiple of 10. So, if the Caller draws a 3 and a 7, the problem is $30-7$.

ELL SUPPORT Ask: *Why is one player called "the Brain"?* (Because he or she is expected to solve the problem using his or her brain rather than a calculator or paper and pencil.) *What are some addition problems that would be faster to solve using your brain? Using a calculator?*

◆ Gameboards

The *Everyday Mathematics* Games Kits provide colorful two-sided gameboards for some of the most popular games. Each side of a gameboard is in a write-on/wipe-off format and includes the directions, recording areas, and playing surfaces for one game.

Early Childhood Gameboards

- Cover-All Game
- Dice Race
- How Many More?
- Money Cube
- Monster Squeeze
- Number Board Games
- Number-Grid Search
- Plus or Minus Game
- Racing Cars
- Spin a Number
- Teen Frame Game
- Train Games

Grade 1 Gameboards

- Addition Spin
- Bunny Hop
- Coin Exchange Games
- Coin Grab Games
- Difference Game
- Domino Concentration
- Exchange Games
- Fact Extension Game
- Fact Power Game
- High Roller
- Monster Squeeze
- Number-Grid Game
- Penny Plate
- Rolling for 50
- 3, 2, 1 Game
- Tric-Trac

Grade 2 Gameboards

- Addition Card Draw
- Addition Spin
- Array Bingo: Advanced Version
- Basketball Addition
- Coin Exchange Games
- Exchange Games
- Fact Extension Game
- Hit the Target
- Money Exchange Games
- Name That Number
- Number-Grid Difference
- Number-Grid Game
- Number Top-It
- Penny Plate
- Pick-a-Coin
- Spinning for Money

Grade 3 Gameboards

- Angle Race
- Array Bingo: Advanced Version
- Base-10 Games
- Baseball Multiplication
- Basketball Addition
- Division Arrays
- Factor Bingo
- Multiplication Bingo
- Multiplication Draw
- Name That Number
- Number-Grid Difference
- Number Top-It
- Shading Shapes
- Spinning for Money
- Target 50
- Three Addends

Grade 4 Gameboards

- Base-10 Decimal Exchange
- Baseball Multiplication
- Chances Are
- Credits/Debits Game
- Division Arrays
- Division Dash
- Fraction Of
- Grab Bag
- Grid Search
- High-Number Toss
- Multiplication Wrestling
- Name That Number
- Number Top-It
- Over and Up Squares
- Polygon Pair-Up
- Rugs and Fences

Grade 5 Gameboards

- Algebra Election
- Build-It
- Credits/Debits Game: Advanced Version
- Divisibility Dash
- Exponent Ball
- Factor Captor
- Frac-Tac-Toe 2-4-5-10
- Frac-Tac-Toe 2-4-8 and 3-6-9
- Fraction Capture
- Fraction Of
- Fraction Spin
- Hidden Treasure
- High-Number Toss
- Mixed-Number Spin
- Multiplication Wrestling
- Name That Number

Grade 6 Gameboards

- Algebra Election
- Angle Tangle
- Build-It
- Credits/Debits Game: Advanced Version
- Doggone Decimal
- Exponent Ball
- Factor Captor
- Frac-Tac-Toe 2-4-5-10
- Frac-Tac-Toe 2-4-8 and 3-6-9
- Fraction Capture
- High-Number Toss
- Landmark Shark
- Mixed-Number Spin
- Name That Number
- Spreadsheet Scramble
- 3-D Shape Sort

▲ Number Card Deck

▲ number cards from the Everything Math Deck

▲ fraction card from the Everything Math Deck

▲ Money Card Deck

▲ Time Card Deck

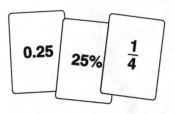

▲ Fraction/Decimal/Percent Card Deck

◆ **Other Games Kit Components**

Posters

A different poster is included in each Games Kit. General rules for playing any game are given on one side; the other side gives directions for Top-It games appropriate for your grade level.

Card Decks

Each kit includes new decks of durable, laminated cards.

To help students avoid mixing the cards from identical decks together, use permanent markers to mark all of the cards in each deck. For example, on one deck draw red lines across the top of the deck as well as on the outside of the box. On another deck, draw green lines, and so on. Now the cards can be combined for playing the games and then sorted later.

The Card Deck Activity Books, available separately, provide additional activities and uses for each card deck.

Number Card Deck (Early Childhood Games Kit)

This deck contains 4 cards for each number 0–10 and 1 card for each number 11–20.

Everything Math Deck (Grades 1–6 Games Kits)

This 2-sided card deck is used in games and activities throughout *Everyday Mathematics*. On one side of the cards is a number deck with 4 cards for each number 0–10 and 1 card for each number 11–20. Numbers are printed in blue or black to easily represent positive or negative numbers.

On the reverse of the 1–10 cards, fractions are represented in a variety of ways.

Money Card Deck (Grades 1–3 Games Kits)

Money cards show various combinations of pennies, nickels, dimes, and quarters.

Time Card Deck (Grades 1–3 Games Kits)

Time cards represent 18 different times in 3 ways: in words, on a digital clock, and on an analog clock.

Fraction/Decimal/Percent Card Deck
(Grades 4–6 Games Kits)

These cards show 18 different sets of equivalent fractions, decimals, and percents.

Cardstock Pages

Some games require unique sets of cards. These cards are provided on Game Masters in the *Teacher's Guide to Games*. For selected games, these cards are also provided on perforated cardstock pages. Materials are provided on cardstock for the following games:

Early Childhood
- dominoes for *Domino Concentration*
- monsters for *Monster Squeeze*
- cars for *Racing Cars*

Grade 1
- bunnies for *Bunny Hop*
- dominoes for *Domino Concentration*
- monsters for *Monster Squeeze*

Grade 2
- *Array Bingo* cards

Grade 3
- *Angle Race* cards
- *Array Bingo* cards

Grade 4
- *Chances Are* cards
- *Fraction Of* cards
- *Grab Bag* cards
- *Polygon Pair-Up* cards
- *Rugs and Fences* cards

Grade 5
- *Algebra Election* cards
- *Build-It* cards
- *First to 100* cards
- *Fraction Of* cards
- *Fraction Action, Fraction Friction* cards
- *Polygon Capture* cards
- *Spoon Scramble* cards
- *3-D Shape Sort* cards

Grade 6
- *Algebra Election* cards
- *Build-It* cards
- *First to 100* cards
- *Fraction Action, Fraction Friction* cards
- *Landmark Shark* cards
- *Polygon Capture* cards
- *Solution Search* cards
- *Spoon Scramble* cards
- *3-D Shape Sort* cards

NOTE: You may wish to store the 5 sets of materials and/or cards for each game in 5 separate plastic bags.

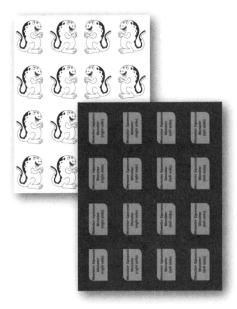

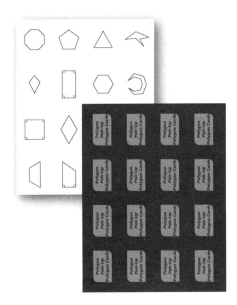

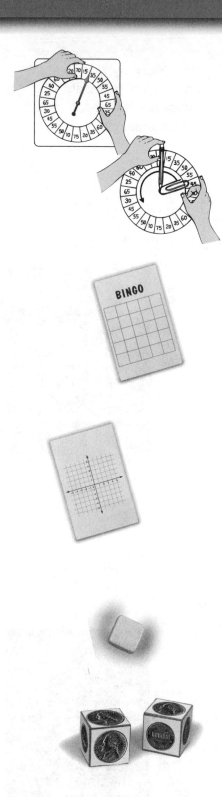

Transparent Spinners

Each Games Kit contains transparent spinners that can be taped or held in place over a spinner face on a gameboard or Game Master.

Alternatively, a paper clip and pencil can be used to create a spinner. Place the point of the pencil in the middle of a spinner face and inside of a paper clip. Students flick the paper clip with a finger to spin the spinner.

Write-On/Wipe-Off Sleeves

Each Games Kit includes write-on/wipe-off sleeves for repeat use of items such as Game Masters.

Bingo Pads

The Games Kits for Grades 3–5 provide Bingo pads for games such as *Multiplication Bingo*.

Coordinate Grid Pads

The Grades 5 and 6 Games Kits provide Four-Quadrant Grid Pads for games such as *Hidden Treasure*.

Blank Dice

Each Games Kit contains 16 blank dice that you can customize for different games. Using stickers to mark these dice will allow you to reuse them for different games.

Inch Cubes

Pictures of coins can be glued to inch cubes from the Early Childhood Games Kit for games such as the *Matching Coin Game*.

◆ Online Features

Gameboards for Demonstration

Gameboards that you can use to demonstrate the games are available online. For games with more intricate steps, an image of a sample turn is also available. You can display the sample turn on your whiteboard as you guide your students through the steps of the game. Keep the sample turn displayed and encourage students to refer to it as they play.

The *Teacher's Guide to Games*

The entire *Teacher's Guide to Games* is available online and can be accessed from any computer.

Family Math Night

Planning a Family Math Night in your classroom is a wonderful way to introduce parents and guardians to the games. Here are some tips for organizing this special event:

◆ **Invite students and their parents or guardians to attend.** In your invitation letter, mention that parents will have the opportunity to learn about the games that are an important part of *Everyday Mathematics.* Suggest that parents ask their children about games that have already been played in your class.

◆ **On Family Math Night, give a brief overview of the games.** Describe how games will be used to practice math skills, how they are a motivating alternative to traditional drill and worksheets, and how they make learning fun.

◆ **Demonstrate a few games that are already familiar to your students.** Have family members play as you describe the rules. For example, for Early Childhood, play *Train Games* or *Plus or Minus Game;* for Grades 1–3, play *Top-It* or *Pick-a-Coin;* for Grades 4–6, play *Baseball Multiplication* or *Number Top-It.*

◆ **Set up game stations where students can teach their parents how to play different games.** Include directions, gameboards, and materials at each station.

Modifying the Games

Here are some strategies for adapting the games to your students' needs:

◆ Use the suggestions in the Differentiation Options feature whenever you need a more basic or a more challenging version of a game.

◆ To encourage cooperation, have students record group scores rather than individual scores, or redefine the game objective. For example, ask groups to play a sequence of games and report their highest and lowest single game totals.

◆ The best modifications can come from your own classroom experiences. Involve your students in the games revision process, perhaps by holding a group discussion after playing a new game. If students realize that their input will result in improved games, they will become more eager players and learners.

Program Goals

Everyday Mathematics organizes content through Program Goals. The Program Goals Chart shows the games in which goal content is taught and then practiced. For more information, see the *Assessment Handbook*.

The Program Goals are divided according to the content strands below.

Content Strands

◆ Number and Numeration*

◆ Operations and Computation*

◆ Data and Chance

◆ Measurement and Reference Frames

◆ Geometry

◆ Patterns, Functions, and Algebra

*Since the games are intended to help students develop basic skills, they focus primarily on the Number and Numeration and the Operations and Computation strands.

How to Use the Program Goals Chart

Find your students' grade level. Then look over the Program Goals to find games that will help your students practice the content of each goal.

TIP: A Games Correlation Chart for Grades K–3 or Grades 4–6 can be found in every *Teacher's Lesson Guide, Volume 1.* These charts indicate the grade levels at which each game is included in *Everyday Mathematics,* the lesson in which each game is first played at a grade level, and the skill and concept areas that each game addresses.

Grade 3

Number and Numeration

Program Goal ▶ Understand the Meanings, Uses, and Representations of Numbers

Base-10 Exchange Games; Coin Top-It; Factor Bingo; Fraction Top-It; Number Top-It; Number Top-It: Decimals; One-Dollar Exchange Games; Target 50

The content of the Program Goal

Games that support the Program Goal

Content strand

Pre-Kindergarten

Number and Numeration

Program Goal	Understand the Meanings, Uses, and Representations of Numbers
	Building Towers; Child Bingo; Count Down; Counting Around; Cover All; Dice Movement; Dice Race; Find the Bear; High Five; High Low; How Many More?; Itsy Bitsy Spider; Making Trains; Match Up; Matching Dominoes; Matching Sets; Missing Number; More or Less; Mother, May I?; Mystery Change; Number Board Games; Number-Grid Search; Racing Cars; Show Me More/Less; Spin a Number; Teen Frame; Train Games
Program Goal	Understand Common Numerical Relations
	Building Towers; Find the Bear; High Low; Making Trains; Matching Dominoes; Matching Sets; Missing Number; Monster Squeeze; More or Less; Mystery Change; Show Me More/Less; Teen Frame

Operations and Computation

Program Goal	Understand Meanings of Operations
	How Many More?; Mystery Change; Plus or Minus Game; Train Games

Data and Chance

Program Goal	Select and Create Appropriate Graphical Representations of Collected or Given Data
	Dice Race
Program Goal	Analyze and Interpret Data

Measurement and Reference Frames

Program Goal	Understand the Systems and Processes of Measurement; Use Appropriate Techniques, Tools, Units, and Formulas in Making Measurements
	Building Towers; Making Trains; Money Cube
Program Goal	Use and Understand Reference Frames
	Time Match (Kindergarten); *Walk Around the Clock* (Kindergarten)

Geometry

Program Goal	Investigate Characteristics and Properties of Two- and Three-Dimensional Geometric Shapes
	I Spy; Shape Concentration; Shape Switch
Program Goal	Apply Transformations and Symmetry in Geometric Situations
	Building Towers; Child Bingo; Making Trains; Number-Grid Search

Patterns, Functions, and Algebra

Program Goal	Understand Patterns and Functions
	Number-Grid Search; Officer, Officer; Shape Concentration; What's My Rule? with Attributes

Kindergarten

Number and Numeration

Program Goal	Understand the Meanings, Uses, and Representations of Numbers
	Addition Top-It; Clear the Board/Cover the Board; Count and Sit; Cover All; Cover Half; Dice Race; Domino Concentration; Follow the Leader; Give the Next Number; Go Forward, Back Up; Guess My Number; High Low; How Many More?; Money Cube; Monster Squeeze; Number Board Games; Number-Grid Game; Number-Grid Grab; Number-Grid Search; Number Gymnastics; One-Dollar Game; Ones, Tens, Hundreds Game; Paper Money Exchange Game; Penny Exchange Games; Spin a Number; Teen Frame; Teen Tangle; Racing Cars; The Raft Game; Top-it; Train Games; Walk Around the Clock
Program Goal	Understand Equivalent Names for Numbers
	Domino Concentration; Guess My Number; Money Cube; Money Grid; One-Dollar Game; Teen Frame; The Raft Game
Program Goal	Understand Common Numerical Relations
	Addition Top-It; Dice Addition; High Low; Matching Coin Game; Monster Squeeze; Number-Grid Grab; Teen Frame; Top-It

Operations and Computation

Program Goal	Compute Accurately
	Addition Top-It; Dice Addition; Go Forward, Back Up; Guess My Number; High Roller; How Many More?; Number Gymnastics; Plus or Minus Game; Train Games
Program Goal	Understand Meanings of Operations
	Go Forward, Back Up; How Many More?; Plus or Minus Game; Train Games

Data and Chance

Program Goal	Select and Create Appropriate Graphical Representations of Collected or Given Data
	Dice Race
Program Goal	Analyze and Interpret Data
Program Goal	Understand and Apply Basic Concepts of Probability
	Soccer Spin (Grade 2)

Measurement and Reference Frames

Program Goal	Understand the Systems and Processes of Measurement; Use Appropriate Techniques, Tools, Units, and Formulas in Making Measurements
	Matching Coin Game; Money Cube; Money Grid; One-Dollar Game; Paper Money Exchange Game; Penny Exchange Games
Program Goal	Use and Understand Reference Frames
	Time Match; Walk Around the Clock

Geometry

Program Goal	Investigate Characteristics and Properties of Two- and Three-Dimensional Geometric Shapes
	Attribute Spinner Game; I Spy; Pattern Cover Up; Read My Mind; Stand Up If . . .
Program Goal	Apply Transformations and Symmetry in Geometric Situations
	Building Towers (Pre-Kindergarten); *Child Bingo* (Pre-Kindergarten); *Making Trains* (Pre-Kindergarten); *Number-Grid Search* (Pre-Kindergarten); *Make My Design* (Grade 1)

Patterns, Functions, and Algebra

Program Goal	Understand Patterns and Functions
	Attribute Spinner Game; Attribute Train Game; Find the Block; Number-Grid Search; Number-Grid Game; Pattern Cover Up; Read My Mind; What's My Rule? Fishing; Who Am I Thinking Of?
Program Goal	Use Algebraic Notation to Represent and Analyze Situations and Structures
	Go Forward, Back Up; Plus or Minus Game; Train Games

Grade 1

Number and Numeration

Program Goal	Understand the Meanings, Uses, and Representations of Numbers
	Base-10 Exchange Games; Before and After; Bunny Hop; Coin-Dice; Coin Exchange; Digit Game; Domino Concentration; Money Cube; Number-Grid Game; $1, $10, $100 Exchange Game; One-Dollar Exchange Games; Paper Money Exchange Game; Penny-Dice Game; Penny Exchange Games
Program Goal	Understand Equivalent Names for Numbers
	Broken Calculator; Coin-Dice; Coin Exchange; Domino Concentration; Money Cube; One-Dollar Exchange Games; Penny Exchange Games; Tric-Trac
Program Goal	Understand Common Numerical Relations
	Addition Top-It; Animal Weight Top-It; Broken Calculator; Coin Top-It; Digit Game; Domino Top-It; Monster Squeeze; Penny-Dice Game; Penny Grab; Rolling for 50; Shaker Addition Top-It; Subtraction Top-It; Top-It

Operations and Computation

Program Goal	Compute Accurately
	Addition Spin; Addition Top-It; Animal Weight Top-It; Beat the Calculator: Addition; Bunny Hop; Coin Top-It; Difference Game; Dime-Nickel-Penny Grab; Domino Concentration; Domino Top-It; Fact Power Game; High Roller; Nickel-Penny Grab; Number-Grid Difference; Number-Grid Game; Penny Grab; Penny Plate; Quarter-Dime-Nickel-Penny Grab; Shaker Addition Top-It; Subtraction Top-It; 3, 2, 1 Game; Tric-Trac
Program Goal	Make Reasonable Estimates
	Broken Calculator
Program Goal	Understand Meanings of Operations
	Difference Game

Data and Chance

Program Goal	Select and Create Appropriate Graphical Representations of Collected or Given Data
	Dime-Nickel-Penny Grab; Nickel-Penny Grab; Quarter-Dime-Nickel-Penny Grab; Rock, Paper, Scissors
Program Goal	Analyze and Interpret Data
	Landmark Shark (Grade 6)
Program Goal	Understand and Apply Basic Concepts of Probability
	Soccer Spin (Grade 2)

Measurement and Reference Frames

Program Goal	Understand the Systems and Processes of Measurement; Use Appropriate Techniques, Tools, Units, and Formulas in Making Measurements
	Coin-Dice; Coin Exchange; Coin Top-It; Dime-Nickel-Penny Grab; Money Cube; Nickel-Penny Grab; One-Dollar Exchange Games; $1, $10, $100 Exchange Game; Paper Money Exchange Game; Penny-Dice Game; Penny Exchange Games; Penny Grab; Quarter-Dime-Nickel-Penny Grab
Program Goal	Use and Understand Reference Frames
	Time Match

Geometry

Program Goal	Investigate Characteristics and Properties of Two- and Three-Dimensional Geometric Shapes
	Attribute Train Game; I Spy; Make My Design
Program Goal	Apply Transformations and Symmetry in Geometric Situations
	Make My Design

Grade 1 (continued)

Patterns, Functions, and Algebra

Program Goal	Understand Patterns and Functions
	Number-Grid Game
Program Goal	Use Algebraic Notation to Represent and Analyze Situations and Structures
	Addition Top-It; Broken Calculator; Domino Top-It; Number-Grid Difference

Grade 2

Number and Numeration

Program Goal	Understand the Meanings, Uses, and Representations of Numbers
	Base-10 Exchange Games; Coin Exchange; Difference Game; Digit Game; Equivalent Fractions Game; Fraction Top-It; High Roller; Money Cube; Money Exchange Game; Number-Grid Game; Number-Grid Difference; Number Top-It; $1, $10, $100 Exchange Game; One-Dollar Exchange Games; Paper Money Exchange Game; Penny Exchange Games; Penny Plate; Spinning for Money
Program Goal	Understand Equivalent Names for Numbers
	Broken Calculator; Coin Exchange; Equivalent Fractions Game; Dollar Rummy; Money Exchange Game; Name That Number; One-Dollar Exchange Games; Penny Exchange Games; Tric-Trac
Program Goal	Understand Common Numerical Relations
	Addition Top-It; Coin Top-It; Digit Game; Domino Top-It; Equivalent Fractions Game; Fraction Top-It; Number-Line Squeeze; Number Top-It; Shaker Addition Top-It; Subtraction Top-It; Top-It

Operations and Computation

Program Goal	Compute Accurately
	Addition Card Draw; Addition Spin; Addition Top-It; Basketball Addition; Beat the Calculator: Addition; Coin Top-It; Dollar Rummy; Domino Top-It; Doubles or Nothing; Fact Extension Game; Hit the Target; Name That Number; Number-Grid Difference; Number-Grid Game; Penny Plate; Pick-a-Coin; Shaker Addition Top-It; Subtraction Top-It; Three Addends; 3, 2, 1 Game; Tric-Trac
Program Goal	Make Reasonable Estimates
	Broken Calculator; Hit the Target
Program Goal	Understand Meanings of Operations
	Array Bingo; Broken Calculator; Difference Game; Penny Plate

Data and Chance

Program Goal	Select and Create Appropriate Graphical Representations of Collected or Given Data
	Dime-Nickel-Penny Grab (Grade 1); *Nickel-Penny Grab* (Grade 1); *Quarter-Dime-Nickel-Penny Grab* (Grade 1); *Rock, Paper, Scissors* (Grade 1)
Program Goal	Analyze and Interpret Data
	Landmark Shark (Grade 6)
Program Goal	Understand and Apply Basic Concepts of Probability
	Soccer Spin

Grade 2 (continued)

Measurement and Reference Frames

Program Goal	Understand the Systems and Processes of Measurement; Use Appropriate Techniques, Tools, Units, and Formulas in Making Measurements
	Coin Exchange; Money Cube; Money Exchange Game; One-Dollar Exchange Games; $1, $10, $100 Exchange Game; Paper Money Exchange Game; Penny Exchange Games; Pick-a-Coin; Spinning for Money
Program Goal	Use and Understand Reference Frames
	Time Match

Geometry

Program Goal	Investigate Characteristics and Properties of Two- and Three-Dimensional Geometric Shapes
	What's My Attribute Rule?
Program Goal	Apply Transformations and Symmetry in Geometric Situations
	Make My Design (Grade 1)

Patterns, Functions, and Algebra

Program Goal	Understand Patterns and Functions
	Array Bingo; Number-Grid Game
Program Goal	Use Algebraic Notation to Represent and Analyze Situations and Structures
	Addition Top-It; Array Bingo; Broken Calculator; Domino Top-It; Name That Number

Grade 3

Number and Numeration

Program Goal	Understand the Meanings, Uses, and Representations of Numbers
	Base-10 Exchange Games; Coin Top-It; Factor Bingo; Fraction Top-It; Number Top-It; Number Top-It: Decimals; One-Dollar Exchange Games; Target 50
Program Goal	Understand Equivalent Names for Numbers
	Broken Calculator; Equivalent Fractions Game; Name That Number
Program Goal	Understand Common Numerical Relations
	Addition Top-It: Decimals; Baseball Multiplication; Coin Top-It; Decimal Solitaire; Fraction Top-It; Less Than You!; Name That Number; Number-Line Squeeze; Subtraction Top-It

Operations and Computation

Program Goal	Compute Accurately
	Addition Top-It; Array Bingo; Baseball Multiplication; Basketball Addition; Beat the Calculator: Addition; Coin Top-It; Factor Bingo; Less than You!; Memory Addition/Subtraction; Multiplication Bingo; Multiplication Draw; Multiplication Top-It; Name That Number; Number-Grid Difference; Pick-a-Coin; Roll to 100; Subtraction Top-It; Target 50; Three Addends
Program Goal	Make Reasonable Estimates
	Broken Calculator; Less Than You!; Target 50
Program Goal	Understand Meanings of Operations
	Array Bingo; Broken Calculator; Division Arrays

Grade 3 (continued)

Data and Chance

Program Goal	Select and Create Appropriate Graphical Representations of Collected or Given Data
	Venn Diagram Challenge (Grade 6)
Program Goal	Analyze and Interpret Data
	Landmark Shark (Grade 6)
Program Goal	Understand and Apply Basic Concepts of Probability
	Block-Drawing Game; Soccer Spin; Spinning to Win

Measurement and Reference Frames

Program Goal	Understand the Systems and Processes of Measurement; Use Appropriate Techniques, Tools, Units, and Formulas in Making Measurements
	Angle Race; Robot Game
Program Goal	Use and Understand Reference Frames
	Time Match (Grade 2)

Geometry

Program Goal	Investigate Characteristics and Properties of Two- and Three-Dimensional Geometric Shapes
	Angle Race; Shading Shapes
Program Goal	Apply Transformations and Symmetry in Geometric Situations
	Dart Game (Grade 4); Pocket-Billiards Game (Grade 4); Robot Game

Patterns, Functions, and Algebra

Program Goal	Understand Patterns and Functions
	Array Bingo (Grade 2); Number-Grid Game (Grade 2); Buzz Games (Grade 4)
Program Goal	Use Algebraic Notation to Represent and Analyze Situations and Structures
	Array Bingo; Beat the Calculator: Addition; Beat the Calculator: Multiplication; Broken Calculator; Multiplication Draw; Name That Number

Grade 4

Number and Numeration

Program Goal	Understand the Meanings, Uses, and Representations of Numbers
	Base-10 Exchange Games; Buzz Games; Factor Bingo; Fishing for Digits; Fraction Match; Fraction Of; High-Number Toss; Number Top-It: Decimals
Program Goal	Understand Equivalent Names for Numbers
	Broken Calculator; Fraction Match; Fraction/Percent Concentration; Multiplication Wrestling; Name That Number
Program Goal	Understand Common Numerical Relations
	Addition Top-It: Decimals; Baseball Multiplication; Coin Top-It; Fraction Top-It; High-Number Toss; Subtraction Top-It

Grade 4 (continued)

Operations and Computation

Program Goal	Compute Accurately
	Addition Top-It; Baseball Multiplication; Buzz Games; Credits/Debits Game; Division Dash; Factor Bingo; Fraction Addition Top-It (Advanced Version of Fraction Top-It); High-Number Toss: Decimal Version; Multiplication Top-It; Multiplication Wrestling; Name That Number; Product Pile-Up; Subtraction Target Practice; Subtraction Top-It
Program Goal	Make Reasonable Estimates
	Broken Calculator; Calculator 10,000; Subtraction Target Practice
Program Goal	Understand Meanings of Operations
	Division Arrays; Broken Calculator

Data and Chance

Program Goal	Select and Create Appropriate Graphical Representations of Collected or Given Data
	Venn Diagram Challenge (Grade 6)
Program Goal	Analyze and Interpret Data
	Landmark Shark (Grade 6)
Program Goal	Understand and Apply Basic Concepts of Probability
	Chances Are; Grab Bag; Seega

Measurement and Reference Frames

Program Goal	Understand the Systems and Processes of Measurement; Use Appropriate Techniques, Tools, Units, and Formulas in Making Measurements
	Angle Tangle; Rugs and Fences
Program Goal	Use and Understand Reference Frames
	Grid Search; Over and Up Squares

Geometry

Program Goal	Investigate Characteristics and Properties of Two- and Three-Dimensional Geometric Shapes
	Angle Tangle; Polygon Pair-Up; Sprouts; Sz'kwa
Program Goal	Apply Transformations and Symmetry in Geometric Situations
	Dart Game; Pocket-Billiards Game; Robot Game

Patterns, Functions, and Algebra

Program Goal	Understand Patterns and Functions
	Buzz Games
Program Goal	Use Algebraic Notation to Represent and Analyze Situations and Structures
	Broken Calculator; Grab Bag; Multiplication Wrestling; Name That Number

Grade 5

Number and Numeration

Program Goal	Understand the Meanings, Uses, and Representations of Numbers
	Estimation Squeeze; Factor Bingo; Factor Captor; Factor Top-It; High-Number Toss; High-Number Toss: Decimal Version; Number Top-It: Decimals; Scientific Notation Toss
Program Goal	Understand Equivalent Names for Numbers
	Broken Calculator; Exponent Ball; Frac-Tac-Toe; Fraction Action, Fraction Friction; Fraction Capture; Fraction/Percent Concentration; Name That Number; Scientific Notation Toss; Spoon Scramble
Program Goal	Understand Common Numerical Relations
	Build-It; Frac-Tac-Toe; Fraction Capture; Fraction Multiplication Top-It; Fraction Spin; Fraction Top-It; High-Number Toss; High-Number Toss: Decimal Version; Mixed-Number Spin; Scientific Notation Toss; Subtraction Top-It

Operations and Computation

Program Goal	Compute Accurately
	Addition Top-It; Algebra Election; Baseball Multiplication; Credits/Debits Games; Divisibility Dash; Division Dash; Division Top-It; Factor Bingo; Factor Captor; Factor Top-It; First to 100; 500; Fraction Addition Top-It (Advanced Version of Fraction Top-It); Fraction Multiplication Top-It; Fraction Spin; High-Number Toss: Decimal Version; Mixed-Number Spin; Multiplication Bull's-Eye; Multiplication Top-It; Multiplication Wrestling; Name That Number; Subtraction Target Practice; Subtraction Top-It; Top-It Games with Positive and Negative Numbers
Program Goal	Make Reasonable Estimates
	Broken Calculator; Estimation Squeeze; Fraction Action, Fraction Friction; Fraction Spin; Mixed-Number Spin; Multiplication Bull's-Eye
Program Goal	Understand Meanings of Operations
	Fraction Of

Data and Chance

Program Goal	Select and Create Appropriate Graphical Representations of Collected or Given Data
	Venn Diagram Challenge (Grade 6)
Program Goal	Analyze and Interpret Data
	Landmark Shark (Grade 6)
Program Goal	Understand and Apply Basic Concepts of Probability
	Exponent Ball; Grab Bag

Measurement and Reference Frames

Program Goal	Understand the Systems and Processes of Measurement; Use Appropriate Techniques, Tools, Units, and Formulas in Making Measurements
	Angle Tangle; Rugs and Fences
Program Goal	Use and Understand Reference Frames
	Hidden Treasure; Over and Up Squares

Geometry

Program Goal	Investigate Characteristics and Properties of Two- and Three-Dimensional Geometric Shapes
	Angle Tangle; Polygon Capture; 3-D Shape Sort
Program Goal	Apply Transformations and Symmetry in Geometric Situations
	Dart Game (Grade 4); *Pocket-Billiards Game* (Grade 4); *Robot Game* (Grade 4)

Grade 5 (continued)

Patterns, Functions, and Algebra

Program Goal	Understand Patterns and Functions
	Buzz Games (Grade 4)
Program Goal	Use Algebraic Notation to Represent and Analyze Situations and Structures
	Algebra Election; Broken Calculator; First to 100; Grab Bag; Name That Number

Grade 6

Number and Numeration

Program Goal	Understand the Meanings, Uses, and Representations of Numbers
	Exponent Ball; High-Number Toss; High-Number Toss: Decimal Version; Number Top-It: Decimals; Percent/Sector Match Up; Scientific Notation Toss
Program Goal	Understand Equivalent Names for Numbers
	Frac-Tac-Toe; Fraction Capture; Scientific Notation Toss; Spoon Scramble
Program Goal	Understand Common Numerical Relations
	Build-It; Fraction Multiplication Top-It; Mixed-Number Spin; Scientific Notation Toss

Operations and Computation

Program Goal	Compute Accurately
	Algebra Election; Credits/Debits Games; Divisibility Dash; Division Top-It; Doggone Decimal; Factor Captor; First to 100; Fraction Capture; Fraction Multiplication Top-It; High-Number Toss: Decimal Version; Mixed-Number Spin; Multiplication Bull's-Eye; Multiplication Top-It; Multiplication Wrestling; Solution Search; Spoon Scramble; Spreadsheet Scramble; Top-It Games with Positive and Negative Numbers
Program Goal	Make Reasonable Estimates
	Doggone Decimal; Fraction Action, Fraction Friction; Getting to One; Mixed-Number Spin; Multiplication Bull's-Eye
Program Goal	Understand Meanings of Operations
	Division Arrays (Grade 4); *Fraction Of* (Grade 5)

Data and Chance

Program Goal	Select and Create Appropriate Graphical Representations of Collected or Given Data
	Venn Diagram Challenge
Program Goal	Analyze and Interpret Data
	Landmark Shark
Program Goal	Understand and Apply Basic Concepts of Probability
	Exponent Ball; Grab Bag; Greedy

Measurement and Reference Frames

Program Goal	Understand the Systems and Processes of Measurement; Use Appropriate Techniques, Tools, Units, and Formulas in Making Measurements
	Angle Tangle
Program Goal	Use and Understand Reference Frames
	Over and Up Squares; X and O—Tic Tac Toe

Grade 6 (continued)

Geometry

Program Goal	Investigate Characteristics and Properties of Two- and Three-Dimensional Geometric Shapes
	Angle Tangle; Polygon Capture; 3-D Shape Sort
Program Goal	Apply Transformations and Symmetry in Geometric Situations
	Dart Game (Grade 4); *Pocket-Billiards Game* (Grade 4); *Robot Game* (Grade 4)

Patterns, Functions, and Algebra

Program Goal	Understand Patterns and Functions
	Buzz Games (Grade 4)
Program Goal	Use Algebraic Notation to Represent and Analyze Situations and Structures
	Algebra Election; First to 100; Getting to One; Multiplication Wrestling; Name That Number; Solution Search

Whole-Class Games for Early-Childhood Classrooms

Pre-Kindergarten

 GRADE PK **Child Bingo**

Skill   Associating number names with written numerals; using spatial reasoning

Materials   ◇ 18 index cards   ◇ tape   ◇ 9 chairs

Set up 9 chairs in 3 rows of 3. Label them randomly with index cards numbered 1–9. Place another set of cards numbered 1–9 in a container. Call one player at a time to pick a number from the container without looking, read the number aloud, and find and sit in the matching chair. Players get Bingo by filling 3 chairs in a row—across, up and down, or diagonally.

ENRICHMENT   Use 16 chairs and cards numbered through 16.

 GRADE PK **Count Down**

Skill   Counting backward with one-to-one correspondence

Have players sit in a circle in an area where there is space to run. Walk around the circle, tapping each player's head. As you tap, count down from 5 (or another number) to 1. Say "Blast off!" as you tap the next player's head. That player gets up and chases you around the circle, trying to catch you before you sit in the empty spot. Then the player takes a turn counting down to blastoff.

ENRICHMENT   Have players count back from higher numbers. Allow players to call "Blast off!" before they reach 1.

 GRADE PK **Counting Around**

Skill   Counting in sequence

Have players stand in a circle. Introduce the game by having all players count in unison to 5 and clap as they say "five." To play the game, have players count around the circle, with the first player saying "one," the next player saying "two," and so on. The player who says "five" sits down, and the count begins again. The players who are sitting do not say a number. Continue until all players are sitting.

ENRICHMENT   Vary the sit-down number. Ask players to think about when they will sit, and who will be the last player standing.

Find the Bear

Skill Reading numerals; comparing numbers

Materials ◇ 6 small cups labeled 1–6 ◇ 1 bear counter

Turn the cups upside down. Hide a bear under one cup. Players take turns guessing the number of the cup the bear is under. Give number clues such as: *It is under a cup with a lower number.*

ENRICHMENT Use more cups with higher numbers.

High Five

Skill Counting in sequence

Gather players in a circle. One player counts aloud to 5, opening one finger for each number. When that player reaches 5, he or she picks another player and gives that player a high five. The player who received the high five then takes a turn as the counter.

ENRICHMENT Players count to 10 and slap both hands of the next player.

Missing Number

Skill Reading numerals; comparing numbers

Materials ◆ number cards 0–6

Place the cards in a row in order. Have players close their eyes while you remove a card and close up the empty space. Players open their eyes and take turns guessing the missing number. Give clues such as: *The missing number is higher than 3.*

ENRICHMENT Add more cards with higher numbers.

Mother, May I?

Skill Counting with one-to-one correspondence

Players line up facing you and take turns asking for permission to take a certain number of steps toward you. For example, a player may ask, "Mother, may I take 3 giant steps?" or "Mother, may I take 10 baby steps?" You answer "Yes, you may," or "No, you may not." A player who takes steps without permission must return to the starting line. The first player to reach you becomes the next "mother."

GRADE PK

Officer, Officer

Skill Using attribute-based clues

Have players sit in a circle. Explain that they will pretend to be police officers, and they will use clues to help you find a "lost" child. Choose the first "Officer." Have that player sit in the middle of the circle. Think of one of the other players to be your missing child, but do not tell who it is. Begin the game by saying: *Officer, Officer, my child is lost. Can you help me? My child is wearing a **red shirt**.* (Use an appropriate clue.) Have the Officer make a guess by naming a player. Respond to the guess, and continue giving clues until the Officer finds the lost child. The lost child becomes the next Officer.

 GRADE PK

Shape Switch

Skill Identifying shapes

Materials ◆ Game Masters 205–207 (1 large paper shape per player)

Have players stand in a circle. Each player holds a paper shape. When you name a shape, all players holding that shape change places with each other. You can also call out properties of a shape; for example, *If you have a shape with 3 sides, switch places.*

 GRADE PK

Show Me More/Less

Skill Counting and comparing groups of objects

Show a number of fingers on one hand. Ask players to show you more fingers. Explain that there is more than one correct response. Repeat with different numbers of fingers, each time asking players to show more (or less). Progress to using fingers on both hands.

 GRADE PK

What's My Rule? with Attributes

Skill Identifying and describing attributes of children and clothing; identifying sorting rules

Select a group of players according to a secret sorting rule, such as everyone wearing red shirts. Have these players stand up or come to the front of the group. When all players who fit the rule are in the group, ask whether anyone knows how you sorted them: *How are all of the children in this group alike?* Give clues as needed to help players identify the rule.

ENRICHMENT Use two attributes in your sorting rule; for example, select all players wearing red shirts who are also girls.

Pre-Kindergarten and Kindergarten

I Spy

Skill *You can use this game to provide practice for many different skills.*

Give a clue and ask players to guess what you see. Use numbers, colors, shapes, and sizes in your clues. For example:

- *I spy a red circle.*

- *I spy four things at the table that are brown.*

- *I spy a 3-dimensional object on my desk with squares on all sides.*

- *I spy a pattern that follows the same rule as this:* (Show a color or movement pattern and describe its rule.)

Simon Says

Skill *You can use this game to provide practice for many different skills.*

Give a series of directions. Players follow directions preceded by *Simon says* and ignore any other directions. When you do not say *Simon says*, players who follow that direction must sit down.

- Have players perform various actions a number of times: *Simon says, take 4 giant steps.*

- Use attributes: *Simon says, children wearing red and wearing belts jump up.*

- Have players draw: *Simon says, make 5 tally marks. Draw coins to show 7 cents.*

Kindergarten

Count and Sit

Skill Counting by ones

Have players stand in a circle. Choose a target number, such as 8. Begin counting with 1 and go around the circle with each player saying the next number in sequence. The player who says the target number sits down. The count begins again at 1, and the seated player is skipped. Continue until all players are sitting.

ENRICHMENT Use higher target numbers, higher starting numbers, counting backward, or skip counting.

Find the Block

Skill Using multiple attributes to find and describe objects; applying sorting rules

Materials ◇ 1 set of attribute blocks

Randomly distribute the attribute blocks to players. Think of a "mystery block." Give directions based on attribute clues to help players figure out the mystery block. For example: *All children with a **large** block stand and hold up their blocks. All children with a **large, blue** block remain standing. All children with a **large, blue circle** remain standing. All children with a **large, blue, thin circle** remain standing.* The player who is still standing has the mystery block. Have that player repeat the block description.

Follow the Leader

Skill Counting by ones

Have players sit in a circle. Model an action such as wiggling your fingers, and have players join in. Direct them to begin counting (as they continue the movement) and go around the circle, with players taking turns saying the next number. The player who says "ten" may change the movement, and the count starts over from 1.

ENRICHMENT Use higher target numbers, higher starting numbers, counting backward, or skip counting.

Give the Next Number

Skill Counting by ones

Have players sit in a circle. Walk around the circle slowly, counting the players (or their feet) in a soft voice: Players count along in soft voices. Every so often, tap a player to stand up and say the next number aloud. The standing player also taps or claps the number.

ENRICHMENT Have players count silently, count backward from 10, count beyond 10, or skip count.

Guess My Number

Skill Using addition and subtraction; recognizing equivalent names for numbers; combining digits to make numbers

Write down a secret number. Give different types of clues to help players guess the number. For example:

- The number that is 2 less than 5

- The number between 7 and 9

- A number in the teens with 6 in it

- A number with a 2 and a 4 as the digits

When a player guesses correctly, show the number and have players read it aloud. Ask: *Are there other clues that could describe this number?* Record players' suggestions.

Number Gymnastics

Skill Manipulating digits in numbers; mental addition and subtraction

Begin with a number clue, such as: *I'm thinking of a number with 2 as its first digit and 3 as its second digit. What is my number?* (23) Give step-by-step instructions for changing the number. Ask players to say the number after each step. For example: *What is the number if I reverse the digits?* (32) *What number comes before that number?* (31) *Now add 2.* (33) You may want to try to get back to the starting number. For number-writing practice, have players record each number.

Stand Up If . . .

Skill Identifying solid figures

Materials ◇ items representing common 3-dimensional shapes (1 per player)

Give each player a 3-dimensional shape. Say: *Stand up if you have a sphere (cube, cylinder . . .).* Hold up an example of the shape. Have players name the object they are holding and its shape when they stand up.

Teen Tangle

GRADE K

Skill Reading teen numbers

Materials ◆ Game Master 222 (11–20 Spinner) ◇ paper

Label sheets of paper in order to make several sets of sheets labeled 11–20. Place the sheets on the floor in random order. One player spins the spinner while the other players (one at a time) place a finger, foot, or other body part on the number the spinner points to. The goal is for players to touch as many numbers as they can without falling.

What's My Rule? Fishing

GRADE K

Skill Identifying and applying sorting rules

Explain that players will pretend to be fish, and you will try to catch one kind of fish at a time. Players will watch and try to guess the kind of fish you are looking for. "Catch" some fish by calling them up to the front of the room. Ask: *What sort of fish am I fishing for?* or: *What's my fishing rule?* Continue fishing until the rule is guessed. Then ask players to say what is the same about the players who were caught, and what is the same about the players who were not caught.

You can also fish for attribute blocks instead of players.

(ENRICHMENT) Fish for two attributes, such as short, brown hair.

Who Am I Thinking Of?

GRADE K

Skill Identifying and applying sorting rules

Secretly write down one player's name. Have all players stand. Players ask "yes" or "no" questions to try to guess the name. Players sit when they are in the "no" group. For example, if someone asks *Is it a girl?* and you answer *yes,* the girls remain standing while the boys sit down. If a player then asks *Is she wearing blue?* and your answer is *no,* then all the girls wearing blue sit down. Continue until the player whose name you wrote is the only one standing.

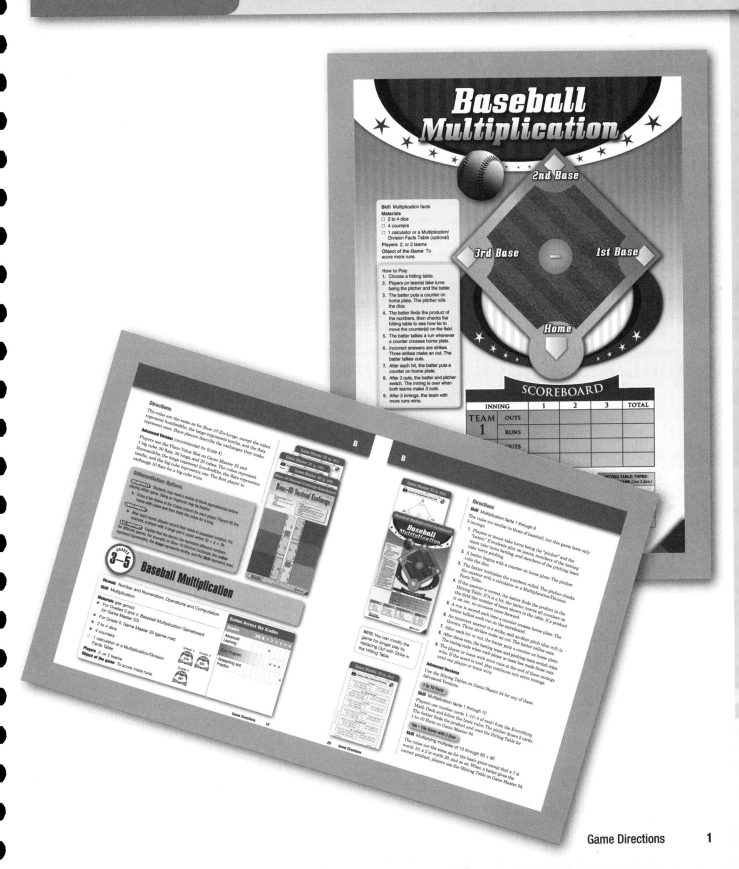

A

GRADE **2**

Addition Card Draw

Games Across the Grades								
Grades	PK	K	1	2	3	4	5	6
Advanced Learning			◆					
Core Program				◆				
Reteaching and Practice					◆	◆		

Strand Operations and Computation

Skill Adding 3 numbers

Materials (per pair)

◆ *Addition Card Draw* Gameboard (or Game Master 1, 2 copies)

◆ Everything Math Deck

◇ 1 calculator

◇ 2 slates or scratch paper

Players 2

Object of the game To get the higher total.

Game Master 1 (p. 260)

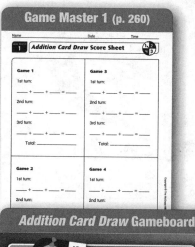

Addition Card Draw Gameboard

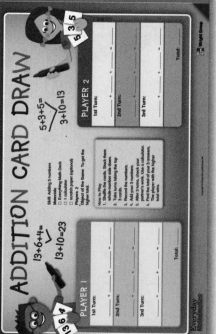

Directions

1. Players shuffle the deck and place it whole-number side down. Players take turns.

2. Player 1 draws the top 3 cards from the deck.

3. Player 1 records the numbers on the score sheet and puts the 3 cards in a separate pile.

4. Player 1 finds the sum of the 3 numbers on a slate or scratch paper.

5. Player 2 repeats Steps 2–4.

6. After 3 rounds, players check each other's work with a calculator.

7. Each player finds the total of his or her 3 answers and writes it on the score sheet. The player with the higher total wins.

Differentiation Options

READINESS Students may need a review of strategies for adding 1- and 2-digit numbers. Beginning with smaller numbers may be helpful:

▶ Players roll a die instead of drawing cards.

ENRICHMENT

▶ Players use each card as the first digit(s) of a multiple of 10—for example, if you draw 13, your number is 130. Players find the sum of their multiples.

ELL SUPPORT English Learners may know how to "draw a card" with crayons, but in card games, ***draw a card*** means to select one from a stack.

2 **Game Directions**

GRADES 1–2 Addition Spin

Strands Number and Numeration; Operations and Computation

Skill Mental addition

Materials (per pair)

◆ *Addition Spin* Gameboard (or Game Masters 2 and 3, and 2 sheets of paper)

◆ 1 transparent spinner (or a paper clip and pencil)

◇ 1 calculator

Players 2

Object of the game To have the larger total.

Grades 1–2
MRB
120

Games Across the Grades

Grades	PK	K	1	2	3	4	5	6
Advanced Learning		◆						
Core Program			◆	◆				
Reteaching and Practice					◆			

Directions

> **NOTE:** For Grade 1, begin with the spinner showing multiples of 5.

1. Players choose one spinner face to use. Players may hold or tape the transparent spinner in place over the spinner face, or use the paper clip and pencil to make a spinner.

2. Players take turns being the "Spinner" and the "Checker."

3. The Spinner spins twice and writes both numbers on which the pointer lands. If it points to more than one number, the Spinner writes the smaller number.

4. The Spinner adds the 2 numbers and writes the sum. The Checker checks the sum with a calculator.

5. If the sum is correct, the Spinner circles it. If the sum is incorrect, the Spinner corrects it but does not circle it.

6. Players switch roles. After 5 rounds, each player uses a calculator to find the total of his or her circled scores. The player with the larger total wins.

Another Way to Play

Fill in a blank spinner face on the gameboard or Game Master 3 with different numbers and have students play again.

Game Master 3 (p. 262)

Game Master 2 (p. 261)

Addition Spin Gameboard

Differentiation Options

READINESS Students may need a review of strategies for 2-digit addition. Starting with smaller numbers may also be helpful:

▶ Label a blank spinner face with smaller numbers.

▶ Players use one spinner showing multiples of 10 and one spinner showing 1-digit numbers. They spin each spinner once and find the sum.

ENRICHMENT

▶ Label a blank spinner face with larger numbers to provide practice in adding 2-digit numbers with regrouping or 3-digit numbers.

▶ Players spin 3 times and add 3 numbers.

ELL SUPPORT Explain the different uses of *sum* and *total* in this game. Players will find the *sum* for each turn. After 5 turns, they will find their *total* score.

GRADES K–5 Addition Top-It

Games Across the Grades								
Grades	PK	K	1	2	3	4	5	6
Advanced Learning								
Core Program		◆	◆	◆	◆	◆	◆	
Reteaching and Practice								◆

Strands Number and Numeration; Operations and Computation; Patterns, Functions, and Algebra

Skill Adding; comparing sums

Materials (per group)

◆ Everything Math Deck (number cards 0–10, 4 of each)

◆ Game Master 4 (Record Sheet, optional)

◇ 1 calculator or Addition Facts Table (optional)

Players 2–4

Object of the game To collect the most cards.

Grades 1–2 **MRB** 122   Grade 3 **SRB** 270

Grade 4 **SRB** 263   Grade 5 **SRB** 333

NOTE: For Kindergarten and Grade 1, you may want to begin with cards 0–5 and only 2 players. Sticking dots on the cards to represent the numbers may help with addition.

Facts 0–10 (recommended for Grades K–5)

Skill Addition facts 0 to 10

Directions

1. One player shuffles the cards and places the deck whole-number side down.

2. Each player turns over 2 cards and calls out the sum of the numbers. Players check each other's sums, using an Addition Facts Table or a calculator if needed.

3. The player with the greatest sum wins the round and takes all of the cards.

4. In case of a tie for the greatest sum, each tied player turns over 2 more cards and calls out their sum. The player with the greatest sum takes all of the cards from both plays.

5. The game ends when not enough cards are left for each player to have another turn.

6. The player with the most cards wins.

Other Ways to Play

- Players use double-9 dominoes instead of number cards.
- Supply 40 pennies for players to model the addition problems.
- Players can flip a coin at the end of the game to determine whether the player with the most or fewest cards wins.

3 Addends (recommended for Grades 2–5)

Skill Adding three numbers; comparing sums

Each player turns over 3 cards and finds the sum. Or, players roll 3 dice; one or more of the dice may be polyhedral.

2-Digit Numbers (recommended for Grades 4 and 5)

Skill Adding two 2-digit numbers; using place-value concepts; comparing sums

Players use only the number cards 1–9. Each player turns over 4 cards, forms two 2-digit numbers, and finds the sum.

Decimals (recommended for Grades 4 and 5)

Skill Adding and comparing decimals; place-value concepts

Players use Game Master 5 and 2 pennies or counters per player. Each player draws 4 cards and forms 2 numbers, each with a whole-number portion and a decimal portion. Players use the pennies or counters as decimal points. Each player finds the sum of his or her two decimals. Players compare their decimals.

NOTE: Players at any level can use Game Master 4 to record and compare their addition sentences.

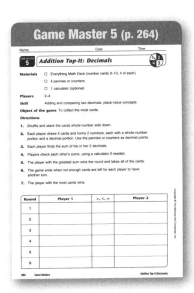

Differentiation Options

READINESS Students may need a review of strategies for addition. Keeping one addend constant may be helpful:

► Players choose one addend to keep constant and turn over only the second addend for each round. For example, for each round, the players draw one card and add that number to 5.

ENRICHMENT Challenge students to work with greater numbers:

► Players use all of the number cards in the Everything Math Deck or two polyhedral dice with the numbers 0–20.

► Players draw one extra card on each turn and include an extra digit in one of the addends they make.

ELL SUPPORT Explain that *Top-It* is an expression that means "beat that." For example, a sum of 14 "tops" a sum of 13.

GRADES 5–6 Algebra Election

Games Across the Grades										
Grades	PK	K	1	2	3	4	5	6
Advanced Learning						◆		
Core Program							◆	◆
Reteaching and Practice								

Strands Number and Numeration; Operations and Computation; Patterns, Functions, and Algebra

Skill Variable substitution; solving equations

Materials (per group)

◆ *Algebra Election* Gameboard (or Game Masters 6 and 7)

◆ For Grade 5: *First to 100* Problem Cards (or Game Masters 8 and 9)

◆ For Grade 6: *Algebra Election* Problem Cards (or Game Masters 10 and 11; also available in Grade 6 Math Journal 2, Activity Sheets 3 and 4)

◆ 1 die

◆ 4 counters

◇ 1 calculator

◇ 2 pieces of paper

Players 2 teams, each with 2 players

Object of the game To be the first team to collect 270 or more electoral votes and become president and vice president.

Grade 6

SRB
304

Directions

1. Players shuffle the cards and stack them facedown.

2. Each player puts a counter on Iowa on the map of the United States.

3. One member of each team rolls the die. The team with the higher number goes first. Team members play on alternate turns: Team 1, Player 1; Team 2, Player 1; Team 1, Player 2; Team 2, Player 2.

4. The first player rolls the die. The roll tells how many moves the player must make from the current state. Each new state counts as one move. Moves can be in any direction as long as they pass between states that share a common border. However, players can get to and from Alaska by way of Washington state and to and from Hawaii by way of California. A player may not return to a state on the same turn.

5. The map shows how many electoral votes each state has. The player takes the top Problem Card and substitutes the state's number of electoral votes for the variable x in the problem(s) on the card. The player solves the problem(s), and the other team checks the answer(s) with a calculator.

6. If there are no errors, the player's team wins the state's electoral votes. Team members write the state's name and its electoral votes on a piece of paper and write their first initials on the state to show that they have won it. Once a state is won, the opposing team may land on it but cannot get its votes.

7. If the player did not solve the problem(s) correctly, the state remains open. Players may still try to win its votes.

8. A player on the next team takes a turn rolling the die and moving his or her counter. Each player begins a turn from the last state he or she landed on.

9. When all of the Problem Cards have been used, players shuffle the deck and use it again.

10. The first team to get at least 270 votes wins the election.

Additional Information

- "A state" means "a state or the District of Columbia (D.C.)."

- Partners may discuss the problems. Each player, however, has to answer the problem(s) on his or her own.

- If a player does not want to answer a particular Problem Card, he or she may say "Pass" and draw another card. A player may pass 3 times during a game.

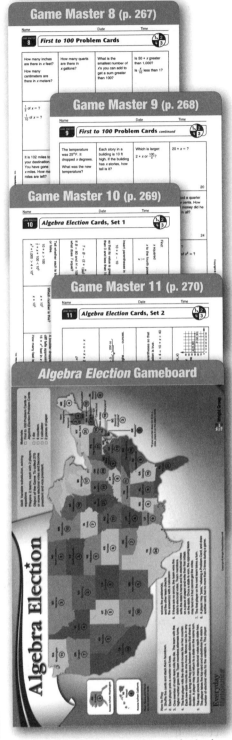

▲ You can also create this map by taping Game Masters 6 and 7 together.

NOTE: The distribution of electoral votes shown on the map is likely to change as a result of the 2010 census.

- If a Problem Card contains several problems, a player must solve all of the problems correctly to win a state's votes.
- Suggested strategy: A player looks at the map to see which states have the most votes, and then works with his or her partner to win those states.

Other Ways to Play

- Players agree on a time limit for answering problems.
- A team receives 1 extra point if the player can name the capital of the state landed on.
- A shorter version of the game can be played by going through all 32 cards just once. The team with the most votes at that time wins.

Differentiation Options

READINESS Students may need a review of variable substitution:

▶ Players use copies of the cards and write the *x*-values directly on them.

▶ Replace some or all of the cards with simpler variable substitution problems on index cards.

ENRICHMENT

▶ Players multiply the number rolled by 10 (or by 100).

ELL SUPPORT Explain the U.S. electoral voting system, including the fact that more populous states have more electoral votes.

GRADE 3 — Angle Race

Strands Measurement and Reference Frames; Geometry

Skill Recognizing angle measures

Materials (per pair)

◆ *Angle Race* Gameboard (or Game Master 12, or a 24-pin circular geoboard)

◆ *Angle Race* Cards (or Game Master 13)

◇ 1 straightedge (or rubber bands for the geoboard)

Players 2

Object of the game To complete an angle exactly at the 360° mark.

Grade 3

SRB
271

Directions

1. Players shuffle the deck and place it facedown.

2. A player draws a line segment from the center dot to the 0° dot. This will be one side of the first angle.

3. Players take turns. On each turn, the player selects the top card and draws an angle with that measure. The player uses the last segment drawn as one side of the angle and goes clockwise around the board.

Example

On the first turn, Ken draws a 30° card. He makes a 30° angle by drawing a line segment from the center dot to the 30° dot. Jael draws a 75° card. She makes a 75° angle by drawing a line segment from the center dot to the 105° dot—and so forth, clockwise around the board.

4. Angles may not go past the 360° (or 0°) mark. If a player can't make an angle without going past the 360° mark, the player loses his or her turn.

5. The first player to complete an angle exactly on the 360° mark wins.

Differentiation Options

READINESS Students may need to practice counting on by 15s on the geoboard. It may be helpful to begin with only the *Angle Race* Cards that are easy to relate to right angles:

▶ Players use only the 30°, 45°, 90°, and 180° cards.

ENRICHMENT

▶ Players may go past 360°. They may add or subtract the angle on their card once they have passed 360°. The first player to reach exactly 360° wins.

ELL SUPPORT Using a circular geoboard, create several angles that will total 360°; for example, 60°, 50°, 40°, 100°, 90°, and 20°. Explain that the total measure of those six angles is 360°. Tell students that in *Angle Race,* players are in a race to get to 360° first.

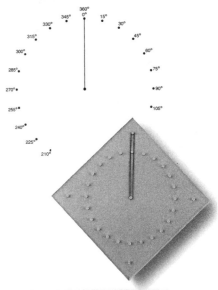

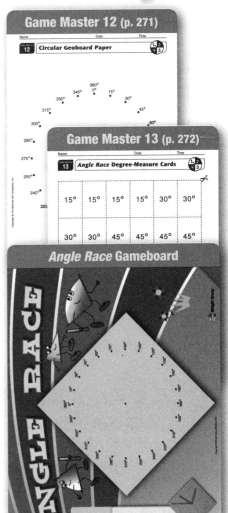

Game Master 12 (p. 271)

Game Master 13 (p. 272)

Angle Race Gameboard

GRADES 4–6 Angle Tangle

Games Across the Grades

Grades	PK	K	1	2	3	4	5	6
Advanced Learning					◆			
Core Program						◆	◆	◆
Reteaching and Practice								

Strands Measurement and Reference Frames; Geometry

Skill Estimating and measuring angle size

Materials (per pair)

◆ For Grades 4 and 5: Game Master 14 (Record Sheet, 2 copies)

◆ For Grade 6: *Angle Tangle* Gameboard (or Game Master 14, 2 copies)

◇ 1 protractor

◇ 1 straightedge

Players 2

Object of the game To get the lower total score by accurately estimating angle sizes.

Grade 4 — SRB 230
Grade 5 — SRB 296
Grade 6 — SRB 306

Directions

1. Player 1 uses a straightedge to draw an angle on Player 2's Record Sheet.

2. Player 2 estimates the degree measure of the angle.

3. Player 1 measures the angle with a protractor. Players agree on the measure.

4. Player 2's score is the difference between the estimate and the actual measure of the angle. (The difference will be 0 or a positive number.)

5. Players trade roles and repeat Steps 1–4.

6. Players add their scores at the end of 5 rounds. The player with the lower total score wins.

Game Master 14 (p. 273)

Angle Tangle Gameboard

Differentiation Options

READINESS Students may need a review of using a protractor to measure an angle. A diagram on the gameboard shows how to use a half-circle protractor. Starting with a review of benchmark angle measures may also be helpful:

▶ Players score 1 point for correctly estimating whether an angle is larger or smaller than a right angle. They can use the corner of a piece of paper to check their estimates. The player with more points wins.

▶ Players make angle templates by drawing and cutting out 20°, 30°, 45°, 60°, 90°, 135°, 180°, 225°, and 270° angles. They trace one of these templates on each turn.

ENRICHMENT

▶ Players measure reflex angles.

▶ Each player draws an angle. Both players estimate the difference between the angle measures. The player with the closer estimate scores 1 point. The player with more points wins.

ELL SUPPORT Explain how an *estimate* and an *actual measure* are different. Ask: *What strategies can you use to estimate the measures of angles? Which angle measures are easy to estimate? More difficult to estimate?*

GRADE 1

Animal Weight Top-It

Strands Number and Numeration; Operations and Computation

Skill Adding, subtracting, and comparing 2-digit numbers

Materials (per pair)

◆ Game Masters 15–18 (Animal Cards, 2 sets; also available in Grade 1 *Math Journal 2,* Activity Sheets 7 and 8)

◆ Game Master 4 (Record Sheet, optional)

◆ Game Master 19 (directions, optional)

Players 2

Object of the game To earn more points than the other player.

Games Across the Grades

Grades	PK	K	1	2	3	4	5	6
Advanced Learning								
Core Program			◆					
Reteaching and Practice					◆	◆		

NOTE: To play Animal Weight Top-It, students need only Game Masters 15 and 17. To play both versions of this game, pair Game Masters 15 and 16 and Game Masters 17 and 18 to create cards with weights on the front and lengths on the back.

Players can use Game Master 4 to record and compare the animal weights and lengths.

Directions

1. One player shuffles the cards and stacks them weight-side down.

2. Player 1 turns over the two top cards. Player 2 turns over the next card.

3. Player 1 finds the total weight of the animals on his or her cards and tells whether these two animals together weigh more or less than Player 2's animal.

4. If they weigh more, Player 1 scores the difference between his or her total and Player 2's cards. If they weigh less, Player 2 scores the difference between his or her card and Player 1's total. In case of a tie, neither player scores.

5. Players trade roles and play continues.

6. The game ends when all cards from the stack have been played. The player with more points wins.

Another Way to Play

Players use the sides of the cards showing animals' lengths to play a version of the game comparing the lengths of animals.

Differentiation Options

READINESS Students may need a review of comparing, adding, or subtracting 1- and 2-digit numbers. Beginning with smaller numbers or simplifying the comparisons may be helpful:

► Players use number cards 0–10 instead of Animal Cards to learn the rules of the game.

► Players use a set of Animal Cards on which you have rounded each weight to the nearest ten.

► Each player draws only one card for each round.

ENRICHMENT

► Each player draws two cards in each round.

ELL SUPPORT Ask students to identify some of their favorite animals and to estimate how many pounds each animal weighs. Provide sample animal weights using the game cards or information from the Internet.

GRADES 2–3

Array Bingo

Strands Number and Numeration; Operations and Computation; Patterns, Functions, and Algebra

Skill Multiplication with arrays

Materials (per group)

◆ *Array Bingo* Cards (1 set per player)
  • For Level 1: Use Set A (or Game Master 20).
  • For Level 2: Use Sets A and B (or Game Master 20).
  • For Level 3: Use Set C (or Game Master 21).

◆ Everything Math Deck (number cards 1–20, 1 of each)

Players 2 or 3

Object of the game To turn over a row, column, or diagonal of cards.

Grade 3

SRB
273

Games Across the Grades

Grades	PK	K	1	2	3	4	5	6
Advanced Learning								
Core Program				◆	◆			
Reteaching and Practice						◆	◆	

Array Bingo: Original Version

Directions

Advance Preparation: Have students begin with the "A" cards in a 3-by-3 arrangement. Add the "B" cards to make 4-by-4 arrangements when students are ready. Replace these cards with set C to introduce the × symbol. The cards in set D are for the Advanced Version, but their back sides can be used to play the basic version with greater products. If you use the "D" cards, you will need the number cards on cardstock (or Game Master 24) instead of the Everything Math Deck.

1. Each player arranges his or her array cards faceup in a square array.
   ◆ Level 1: Each player uses the 9 "A" cards in a 3-by-3 array.
   ◆ Level 2: Each player uses all 16 "A" and "B" cards.
   ◆ Level 3: Each player uses all 16 "C" cards.

2. One player shuffles the number cards and stacks them whole-number side down.
   ◆ For Level 1: Players use cards 1–12.
   ◆ For Level 2: Players use cards 1–20.
   ◆ For Level 3: Players use cards 1–20.

3. Players take turns drawing a number card, looking for an array with that number of dots, and turning the matching array card facedown. If there is no matching array card, the player's turn ends. The number card is placed in a discard pile.

Game Master 20 (p. 279)

Array Bingo Cards (A and B)

A 2 by 2	A 2 by 3	A 2 by 4	B 4 by 4
A 2 by 5	A 2 by 6	B 3 by 5	B 6 by 3
A 3 by 3	A 1 by 7	A 4 by 3	A 3 by 6
B 5 by 3	A 6 by 1	B 4 by 5	B 5 by 4

Game Master 21 (p. 280)

Array Bingo Cards (C)

C 2 × 2	C 2 × 3	C 2 × 4	C 4 × 4
C 2 × 5	C 2 × 6	C 3 × 5	C 6 × 3
C 3 × 3	C 1 × 7	C 4 × 3	C 3 × 6
C 5 × 3	C 6 × 1	C 4 × 5	C 5 × 4

NOTE: The *Array Bingo Gameboard* shows directions and playing space for the Advanced Version. You can simplify the rules of the Advanced Version by allowing players to turn the "D" cards over to check the arrays *as* they choose a card. As players become proficient, you can begin to limit the number of cards that can be checked per turn.

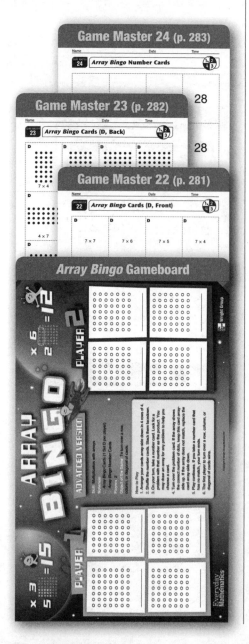

4. The first player to turn an array card facedown so that a row, column, or diagonal of cards is all facedown calls out "Bingo!"

5. If all of the number cards are used before someone wins, players shuffle them and play continues.

Array Bingo: Advanced Version

Materials

◆ *Array Bingo* Gameboard (optional)

◆ *Array Bingo* Cards, Set D (or Game Masters 22 and 23, 1 set per player)

◆ *Array Bingo* Number Cards (or Game Master 24, 1 set per group)

1. Each player arranges his or her cards array-side down in a 4-by-4 array.

2. One player shuffles and stacks the number cards facedown.

3. Players take turns drawing a number card and looking for a problem with that number as the product. Encourage players to draw an array for any problem to help them choose a card.

4. After choosing a problem card, a player turns it over. If the array shows the correct number of dots, this card stays array-side up. If the array does not match, the player replaces the card array-side down.

5. Play continues. If a player's number card has no match, that player's turn ends.

6. The first player to turn over a row, column, or diagonal of cards wins.

7. If all of the number cards are used before someone wins, players shuffle them and play continues.

Differentiation Options

READINESS Students may benefit from a review of skip-counting and the meaning of *array.* Further practice with basic facts may be helpful:

▶ Players make their own cards for all basic facts with products through 9, and use these with number cards through 9.

ENRICHMENT

▶ Players prepare additional cards in the style of set D and use them to play the Advanced Version with different facts.

▶ A player may earn a bonus point for drawing a second array for the number on his or her card.

ELL SUPPORT Use the cards to model a winning *row, column,* and *diagonal.*

GRADE K

Attribute Spinner Game

Strands Geometry; Patterns, Functions, and Algebra

Skill Choosing blocks based on attributes (color, shape, and size)

Materials (per group)

◆ Games Masters 25 and 26 (spinners)

◆ 1 transparent spinner (or a paper clip and pencil)

◇ 1 set of attribute blocks

Players 2–5

Object of the game To collect the most blocks.

Games Across the Grades

Grades	PK	K	1	2	3	4	5	6
Advanced Learning		◆						
Core Program			◆					
Reteaching and Practice			◆					

Directions

Advance Preparation: To create spinners, tape each spinner face from Game Masters 25 and 26 to the back of a transparent spinner, or show students how to hold the transparent spinner in place over a spinner face. Alternatively, model how to use a paper clip and pencil to spin (see the drawing on Game Master 2).

1. Players take turns. For each turn, a player spins the attribute spinners for shape, color, and size. He or she chooses the shape that matches the attributes shown on all three spinners; for example, a large, blue triangle.

2. If all blocks matching the three attributes have already been taken, the player does not take a block, and his or her turn is over.

3. The game ends when all of the blocks have been chosen. The player with the most blocks wins.

NOTE: For Step 2, players may decide as a group what to do if all of the matching blocks have already been taken: skip a turn, spin one spinner again, and so on.

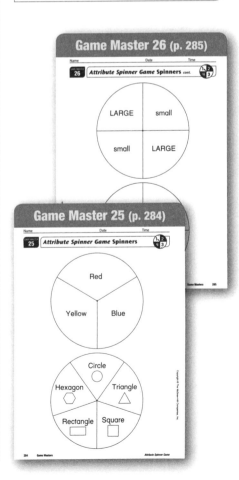

Game Master 26 (p. 285)

Game Master 25 (p. 284)

Differentiation Options

READINESS Students may need practice in describing the shapes, colors, and sizes of the blocks before playing. Limiting the number of attributes may also be helpful:

▶ Use only the spinners for shape and color.

ENRICHMENT

▶ Players also use the thickness spinner on Game Master 26 and choose a block matching four attributes.

ELL SUPPORT Use the shapes spinner to discuss the names for different shapes: *circle, triangle, square, rectangle,* and *hexagon.* Ask students to trace each shape with a finger and describe it.

A

GRADES K–1 Attribute Train Game

Games Across the Grades								
Grades	PK	K	1	2	3	4	5	6
Advanced Learning		◆						
Core Program			◆	◆				
Reteaching and Practice					◆			

Strands Geometry; Patterns, Functions, and Algebra

Skill Identifying blocks that differ by just one attribute (shape, size, or color)

Materials (per group)

◆ Game Master 27 (directions, optional)

◇ 1 set of attribute blocks

Players 2–5

Object of the game To put the last block in the train, or to have the fewest blocks left.

Game Master 27 (p. 286)

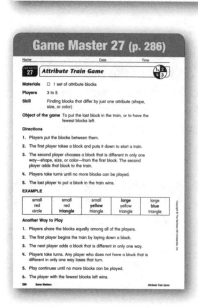

Directions

1. The blocks are placed between the players.

2. The first player takes a block and puts it down to start a train.

3. The second player chooses a block that is different in *only one* way—in shape, size, or color—from the first block. The second player adds that block to the train.

4. Players continue taking turns until no more blocks can be played.

5. The last player to put a block in the train wins.

Example				
Player 1	**Player 2**	**Player 3**	**Player 4**	**Player 5**
small	small	small	**large**	large
red	red	small **yellow**	yellow	**blue**
circle	**triangle**	triangle	triangle	triangle

Another Way to Play

The blocks are shared equally among all of the players. Each player takes a turn by adding one of his or her blocks to the train. If a player cannot add a block to the train, he or she loses that turn. Play continues until no more blocks can be played. The player with the fewest blocks wins.

Differentiation Options

READINESS Students may need practice in describing the shape, color, and size of the blocks before playing. Limiting the number of attributes may be helpful:

▶ Players use only small blocks.

ENRICHMENT

▶ Players consider thickness as well as color, shape, and size.

▶ Players use number cards 1–4 (4 of each). On each turn, they turn over a card to determine how many attributes must be different for the next block.

ELL SUPPORT Explain the meaning of **train** in this context. Explain that a train is formed by linking one or more things together.

GRADES 1–4

Base-10 Exchange Games

Strand Number and Numeration

Skill Place-value concepts; counting and exchanging blocks

Materials (per group)

◆ Gameboard or Place-Value Mat

◆ 2 dice

◇ base-10 blocks

Players 2

Games Across the Grades

Grades	PK	K	1	2	3	4	5	6
Advanced Learning								
Core Program			◆	◆	◆	◆		
Reteaching and Practice							◆	

Base-10 Exchange (recommended for Grades 1–3)

Materials (per pair)

◆ *Exchange Games* Gameboard, *Base-10 Games* Gameboard, or 2 copies of Game Master 28

◆ Game Master 29 (directions, optional)

◆ 2 dice

◇ base-10 blocks: 1 flat, 30 longs, and 30 cubes

Object of the game To make an exchange for a flat.

NOTE: For Grades 1 and 2, you may want to begin with 20 longs, 40 cubes, and no flats. The game ends when there are no more longs in the bank. The player with more longs (or more cubes if there is a tie) wins.

Game Master 29 (p. 288)

Game Master 28 (p. 287)

Base-10 Games **Gameboard**

Base-10 Games

Exchange Games **Gameboard**

Exchange Games

NOTE: You may want to write the words *Hundreds, Tens,* and *Ones* in the appropriate columns of the Place-Value Mat on Game Master 28.

Directions

1. Players put all of the base-10 blocks in a "bank" between them.

2. Players take turns. For each turn, a player rolls the dice and announces the total number of dots.

3. The player who rolled takes that number of cubes from the bank and places them in the Cubes column of his or her mat.

4. Whenever possible, a player exchanges 10 cubes for 1 long and places it in the Longs column. When there are 10 longs, a player exchanges them for 1 flat.

5. The player not rolling the dice checks the exchanges.

6. The first player to make an exchange for a flat wins.

Base-10 Trading (recommended for Grades 1–3)

Materials (per pair)

◆ *Base-10 Games* Gameboard (or Game Master 28, 2 copies)

◆ Game Master 29 (directions, optional)

◆ 2 dice

◇ base-10 blocks: 2 flats, 20 longs, and 40 cubes

Object of the game To clear the game mat.

Directions

1. Players put 20 longs and 40 cubes in a "bank". Each player puts 1 flat on the Flats column of his or her mat.

2. Players take turns. For each turn, a player rolls the dice and announces the total number of dots.

3. The player who rolled returns that number of cubes to the bank. A player exchanges 1 flat for 10 longs and 1 long for 10 cubes from the bank as needed.

4. The player not rolling the dice checks the exchanges.

5. The first player to clear his or her mat wins.

Base-10 Decimal Exchange (recommended for Grades 3 and 4)

Materials (per pair)

◆ *Base-10 Decimal Exchange* Gameboard (or Game Master 30, 2 copies)

◆ Game Master 31 (directions, optional)

◆ 2 dice

◇ base-10 blocks: 1 flat, 30 longs, and 30 cubes

Object of the game To make an exchange for a flat (one).

Directions

The rules are the same as for *Base-10 Exchange,* except the cubes represent hundredths, the longs represents tenths, and the flats represent ones. Have players describe the exchanges they make.

Advanced Version (recommended for Grade 4)

Players use the Place-Value Mat on Game Master 32 and 1 big cube, 30 flats, 30 longs, and 30 cubes. The cubes represent thousandths, the longs represent hundredths, the flats represents tenths, and the big cube represents one. The first player to exchange 10 flats for a big cube wins.

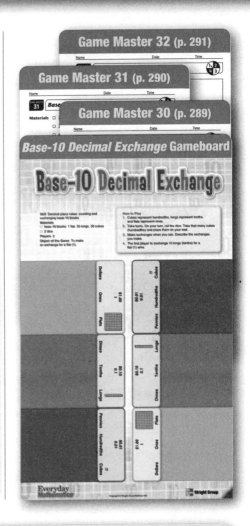

Differentiation Options

READINESS Students may need a review of block equivalencies before playing either game. Using an organizer may be helpful:

> ▶ Draw a ten-frame in the Cubes column for each player. Players fill the frame with cubes and then trade the cubes for a long.

ENRICHMENT

> ▶ After each round, players record their totals in expanded notation. For example, a player with 3 longs and 6 cubes writes $30 + 6 = 36$.

ELL SUPPORT Explain that the blocks can represent different numbers for different games. For example, in *Base-10 Decimal Exchange,* the **cubes** represent hundredths, the **longs** represent tenths, and the **flats** represent ones.

GRADES 3–5 Baseball Multiplication

Strands Number and Numeration; Operations and Computation

Skill Multiplication

Materials (per group)
◆ For Grades 3 and 4: *Baseball Multiplication* Gameboard (or Game Master 33)
◆ For Grade 5: Game Master 33 (game mat)
◆ 2 to 4 dice
◆ 4 counters
◇ 1 calculator or a Multiplication/Division Facts Table

Grade 3 — SRB 274

Grade 4 — SRB 231

Grade 5 — SRB 297

Players 2, or 2 teams
Object of the game To score more runs.

Games Across the Grades

Grades	PK	K	1	2	3	4	5	6
Advanced Learning						◆		
Core Program					◆	◆	◆	
Reteaching and Practice								◆

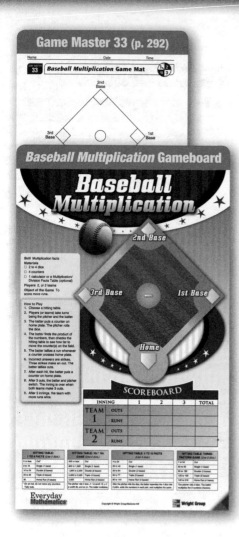

Game Master 33 (p. 292)

NOTE: You can modify the game for longer play by replacing *Out* with *Strike* in the Hitting Table.

Game Master 34 (p. 293)

Directions

Skill Multiplication facts 1 through 6

The rules are similar to those of baseball, but this game lasts only 3 innings.

1. Players or teams take turns being the "pitcher" and the "batter." If students play on teams, members of the batting team take turns batting, and members of the pitching team take turns pitching.

2. A batter begins with a counter on home plate. The pitcher rolls the dice.

3. The batter multiplies the numbers rolled. The pitcher checks the answer with a calculator or a Multiplication/Division Facts Table.

4. If the answer is correct, the batter finds the product in the Hitting Table. If it is a hit, the batter moves all counters on the field the number of bases shown in the table. If a product is an out, no counters move forward.

5. A run is scored each time a counter crosses home plate. The batter tallies each run on the scoreboard.

6. An incorrect answer is a strike, and another pitch (dice roll) is thrown. Three strikes make an out. The batter tallies outs.

7. After each hit or out, the batter puts a counter on home plate.

8. After three outs, the batting team and pitching team switch roles. The inning ends when each player or team has made three outs.

9. The player or team with more runs at the end of three innings wins. If the score is tied, play continues into extra innings until one player or team wins.

Advanced Versions

Use the Hitting Tables on Game Master 34 for any of these Advanced Versions.

1 to 10 Facts

Skill Multiplication facts 1 through 10

Players use number cards 1–10 (4 of each) from the Everything Math Deck and follow the basic rules. The pitcher draws 2 cards. The batter finds the product and uses the Hitting Table for 1-to-10 Facts on Game Master 34.

10s * 10s Game with 2 Dice

Skill Multiplying multiples of 10 through 60 × 60

The rules are the same as for the basic game except that a 1 is worth 10, a 2 is worth 20, and so on. When a batter gives the correct product, players use the Hitting Table on Game Master 34.

1 to 12 Facts

Skill Multiplication facts 1 through 12

Players use a 12-sided die. The pitcher rolls the die twice to get 2 factors. The batter multiplies the numbers rolled and uses the Hitting Table on Game Master 34.

2 to 12 Facts

Skill Multiplication facts 2 through 12

Players use 4 dice and follow the basic rules. The pitcher rolls 4 dice. The batter separates them into 2 pairs, adds the numbers in each pair, and multiplies the sums. Players use the Hitting Table on Game Master 34.

How players pair the numbers can determine the kind of hit they get or whether they get an out.

> **NOTE:** If 11 or 12 is rolled on the 12-sided die, players can pretend that a 10 was rolled.

Example

The pitcher rolls a 1, 2, 3, and 5. The batter could add pairs in different ways and multiply as follows:

one way	a second way	a third way
$1 + 2 = 3$	$1 + 3 = 4$	$1 + 5 = 6$
$3 + 5 = 8$	$2 + 5 = 7$	$2 + 3 = 5$
$3 * 8 = 24$	$4 * 7 = 28$	$6 * 5 = 30$
Out	**Single**	**Single**

Three-Factors Game

Skill Multiplying three numbers from 1 through 6

Players use 3 dice. The pitcher rolls 3 dice. The batter multiplies the 3 numbers (factors) and uses the Hitting Table on Game Master 34.

10s * 10s Game with 4 Dice   (recommended for Grades 4 and 5)

Skill Multiplying two-digit numbers

Players use 4 dice. The rules are the same as for the **2 to 12 Facts** game with 2 exceptions:

- Sums of 2 through 9 represent 20 through 90.
- Sums of 10 through 12 represent themselves.

Example

Player 1 rolls 1, 2, 3, and 5. He or she gets sums of 6 and 5 and multiplies 60 * 50.

Player 2 rolls 3, 4, 6, and 6. He or she gets sums of 7 and 12 and multiplies 70 * 12.

- Players use the Hitting Table on Game Master 34.

Differentiation Options

READINESS Students may need a review of multiplication strategies. It may be helpful to begin with the basic facts:

▶ Players use the number cards 0, 1, 2, and 5 in one pile, and the number cards 0–6 in another pile. The pitcher draws a card from each pile, and the batter multiplies. They use the following Hitting Table:

25 to 30 = Home Run (score a run)	7 to 12 = Single (go to 1st base)
19 to 24 = Triple (go to 3rd base)	0 to 6 = Out (record an out)
13 to 18 = Double (go to 2nd base)	

ENRICHMENT Challenge students to multiply larger multiples of 10:

▶ Tell players that one die in the Three-Factors Game represents a number of tens. For example, if a pitcher rolls 6, 5, and 5, the batter multiplies $60 \times 5 \times 5$. Adjust the Hitting Table by writing a zero at the end of each product: 10 to 540 is an out, 600 to 900 is a single, and so on.

ELL SUPPORT If students are unfamiliar with baseball, explain that *strike, out, hit, single, double, triple,* and *home run* have specific meanings in baseball. Using the game board and counters, explain how to score runs in a baseball game.

GRADES 2–3 Basketball Addition

Games Across the Grades

Grades	PK	K	1	2	3	4	5	6
Advanced Learning			◆					
Core Program				◆	◆			
Reteaching and Practice						◆		

Strand Operations and Computation

Skill Adding three or more 1- and 2-digit numbers

Materials (per group)

◆ *Basketball Addition* Gameboard (or Game Master 35)

◆ 3 dice

Players 2 teams of 3–5 players each

Object of the game To score the greater number of points.

Directions

1. Players on opposite teams take turns rolling the 3 dice.

2. Each player enters the sum of the 3 numbers rolled in the Points Scored table.

3. After all players have rolled the dice, each team finds the team score for the first half and enters it on the Scoreboard.

4. Players continue for the second half of the game.

5. Each team finds its final score. The team with the greater final score wins.

Game Master 35 (p. 294)

Basketball Addition Gameboard

Differentiation Options

READINESS Students may need a review of strategies for adding three numbers or of adding 1- and 2-digit numbers. Starting with smaller numbers may be helpful:

▶ Each player rolls one die one time per turn. The team's score for the first half is the sum of those 3 numbers.

ENRICHMENT

▶ If a player rolls a 1, that player doubles the sum of the other two numbers for his or her score.

ELL SUPPORT Show students pictures of a basketball game and discuss how points are scored. Explain that in *Basketball Addition,* players roll 3 dice to determine how many points they score for each half of the game.

GRADES 1–3 Beat the Calculator: Addition

Strand Operations and Computation; Patterns, Functions, and Algebra

Skill Mental addition

Materials (per group)

◆ Everything Math Deck (number cards 0–10, 4 of each)

◆ Game Master 36 (*Fact Power Table,* optional)

◆ Game Master 37 (*Beat the Calculator* Triangle, optional)

◇ 1 calculator

Players 3

Object of the game To add faster than a player using a calculator.

Grades 1–2 MRB 124   Grade 3 SRB 278

Games Across the Grades

Grades	PK	K	1	2	3	4	5	6
Advanced Learning		◆						
Core Program			◆	◆	◆			
Reteaching and Practice						◆	◆	

NOTE: To begin with easier facts, the Caller may select problems from the unshaded section of Game Master 36 rather than drawing two cards.

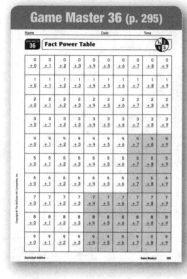

Game Master 36 (p. 295)

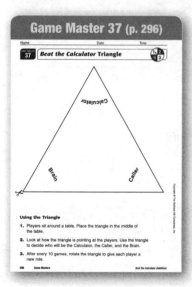

Game Master 37 (p. 296)

Directions

1. One player is the "Caller," one is the "Calculator," and one is the "Brain." (If you are the Caller, divide your class into a Calculator group and a Brain group.)

2. A player shuffles the cards and places them whole-number side down.

3. The Caller draws two cards from the deck and asks for the sum.

4. The Calculator solves the problem *with* a calculator. The Brain solves it *without* a calculator. As soon as a player has found the sum, he or she says it aloud. The Caller decides who got the correct answer first.

5. The player who got the correct answer first wins.

6. Players trade roles every 10 games or so.

Advanced Versions

Mental Subtraction

The Caller draws two cards and asks for the difference.

Fact Extensions

Partners take turns being the Calculator and the Brain while you are the Caller. Call out a basic addition or subtraction fact, and have players respond. Then call out a fact extension for each fact; for example, using the subtraction fact 13 − 6, you can call out 23 − 6 or 130 − 60 as a fact extension.

Differentiation Options

READINESS Students may need a review of addition facts before playing this game. Keeping one addend constant may be helpful:

▶ One number is chosen as the constant. The Caller draws only one card for each game. For example, if 1 is the constant, every addition fact will involve "+ 1."

ENRICHMENT

▶ The Caller uses the full deck of cards (through 20). The Caller draws two cards. The number on the first card becomes a multiple of 10; for example, a 2 becomes 20. The number on the second card will be subtracted from the multiple of 10. So, if the Caller draws a 3 and a 7, the problem is 30−7.

ELL SUPPORT Ask: *Why is one player called "the Brain?"* (Because he or she is expected to solve the problem using his or her brain rather than a calculator or paper and pencil.) *What are some addition problems that would be faster to solve using your brain? Using a calculator?*

Beat the Calculator: Multiplication

GRADES 2–5

Strand Operations and Computation; Patterns, Functions, and Algebra

Skill Mental multiplication

Materials (per group)

- ◆ Everything Math Deck (number cards 1–10, 4 of each)
- ◆ Game Master 37 (*Beat the Calculator Triangle*, optional)
- ◇ 1 calculator

Players 3

Object of the game To multiply faster than a player using a calculator.

Grade 3 **SRB** 279

Grade 4 **SRB** 233

Grade 5 **SRB** 299

Games Across the Grades

Grades	PK	K	1	2	3	4	5	6
Advanced Learning								
Core Program					◆	◆	◆	◆
Reteaching and Practice								◆

Directions

1. One player is the "Caller," one is the "Calculator," and one is the "Brain." (If you are the Caller, divide your class into a Calculator group and a Brain group.)

2. A player shuffles the cards and places them whole-number side down.

3. The Caller draws two cards from the deck and asks for the product.

4. The Calculator solves the problem *with* a calculator. The Brain solves it *without* a calculator. As soon as a player has found the product, he or she says it aloud. The Caller decides who got the correct answer first.

5. The player who got the correct answer first wins.

6. Players trade roles every 10 games or so.

Example

The Caller draws a 10 and a 7 and says, "10 times 7." The Brain and the Calculator each solve the problem and call out their answers. The Caller decides who got the correct answer first.

Advanced Version

Extended Facts (recommended for Grades 4 and 5)

The Caller draws two cards and attaches a 0 to either factor or to both factors before asking for the product. Callers can use Game Master 38 to create the problems.

Game Master 37 (p. 296)

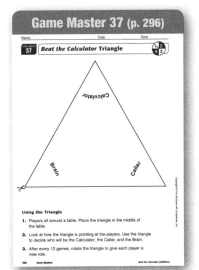

Game Master 38 (p. 297)

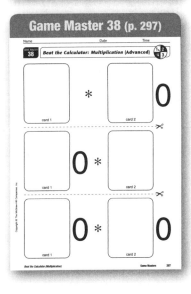

Example

If the Caller turns over a 4 and an 8, he or she may make up any one of the following problems:

| 4 * 80 | 40 * 8 | 40 * 80 |

Differentiation Options

READINESS Students may need a review of strategies for multiplication before playing this game. Keeping one factor constant or using a specific set of multiplication facts may be helpful:

► One number is chosen as the constant. The Caller draws only one card for each game. For example, if 6 is the constant, every multiplication fact will involve "* 6."

► Players make Fact Triangles for a specific set of facts. The Caller draws a Fact Triangle on each turn and calls out a problem from the triangle.

ENRICHMENT Challenge students to multiply a multiple of ten, one hundred, or one thousand by a single-digit factor:

► Players use 3 index cards labeled 10, 100, and 1,000. The Caller first randomly selects an index card and then draws 2 cards. The Caller can make one or both of the factors a multiple of the number on the index card. For example, if the Caller draws 100, 5, and 9, he or she could call 500 * 9, 5 * 900, or 500 * 900.

ELL SUPPORT Ask: *Why is one player called "the Brain?"* (Because he or she is expected to solve the problem using his or her brain rather than a calculator or paper and pencil.)

GRADE **1**

Before and After

Games Across the Grades								
Grades	PK	K	1	2	3	4	5	6
Advanced Learning		◆						
Core Program			◆					
Reteaching and Practice				◆				

Strands Number and Numeration; Operations and Computation

Skill Identifying numbers that are 1 less or 1 more than a given number

---

Materials (per pair)

◆ Everything Math Deck (number cards 0–10, 4 of each)

Players 2

Object of the game To have fewer cards.

Grades 1–2

MRB
126

Directions

1. One player shuffles the cards and deals six cards to each player.

2. The dealer places two cards faceup (whole-number side up) on the table and puts the rest of the deck facedown.

3. Players take turns. For each turn, a player looks for any number in his or her hand that comes just before or just after either of the faceup cards. If the player has such a card, he or she puts it on top of the faceup card. The player puts down as many cards as possible.

Example

If the 2 and 9 cards are showing, a player with 8, 7, and 6 in her hand can play them all in that order on top of the 9.

4. The player draws as many cards as needed from the deck so that he or she has six cards again.

5. If a player can't play any cards on his or her turn, the player takes two cards from the deck and places them faceup on top of the two cards on the table. The player tries to play a card again. If a player still can't play a card, his or her turn is over.

6. The game is over when all cards have been taken from the deck and no player can play any more cards.

7. The player holding fewer cards wins.

Differentiation Options

READINESS Students may need a review of counting forward and back from given numbers. Finding only numbers that are 1 more or only numbers that are 1 less may be helpful:

▶ If players are finding only numbers that are 1 more, then both faceup cards should be 1s. If players are finding only numbers that are 1 less, then both faceup cards should be 10s.

ENRICHMENT Challenge students to identify numbers that are 2 more or 2 less than a given number:

▶ Begin the game with one even and one odd card faceup. Players count by 2s to play cards that are two more or two less than the faceup cards.

ELL SUPPORT Discuss the words *before* and *after.* Compare the everyday use of these words with their mathematical use for counting. Use a number line to illustrate the mathematical use.

The Block-Drawing Game

Games Across the Grades

Grades	PK	K	1	2	3	4	5	6
Advanced Learning			◆					
Core Program				◆				
Reteaching and Practice						◆	◆	

Strand Data and Chance

Skill Using chance data to estimate

Materials (per group)

◇ 1 paper bag

◇ 7 blocks (all the same size and shape) in 3 different colors

◇ 1 slate or piece of paper

Players 3 or more

Object of the game To correctly guess how many blocks of each color are in a bag.

Directions

1. One player is chosen to be the "Director."

2. The Director secretly puts 3, 4, or 5 blocks (not all the same color) into a bag. The Director tells the other players *how many* blocks are in the bag, but *not* their colors.

3. The other players guess how many blocks of *each color* are in the bag. They take turns taking 1 block out of the bag, showing it to all players, and then replacing it.

4. After each draw, the Director records the color and keeps a tally on a slate or piece of paper. The Director shows the tally to all players.

5. A player may try to guess the number of blocks of each color at any time.

6. If a player guesses incorrectly, he or she is out of the game.

7. The first player to guess correctly wins the game.

Example

The Director tells the others that there are 5 blocks in the bag.

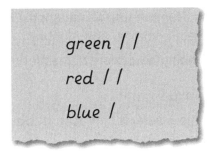

> green / /
>
> red / /
>
> blue /

tally after 5 draws

After five draws, Player 1 guesses 2 green, 2 red, and 1 blue. This guess is incorrect. Player 1 is out of the game.

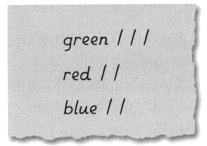

> green / / /
>
> red / /
>
> blue / /

tally after 7 draws

After 7 draws, Player 2 guesses 2 green, 1 red, and 2 blue. This guess is incorrect. Player 2 is out of the game.

Player 3 then guesses 3 green, 1 red, and 1 blue. This guess is correct. Player 3 wins the game.

Differentiation Options

READINESS Students may need a review of using chance data to make predictions. Using fewer blocks and colors may be helpful:

▶ Players use only 4 blocks and 2 colors.

ENRICHMENT Challenge students to record the outcome of the draws in fraction form and to use the fractions to predict:

▶ Players draw 20 times. They record the outcomes in fraction form; for example: $\frac{7}{20}$ *of the time, a red block was drawn.* Then they make a prediction; for example: *It is likely that fewer than half of the blocks are red.*

ELL SUPPORT English learners may be familiar with the word **draw** as a verb that means to create a picture. Explain that, in this game, **draw** means to take 1 cube out of the bag. Explain that more draws will help players to make a better guess.

Broken Calculator

Games Across the Grades

Grades	PK	K	1	2	3	4	5	6
Advanced Learning								
Core Program			◆	◆	◆	◆	◆	◆
Reteaching and Practice								

Strands Number and Numeration; Operations and Computation; Patterns, Functions, and Algebra

Skill Finding equivalent names for numbers

Materials (per group)

◆ Game Master 39 (directions, optional)

◇ 1 calculator

Players 2

Object of the game To have the lower final score.

Game Master 39 (p. 298)

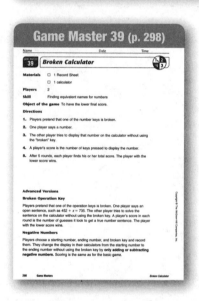

Game Master 40 (p. 299)

Directions

1. Players pretend that one of the number keys is broken.

2. One player says a number.

3. The other player tries to display that number on the calculator without using the "broken" key.

Example

Suppose the 8 key is broken. Here are several ways to display 18 without using the 8 key:

9 [+] 7 [+] 2 [=]

19 [−] 1 [=]

9 [×] 2 [=]

36 [÷] 2 [=]

4. A player's score is the number of keys pressed to display the number.

5. After 5 rounds, each player finds his or her total score. The player with the lower score wins.

Advanced Versions

Broken Operation Key (recommended for Grades 4 and 5)

Players pretend that one of the operation keys is broken. One player says an open sentence. The other player tries to solve the sentence on the calculator without using the broken key.

Players can record their guesses on Game Master 40.

Example

Pretend the $\boxed{-}$ is broken. What is the solution to the open sentence $452 + x = 735$?

Replace the variable x with a number and see if you get a true number sentence. If it is not true, try other numbers until you get a true sentence.

Try **400**: $452 \boxed{+} \textbf{400} \boxed{=} 852$ 400 is too big.

Try **300**: $452 \boxed{+} \textbf{300} \boxed{=} 752$ 300 is 17 away.

Try **317**: $452 \boxed{+} \textbf{317} \boxed{=} 769$ Wrong way!

Try **283**: $452 \boxed{+} \textbf{283} \boxed{=} 735$ True sentence.

283 is the answer.

A player's score in each round is the number of guesses it took to get a true number sentence. The player with the lower score wins.

Negative Numbers (recommended for Grades 5 and 6)

Players choose a starting number, ending number, and broken key and record them on Game Master 41. They change the display in their calculators from the starting number to the ending number without using the broken key by **only adding or subtracting negative numbers.** Scoring is the same as for the basic game.

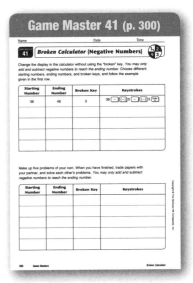

Game Master 41 (p. 300)

Differentiation Options

READINESS Students may need a review of different calculator keys and their functions, and the effect of each operation. Exploring the game as a group may be useful:

▶ Groups of players cooperate to display numbers.

ENRICHMENT

▶ Challenge players to use each operation exactly once to solve each problem in the basic version of the game.

▶ In the Negative Numbers version, players may also multiply or divide by negative numbers.

ELL SUPPORT Explain to students that for each game, they are pretending that one of the calculator keys is broken, or doesn't work. Different keys can be "broken" for different games.

GRADES 5–6 **Build-It**

Games Across the Grades								
Grades	PK	K	1	2	3	4	5	6
Advanced Learning				◆	◆	◆		
Core Program							◆	◆
Reteaching and Practice								

Strand Number and Numeration

Skill Comparing and ordering fractions

Materials (per pair)
- ◆ *Build-It* Gameboard (or Game Master 42)
- ◆ *Build-It* Cards (or Game Master 43)

Players 2

Object of the game To be the first player to arrange 5 fraction cards in order from smallest to largest.

Grade 5 — SRB 300   Grade 6 — SRB 307

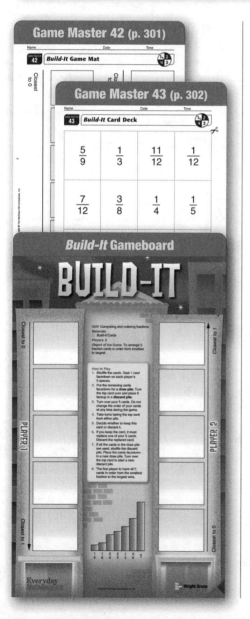

Game Master 42 (p. 301)

42 *Build-It* Game Mat

Game Master 43 (p. 302)

43 *Build-It* Card Deck

$\frac{5}{9}$	$\frac{1}{3}$	$\frac{11}{12}$	$\frac{1}{12}$
$\frac{7}{12}$	$\frac{3}{8}$	$\frac{1}{4}$	$\frac{1}{5}$

Build-It **Gameboard**

BUILD-IT

Directions

1. One player shuffles the cards and deals 1 card facedown on each of the 5 spaces for each player.

2. The dealer puts the remaining cards facedown in a draw pile. He or she turns the top card over and places it faceup in a discard pile.

3. Each player turns over his or her 5 cards. The order of the cards may not be changed at any time during the game.

4. Players take turns. On each turn, a player takes either the top card from the draw pile or the top card from the discard pile.

5. The player decides whether to keep the card or put it faceup on the discard pile.

6. If the player keeps the card, it must replace one of his or her 5 cards. The player puts the replaced card faceup on the discard pile.

7. If all of the draw cards are used, the dealer shuffles the discard pile and places those cards facedown in a new draw pile. The top card is turned over to start a discard pile.

8. The first player to have all 5 cards in order from the smallest fraction to the largest wins.

Differentiation Options

READINESS Students may need to review comparing and ordering fractions with like or compatible denominators:

▶ Players make a deck of *Build-It* cards using halves, fourths, and twelfths as follows: $\frac{1}{2}, \frac{1}{4}, \frac{2}{4}, \frac{3}{4}, \frac{4}{4}, \frac{1}{12}, \frac{2}{12}, \frac{3}{12}, \frac{4}{12}, \frac{5}{12}, \frac{6}{12}, \frac{7}{12}, \frac{8}{12}, \frac{9}{12}, \frac{10}{12},$ and $\frac{11}{12}$.

ENRICHMENT

▶ Players create their own *Build-It* card decks with more challenging fractions, or with a mix of fractions and decimals.

ELL SUPPORT Explain to students that in this game, they will build a list of fractions from smallest to largest, so the fractions will be *in order* from smallest to largest.

GRADE Pre-K Building Towers

Strands Number and Numeration; Measurement and Reference Frames; Geometry

Skills Counting; recognizing numerals; comparing quantities and heights

Materials (per group)
- ◆ Game Master 44 (spinner faces)
- ◆ transparent spinner
- ◇ inch cubes or other small blocks (up to 15 per player)

Players 2–5

Object of the game To build the tower with the most blocks.

Games Across the Grades

Grades	PK	K	1	2	3	4	5	6
Advanced Learning								
Core Program	◆							
Reteaching and Practice		◆						

Advance Preparation Make a spinner by labeling sections on a 6-part spinner face (Game Master 44) with numerals 1–6 and taping it to the back of a transparent spinner.

Directions

1. Players take turns spinning the spinner, reading the numeral, and taking that number of inch cubes.

2. Each player begins building a tower by stacking the cubes he or she collects.

NOTE: Have students play this game in an area away from general block play. Players should sit far enough apart so that their blocks won't get mixed up when their towers fall. See *Making Trains* for a similar game in which children compare horizontal lengths of cube "trains."

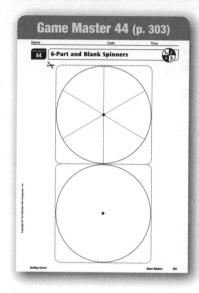

Game Master 44 (p. 303)

3. Players continue spinning the spinner and adding blocks to their towers until one of the towers falls down.

4. After one player's tower has fallen down, each player counts his or her blocks.

5. Players compare their numbers of blocks to see which player's tower used the most blocks. The player who used the most blocks wins.

Differentiation Options

READINESS Students may need a review of numeral recognition or strategies for counting a random assortment of objects. Using smaller numbers or dot patterns may be helpful:

▶ Add the corresponding dot pattern to each numbered section of the spinner.

ENRICHMENT Challenge players to use size comparison language:

▶ As part of each player's turn, the player uses terms such as *taller, shorter,* and *same height* to compare his or her tower to another.

ELL SUPPORT Demonstrate the meaning of *tower.* Ask students to compare two towers of blocks and decide which has more cubes. Explain that in this game, the player who builds the tower with the most cubes wins.

GRADE 1 Bunny Hop

Games Across the Grades									
Grades	PK	K	1	2	3	4	5	6
Advanced Learning	◆	◆						
Core Program			◆					
Reteaching and Practice				◆				

Strands Number and Numeration; Operations and Computation

Skill Counting up and back on a number line

Materials (per pair)
- *Bunny Hop* Gameboard (or Game Master 45, 2 copies)
- 2 bunny markers (available on cardstock or Game Master 45)
- 1 die

Players 2

Object of the game To reach the carrot and return to the rabbit hole.

Directions

Advance Preparation: To use cardstock bunny markers, punch out each card and then clip the bottom of each card along the dotted lines.

To use Game Master 45, cut out and tape together the two number-line sections and cut out the bunny marker for each player.

1. Each player places a bunny marker on 0 on his or her own number line.

2. Players take turns rolling the die and moving the bunny that number of spaces.

3. Each bunny must hop to the carrot and back to the hole. At each end of the number line, players must roll an exact number to reach the carrot or the hole.

4. The first player to get to the carrot and back to the hole wins.

NOTE: As students play, model statements such as, "The bunny hopped 4 spaces from 6 to 10." Make sure students hop toward their destination with each count and do not count the starting point as a hop.

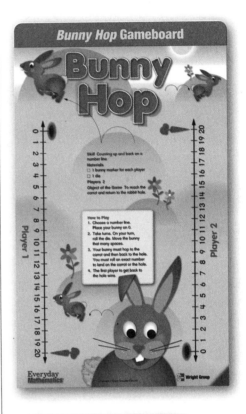

Bunny Hop Gameboard

Differentiation Options

READINESS Students may need a review of counting dots on a die and marks on a number line with one-to-one correspondence, as well as reading numerals through 20. Starting with a simpler number line may be helpful:

▶ Players practice on an unnumbered number line. They draw hops and record the total number of hops above.

▶ Provide a die marked 1, 2, 3, 1, 2, 3 and draw a head of lettuce at 10 on each number line. Players hop to the lettuce and back to the hole.

ENRICHMENT Challenge children to count ahead mentally and explore sums:

▶ After rolling, children predict where the bunny will land. Each correct prediction earns one extra hop.

▶ Draw a head of lettuce at 10 on each number line. After each turn, players state how far the bunny must go to reach the next stop (the lettuce, the carrot, or the hole).

▶ Players write addition number sentences as they move toward the carrot, and subtraction number sentences as they move toward the hole.

ELL SUPPORT Demonstrate the meaning of *rolling an exact number.* Place a bunny at 18 on the number line. Say: *You need to roll an exact number so that the bunny lands on the carrot, What number do you need to roll?* (2) *What happens if you don't roll a 2?* (The bunny remains at 18 until a 2 is rolled.)

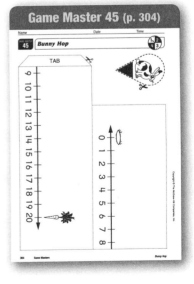

Game Master 45 (p. 304)

GRADE 4

Buzz Games

Strand Number and Numeration; Patterns, Functions, and Algebra

Skill Finding multiples of whole numbers

Materials

Players 5–10

Object of the game To correctly say either "BUZZ" or the next number.

Grade 4

SRB
234

Buzz

Directions

1. Players sit in a circle and choose a leader. The leader names any whole number from 3 to 9. This number is the BUZZ number. The leader also chooses the STOP number. The STOP number should be at least 30.

2. The player to the left of the leader begins the game by saying "one." Play continues clockwise with each player saying either the next whole number or "BUZZ."

3. A player must say "BUZZ" instead of the next number if:
   • The number is the BUZZ number or a multiple of the BUZZ number; or
   • The number contains the BUZZ number as one of its digits.

4. If a player makes an error, the next player starts over with 1.

5. Play continues until the STOP number is reached.

6. For the next round, the player to the right of the leader becomes the new leader.

Example

The BUZZ number is 4. Play should proceed as follows:
"1, 2, 3, BUZZ, 5, 6, 7, BUZZ, 9, 10, 11, BUZZ, 13, BUZZ, 15," and so on.

Bizz-Buzz

Skill Finding common multiples of two whole numbers

Directions

Bizz-Buzz is played like *Buzz,* except that the leader names two numbers: a BUZZ number and a BIZZ number.

Players say:

- "BUZZ" if the number is a multiple of the BUZZ number.
- "BIZZ" if the number is a multiple of the BIZZ number.
- "BIZZ-BUZZ" if the number is a multiple of both the BUZZ number and the BIZZ number.

Example

The BUZZ number is 6, and the BIZZ number is 3. Play should proceed as follows: "1, 2, BIZZ, 4, 5, BIZZ-BUZZ, 7, 8, BIZZ, 10, 11, BIZZ-BUZZ, 13, 14, BIZZ, 16," and so on. The numbers 6 and 12 are replaced by "BIZZ-BUZZ" since 6 and 12 are multiples of both 6 and 3.

Differentiation Options

READINESS Students may need a review of strategies for finding multiples before playing the game. Focusing on multiples or starting with smaller numbers may be helpful:

- ▶ Players say "BUZZ" only for multiples, and NOT when one of the digits is the BUZZ number.
- ▶ For BIZZ-BUZZ, the leader chooses a BIZZ number that is a multiple of the BUZZ number.

ENRICHMENT

- ▶ The leader names 3 numbers. The third number is the BAM number.

ELL SUPPORT Model the game with a small group of students. Ask: *How would you describe the numbers that were not BUZZED in that round?*

GRADE 4
Calculator 10,000

Games Across the Grades									
Grades	PK	K	1	2	3	4	5	6	
Advanced Learning					♦				
Core Program						♦			
Reteaching and Practice							♦	♦	

Strand Operations and Computation

Skill Using estimation with addition, subtraction, multiplication, and division

Materials

◇ 1 calculator per player

Players 1 or 2

Object of the game To get as close to 10,000 as possible, using each operation exactly once.

Grade 4
SRB
235

Directions

1. Each player creates a starting number by picking any number from 1 to 12 and cubing it. For example, if a player picked 5: 5 ⨉ 5 ⨉ 5 = 125. The player's starting number is 125.

2. Before continuing, players decide whether to choose the numbers they will use to add, subtract, multiply, and divide with from either Level 1 or Level 2. (Level 2 is harder.)

   • Level 1: any number except 0

   • Level 2: only numbers from 2 to 100

3. The player picks a number and adds, subtracts, multiplies, or divides his or her starting number with it. For example, if the player starting with 125 picked 100: 125 ⨉ 100 = 12,500.

4. The player picks a different number and uses a different operation from the one used in Step 3 with the result from Step 3. For example, if the player picked 2 and chose to divide: 12,500 ÷ 2 = 6,250.

5. The player continues to pick **different numbers** and use **different operations** until he or she has used each of the four operations once. The operations can be used in any order, but each operation may be used only once.

6. Players should record what they did for each round.

Example

A sample record for one round using Level 1 is shown below. The final result is 10,150.

Pick a Number	Key In	Result
5	5 × 5 × 5 =	125 (starting number)
100	× 100 =	12,500
2	÷ 2 =	6,250
3,000	− 3000 =	3,250
6,900	+ 6900 =	10,150

7. Players play three rounds. For each round, players find the difference between their final result and 10,000. Each player adds his or her three differences to find the total score.

8. If there are 2 players, the player with the lower score wins. If there is 1 player, he or she records the score for the first game, and then tries for a lower score in each subsequent game.

Differentiation Options

READINESS Students may need a review of estimating with different operations. Using fewer operations may be helpful:

► After creating the starting number, players use addition twice and subtraction twice.

ENRICHMENT

► Challenge players to use the operations in a designated order, with addition and subtraction before multiplication and division.

ELL SUPPORT Explain the meaning of *cubing* a number using a cube model.

Chances Are

Games Across the Grades

Grades	PK	K	1	2	3	4	5	6
Advanced Learning				◆	◆			
Core Program						◆		
Reteaching and Practice							◆	

Strand Data and Chance

Skill Describing the probability of events

Materials (per pair)
- ◆ *Chances Are* Gameboard (or Game Master 46, 2 copies)
- ◆ Event Cards (or Game Masters 47 and 48)
- ◆ Probability Cards (or Game Masters 49 and 50)

Players 2

Object of the game To match more cards.

Grade 4

SRB 236

Game Master 46 (p. 305)

Name | Date | Time
46 | *Chances Are Game Mat* | 1 2 4 3

Game Master 47 (p. 306)

Name | Date | Time
47 | *Chances Are Event Cards* | 1 2 4 3

Game Master 48 (p. 307)

Name | Date | Time
48 | *Chances Are Event Cards continued* | 1 2 4 3

Game Master 49 (p. 308)

Name | Date | Time
49 | *Chances Are Probability Cards* | 1 2 4 3

Game Master 50 (p. 309)

Name | Date | Time
50 | *Chances Are Probability Cards continued* | 1 2 4 3

Chances Are Gameboard

Directions

1. One player shuffles the Event Cards and the Probability Cards together and deals 5 cards faceup in front of each player. He or she places the rest of the deck facedown.

2. Players arrange the Event Cards and Probability Cards in the appropriate section of the gameboard.

Example

Each player will have 5 cards at the beginning of a game.

EVENT CARDS

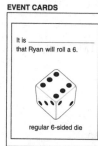

It is _____ that Ryan will roll a 6.

regular 6-sided die

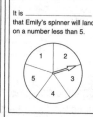

It is _____ that Emily's spinner will land on a number less than 5.

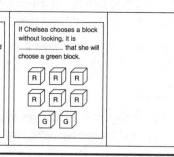

If Chelsea chooses a block without looking, it is _____ that she will choose a green block.

PROBABILITY CARDS

50-50
About half
Even chance

Certain
Sure thing
Positive
Absolutely

3. Players take turns. For each turn, a player draws a card from the deck and places it faceup in the correct section of his or her gameboard. The player tries to match a Probability Card

with an Event Card. A match is made when a player finds a Probability Card with the best description of the chance that the event on the Event Card will happen.

4. If a match is made, the player removes the matching cards from the gameboard and the turn is over. **Only one match may be made per turn.** If no match is made, the turn is over.

Example

Suppose that a player's gameboard looks like the one in the previous example, and the player draws a Probability Card that says "Unlikely".

The player may match this pair of cards and remove them from the gameboard.

It is _____ that Ryan will roll a 6.

regular 6-sided die

Unlikely
Less than half
Slight chance
Not much

Or the player may match this pair of cards and remove them from the gameboard.

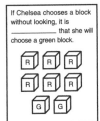

If Chelsea chooses a block without looking, it is _____ that she will choose a green block.

Unlikely
Less than half
Slight chance
Not much

5. The game ends when one player is out of cards or when the deck is gone. The player with more matches wins.

Differentiation Options

READINESS Students may need a review of determining favorable and possible outcomes for each type of event. Limiting the types of events may be helpful:

▶ Players use only the Event Cards showing spinners or dice with all of the Probability Cards.

ENRICHMENT Challenge students to determine the expected probability of events as they play the game:

▶ Players receive a bonus point if they express as a fraction the probability of the event on any Event Cards they match. Bonus points are counted as cards to determine who wins.

ELL SUPPORT Explain the difference between an *Event* Card and a *Probability* Card. Explain that all of the words on a Probability Card are different ways of saying the same thing about how likely it is that something might happen. The words on the Probability Cards go in the blanks on the Event Cards, which describe activities such as spinning a spinner, rolling a die, or choosing a ball or a block from a bag without looking.

GRADE K

Clear the Board/Cover the Board

Games Across the Grades								
Grades	PK	K	1	2	3	4	5	6
Advanced Learning	◆							
Core Program		◆						
Reteaching and Practice			◆					

Strand Number and Numeration

Skill Counting with one-to-one correspondence

Materials (per group)

◆ Game Master 51 (or a checkerboard)

◆ 64 counters (or checkers)

◆ 2 dice

Players 2–5

NOTE: Before either game begins, players can decide whether the checkerboard has to be cleared (or filled) by an exact count to end the game. Players can also decide whether to work together to remove counters, or to play against each other so that the player who removes (or adds) the last counter wins.

Game Master 51 (p. 310)

Clear the Board

Object of the game To remove the last counter from the board.

Directions

1. Players take turns rolling both dice, finding the total number of dots, and removing that number of counters from the board.

2. Play continues until the board is empty.

Cover the Board

Object of the game To place the last counter on the board.

Directions

Players start with an empty board. They roll the dice and add counters to fill the board.

Differentiation Options

READINESS Students may need to review counting before playing either game. It may be helpful to limit how high students need to count:

▶ Players use only one die, or two dice labeled with dot patterns through 3.

ENRICHMENT

▶ Players use one dot die and one die numbered 1–6.

▶ Players roll one die numbered 1–6. They double the number rolled.

ELL SUPPORT Explain that *clear* has different meanings. In this game, it means taking all counters off the board.

Coin-Dice

GRADE **1**

Strands Number and Numeration; Measurement and Reference Frames

Skill Making exchanges with pennies, nickels, and dimes

Materials (per pair)

◆ *Coin Exchange Games* Gameboard (optional)
◆ 60 pennies, 12 nickels, 6 dimes
◆ 2 dice

Players 2

Object of the game To collect more money.

Games Across the Grades

Grades	PK	K	1	2	3	4	5	6
Advanced Learning		◆						
Core Program			◆					
Reteaching and Practice					◆	◆		

Directions

1. Players put all of the coins in a "bank" between them.
2. Players take turns rolling both dice and taking as many pennies from the bank as the total number on the dice.
3. At the end of each turn, a player makes any possible exchanges with the bank—5 pennies for a nickel, 5 pennies and 1 nickel for a dime, 2 nickels for a dime, or 10 pennies for a dime.
4. To pick up the last pennies, the total number on the dice must match the total value of the remaining coins.
5. The player who has more money wins.

Differentiation Options

READINESS Students may need a review of coin values and exchanges before playing the game. Limiting the types of coins used may be helpful:

▶ Players use only pennies and nickels. (At the end of the game, they can make exchanges for dimes.)

ENRICHMENT

▶ Players roll two dice and compare the numbers. They pick up the number of pennies indicated by the smaller number and the number of nickels indicated by the larger number. They exchange for dimes if possible.

▶ Players add two quarters to the bank. (Also see *Coin Exchange*.)

ELL SUPPORT Explain that *bank* has many different meanings; for example, a container (usually with a slot in the top) for keeping money at home, or a building where money is saved. Explain that *exchange* means to trade, such as exchanging one item of clothing at a store for another item. Ask students to identify examples of fair coin exchanges (exchanges of equal value). If students struggle, model exchanging coins with the bank.

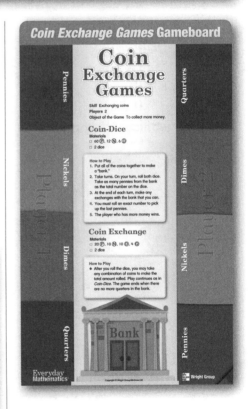

Coin Exchange Games Gameboard

GRADES 1–2

Coin Exchange

Games Across the Grades

Grades	PK	K	1	2	3	4	5	6
Advanced Learning		◆						
Core Program			◆	◆				
Reteaching and Practice				◆				

Strands Number and Numeration; Measurement and Reference Frames

Skill Coin equivalencies

Materials (per pair)

◆ *Coin Exchange Games* Gameboard (optional)

◆ 20 pennies, 10 nickels, 10 dimes, and 4 quarters

◆ 2 dice

Players 2

Object of the game To collect more money.

Grades 1–2

MRB
128

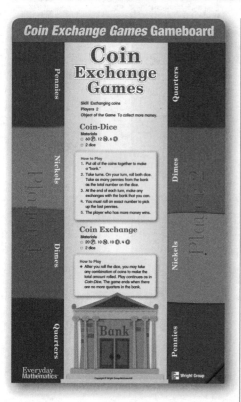

Coin Exchange Games Gameboard

Directions

1. Players put all of the coins in a "bank" between them.

2. Players take turns. For each turn, a player rolls both dice and collects from the bank the amount of money shown on the dice. Players may take any combination of coins adding up to the amount shown.

3. At the end of each turn, a player makes any possible exchanges with the bank—5 pennies for a nickel, 5 pennies and 1 nickel for a dime, 2 nickels for a dime, 10 pennies for a dime, or a combination of nickels and dimes for a quarter.

4. The game ends when there are no more quarters in the bank. The player who has more money wins.

Advanced Version

Players use a larger bank and 2 polyhedral dice.

Differentiation Options

READINESS Students may need a review of money exchanges and comparing the values of groups of coins before playing the game. Limiting the types of coins used may be helpful:

▶ Players use only 30 pennies and 20 dimes. After each round, they compare the total values of their coins.

▶ For a game that uses only pennies, nickels, and dimes, see *Money Cube* or *Coin-Dice.*

ENRICHMENT Challenge students to make more exchanges as they build larger coin collections:

▶ Players use the Everything Math Deck. For each turn, they draw one card and take from the bank a combination of coins with a total value equal to the number on the card. After five rounds, players calculate and compare totals.

ELL SUPPORT Discuss *exchange* in the context of this game. Ask students to exchange coin(s) for other coin(s) of equal value.

GRADES 1–4 Coin Top-It

Strands Number and Numeration; Operations and Computation; Measurement and Reference Frames

Skill Finding and comparing the values of coin combinations

Materials (per pair)
◆ For Grades 1–3: Money Card Deck (or Game Master 52)
◆ For Grade 4: Game Master 52 and/or 53

Players 2

Object of the game To collect more cards than the other player.

Games Across the Grades

Grades	PK	K	1	2	3	4	5	6
Advanced Learning			◆					
Core Program				◆	◆	◆	◆	
Reteaching and Practice							◆	

Directions

1. Players shuffle the cards and stack them coin-side down.

2. Each player draws a card and says the total amount of money shown. The player with the greater amount takes both cards.

3. In case of a tie, each player takes another card. The player with the greater amount takes all 4 cards.

NOTE: For Grade 1, begin with the Money Deck cards showing only pennies and nickels: 2 cards for each value from 7¢ through 20¢. Gradually add cards with dimes and quarters.

C

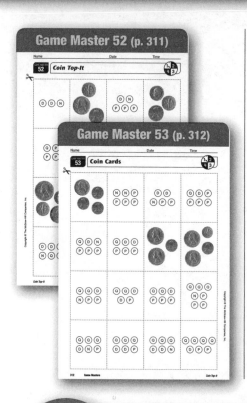

Game Master 52 (p. 311)

Game Master 53 (p. 312)

4. The game ends when there are no cards left to draw. The player with more cards wins.

Differentiation Options

READINESS Students may need a review of coin values and determining the value of a coin collection. Modeling the amounts may be helpful:

► Players use cards with coin amounts through 20 cents and real coins to model the totals on their cards. Players can exchange the coins for pennies to help them find and compare their totals.

ENRICHMENT

► Players draw two cards on every turn. They find the total for all of the coins pictured on both cards and compare totals. They earn a bonus point if they can determine that the total on the two cards could be represented using only nickels or dimes.

ELL SUPPORT Explain that a circled *D* represents a dime, a circled *P* represents a penny, and a circled *Q* represents a quarter.

GRADES PK–K

Cover All

Games Across the Grades								
Grades	PK	K	1	2	3	4	5	6
Advanced Learning								
Core Program	◆	◆						
Reteaching and Practice			◆					

Strand Number and Numeration

Skills Counting with one-to-one correspondence

Materials (per group)
◆ *Cover All* Gameboard (or Game Masters 54 and 55, 1 per player)
◆ 1 dot die
◆ 16 counters per player

Players 2–5

Object of the game To cover all spaces with counters.

NOTE: Before the game begins, players decide whether the game mat has to be filled by an exact count.

Directions

Advance Preparation: Choose one or more appropriate grids. Cross out squares on the gameboards if you need 6- and 9-cell grids.

1. Players take turns. For each turn, a player rolls the die and says the number of dots. He or she takes that number of counters and places them on his or her game mat, one counter per space.

2. Players continue taking turns adding counters to their mats.

3. The first player to cover all of the spaces on his or her game mat wins.

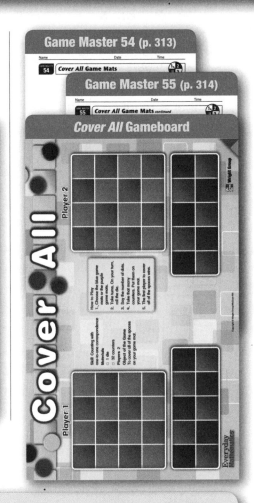

Game Master 54 (p. 313)

54 | Cover All Game Mats

Game Master 55 (p. 314)

55 | Cover All Game Mats *continued*

Cover All Gameboard

Differentiation Options

READINESS Students may need to review counting before playing this game. It may be helpful to limit how high students need to count:

▶ Create dice labeled with 1, 2, or 3 dots. Players use only the 6-square grid.

ENRICHMENT Challenge students to identify numerals or compare numbers as they play the game:

▶ Players use spinners or dice with the numerals 1–6, instead of dot dice, to determine how many counters to add to the grid.

▶ As students play, pose questions such as the following: *How many more counters do you need to fill your grid? Which grid has more (fewer) counters right now?*

ELL SUPPORT Show an example of a winning game mat to demonstrate the meaning of ***cover all of the spaces.***

GRADE **K**

Cover Half

Strand Number and Numeration

Skill Counting with one-to-one correspondence; recognizing half of a group

Materials (per pair)

◆ Game Master 56 (directions and game mat)

◆ 1 die marked 1, 2, 3, 1, 2, 3

◆ counters

Players 2

Object of the game To cover half of the game mat.

Games Across the Grades

Grades	PK	K	1	2	3	4	5	6
Advanced Learning		◆						
Core Program			◆					
Reteaching and Practice				◆				

Directions

1. Players take turns rolling the die.

2. Players place 1, 2, or 3 counters on the game mat, depending on the roll of the die.

NOTE: Before the game begins, players can decide whether rolling an exact number is required to end the game.

3. The game ends when half of the game mat is covered. Players may cover the top, bottom, left, or right half of the game mat or cover half of the squares in a pattern.

Differentiation Options

READINESS Students may need to review counting before playing this game. Using a die with dots may be helpful:

▶ Add the appropriate number of dots to each side of the die so players can match the number of counters they choose to the number of dots.

▶ Players shade half of the game mat before beginning.

ENRICHMENT

▶ To challenge players to think of different ways to show $\frac{1}{2}$, add the rule that players may NOT fill any row or column.

▶ Cut out a mat with an even number of squares from Game Master 51 and have students play with a greater number of counters. You may want to provide a die numbered 1–6 for players using the full 64-square board. Continue challenging players to cover half in different ways.

ELL SUPPORT Show examples of winning game mats to demonstrate the meaning of covering the top, bottom, left, or right half of the game mat, or covering half of the squares in a pattern.

Credits/Debits Games

Games Across the Grades									
Grades	PK	K	1	2	3	4	5	6
Advanced Learning								
Core Program						◆	◆	◆
Reteaching and Practice								

Strand Operations and Computation

Skill Adding and subtracting positive and negative numbers

Materials (per pair)

◆ *Credits/Debits Game* Gameboard (or Game Master 57, 2 copies)

◆ Everything Math Deck

◇ 1 coin (Advanced Version only)

Players 2

Object of the game To have the greater balance.

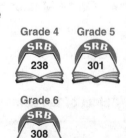

Players pretend they are accountants for a business. Their jobs are to keep track of the company's current balance, also called the "bottom line."

Credits/Debits Game (recommended for Grade 4)

Skill Adding positive and negative numbers

Directions

1. One player shuffles the deck and places it whole-number side down.

2. Each player begins with a balance of +$10.

3. Players take turns. For each turn, a player draws a card. The card tells the dollar amount and whether it is a credit or debit. The black numbers are "credits," and the blue numbers are "debits."

4. The player records the credit (positive) or debit (negative) in the "Change" column. The player adds the credit or debit to adjust the balance, records the result in the "End" column, and copies the result into the "Start" column in the next row.

5. At the end of 10 turns each, the player with more money wins. If both players have negative amounts, the player whose amount is closer to 0 wins.

Example

Beth has a "Start" balance of +$20. She draws a black 4. This is a credit of $4, so she records +$4 in the "Change" column. She adds $4 to the balance: $20 + $4 = $24. She records +$24 in the "End" column, and +$24 in the "Start" column on the next line.

Alex has a "Start" balance of +$10. He draws a blue 12. This is a debit of $12, so he records −$12 in the "Change" column. He adds −$12 to the balance: $10 + (−$12) = −$2. Alex records −$2 in the "End" column. He also records −$2 in the "Start" column on the next line.

Credits/Debits Game: Advanced Version

Skill Adding and subtracting positive and negative numbers

Directions

1. One player shuffles the deck and places it whole-number side down.

NOTE: Both versions can be played on either gameboard. Students in Grades 5 and 6 might need the directions for the basic game that appear on Game Master 58.

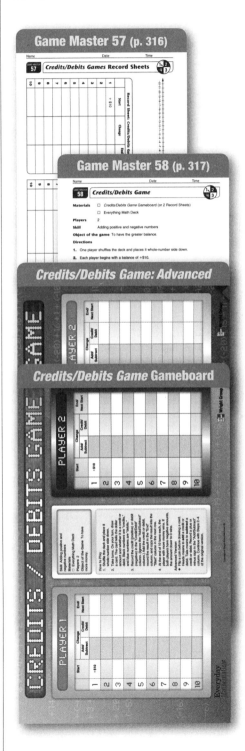

2. Each player begins with a balance of +$10.

3. Players take turns. For each turn, a player flips a coin to see whether to add or subtract. The heads side of the coin tells the player to **add** a credit or debit. The tails side of the coin tells the player to **subtract** a credit or debit. The player records the operation sign in the "Add or Subtract" column.

4. The player draws a card to determine the dollar amount (positive or negative) to add to or subtract from the balance. The black numbers are "credits," and the blue numbers are "debits".

5. The player records the credit or debit in the "Change" column. The player uses the credit or debit to adjust the balance, records the result in the "End" column, and copies the result into the "Start" column in the next row.

6. At the end of 10 turns each, the player with more money wins. If both players have negative amounts, the player whose amount is closer to 0 wins.

Example

Max has a "Start" balance of $5. His coin lands heads up and he records + in the "Addition or Subtraction" column.

He draws a blue 9 and records −$9 in the "Credit or Debit" column. Max adds: $5 + (−$9) = −$4. He records −$4 in the "End" column and also in the "Start" column on the next line.

Amy has a "Start" balance of −$20. Her coin lands tails up, which means subtract. She draws a black 1 (+$1). She subtracts: −$20 − (+$1) = −$21. Her "End" balance is −$21.

Differentiation Options

READINESS Students may need a review of adding and subtracting negative numbers. Modeling the problems may be helpful:

▶ Players use number cards 1–5 (2 black and 2 blue of each number), and 20 each of the following: $1 bills, $10 bills, and $1 IOUs on slips of paper.

▶ Players use the number line on Game Master 57.

ENRICHMENT

▶ Players record number sentences for each round of the game.

▶ Players draw two cards on each turn and use their sum to adjust the balance.

ELL SUPPORT Explain that a *credit* is a positive addition to a bank account and a *debit* removes money from a bank account.

Dart Game

Strand Geometry

Skill Finding lines of reflection

Materials (per pair)

◆ Game Master 59 (dartboard, darts, and directions)

◇ 1 transparent mirror

Players 2

Object of the game To have the higher score by reflecting one of the darts to hit the target.

Games Across the Grades

Grades	PK	K	1	2	3	4	5	6
Advanced Learning					◆			
Core Program							◆	
Reteaching and Practice								◆

Directions

Game Master 59 has two darts, labeled A and B, and a target. The idea is to "hit" the target by reflecting one of the darts with the transparent mirror.

1. Players first practice hitting the target. One player uses Dart A; the other uses Dart B. Players look through the mirror and move it around until the image of the dart hits the target.

2. After practicing, players switch darts—that is, if they practiced with Dart A, they play the game with Dart B (and vice versa).

3. Players take turns. Each player tries to hit the target by placing the transparent mirror on the page **without looking through the mirror.**

4. After a player has placed the mirror on the master, he or she looks through the mirror to find the score.

5. The player with the higher total score after 3 rounds wins.

NOTE: The actual game varies from the practice game in one important respect: When trying to hit the target, players must place the mirror on the master without looking through the mirror. (There would not be much of a game if they could look through the mirror—it would be easy to hit the bull's-eye every time.) Only *after* a player has placed the mirror on the master may he or she look through it in order to find the score.

Differentiation Options

READINESS Students may need a review of the effects of reflection and the use of a transparent mirror. Using a bigger target may be helpful:

▶ Add two larger circles, each worth 10 points, around the target.

ENRICHMENT

▶ Players cut out the targets and darts and tape the targets to a larger playing area. On each turn, a player chooses the starting point, places a dart there, and uses the transparent mirror to hit the target.

ELL SUPPORT Explain to students that *transparent* means you can see through it. Although transparent mirrors are different from other mirrors that students have seen, both types of mirrors involve reflections. Explain that a *reflection* is a flipping motion that makes an image appear to be the "opposite" of the original object.

Game Master 59 (p. 318)

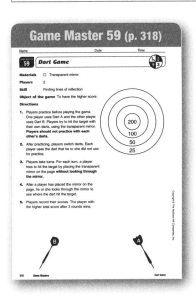

Decimal Solitaire

Games Across the Grades

Grades	PK	K	1	2	3	4	5	6
Advanced Learning								
Core Program					◆			
Reteaching and Practice						◆	◆	◆

Strand Number and Numeration

Skill Comparing decimals

Materials (per player)

- ◆ Everything Math Deck (number cards 0–9, 1 of each)
- ◆ 2 counters to use as decimal points
- ◇ 1 index card with the greater than symbol (>)
- ◇ half-sheet of paper

Players 1

Object of the game To make as many number sentences comparing decimals as possible.

Directions

1. The player shuffles the deck and draws 3 cards.

2. The player makes a number with two decimal places. He or she uses a counter as a decimal point.

3. The player places the greater than (>) card to the right of his or her number.

4. The player draws 3 more cards.

5. He or she uses these three cards and the other "decimal point" (counter) to make a number less than his or her original number. He or she places the number to the right of the greater than (>) card, reads the number sentence aloud, and records it on a half-sheet of paper.

6. The player uses the same 3 cards and the decimal point again, repeating Step 5 until no more true number sentences can be made.

Example

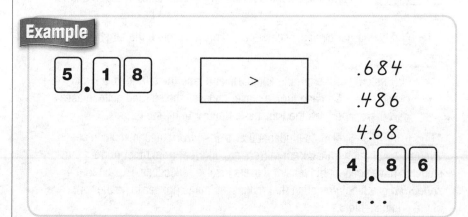

Differentiation Options

READINESS Students may need a review of decimal place value before playing the game. Limiting the number of decimal places may be helpful:

▶ Players draw 2 cards to make each number. Each number should have 1 decimal place.

ENRICHMENT

▶ Players order the numbers they create.

ELL SUPPORT Explain that one meaning of the word *solitaire* is a game that can be played by one person.

GRADE
K

Dice Addition

Strands Number and Numeration; Operations and Computation

Skill Counting, adding, and comparing numbers

Materials

◆ 10 counters per player

◆ 2 dice per player

Players 2–5

Object of the game To collect 10 counters.

Games Across the Grades								
Grades	PK	K	1	2	3	4	5	6
Advanced Learning	◆							
Core Program		◆						
Reteaching and Practice			◆	◆				

Directions

1. Players each roll a pair of dot dice at the same time and announce the sum of the dots on their dice.

2. Players compare their sums. The player with the highest sum takes a counter.

3. Players continue rolling pairs of dice and comparing sums until one player has 10 counters.

Advanced Versions

Counting-On Dice Addition

Players roll a number die and a dot die. They say the number aloud and then "count on" the dots to reach the sum.

Dice Addition with Three Dice

Players roll and add the dots on three dice.

Dice Addition with Polyhedral Dice

Players roll two polyhedral dice with more than six faces.

Differentiation Options

READINESS Students may need to review counting and comparing numbers through 12. Keeping one number constant may be helpful:

▶ Players set one die so that the 1-dot face is showing. On each turn, the player rolls the second die and finds the sum of 1 and the number they rolled. After a few rounds, players can turn the first die to show a different number.

ENRICHMENT

▶ Players write addition sentences to show the total number of dots on their dice.

ELL SUPPORT Contrast the meanings of *sum* and *some.*

GRADE Pre-K Dice Movement

Games Across the Grades								
Grades	PK	K	1	2	3	4	5	6
Advanced Learning								
Core Program	◆							
Reteaching and Practice		◆						

Strand Number and Numeration

Skill Counting with one-to-one correspondence

Materials (per group)
◆ Game Masters 60 and 61 (Movement Cards)
◆ dot die

Players 2–5

Object of the game To collect all of the Movement Cards as a group.

Directions

Advance Preparation Cut apart the Movement Cards from Game Masters 60 and 61. If possible, mount them on large index cards and/or laminate them for durability. You can also make an extra-large die from a large wooden or foam cube, or have children put together two half-pint milk cartons with the tops cut off to make their own large dice.

1. One player stacks the Movement Cards facedown.

2. A second player takes a Movement Card and displays it for the group.

3. The same player rolls the die and announces the number.

4. All players do the movement on the card that number of times. For example, if the picture shows someone clapping and a 3 is rolled, all players clap their hands 3 times.

5. Players take turns choosing a Movement Card and rolling the die. If all players do the movement on the card the correct number of times, the group takes the card. If any player does the movement the wrong number of times, the card is put back in the stack.

6. The game ends when the group has collected all of the Movement Cards for doing each movement the correct number of times.

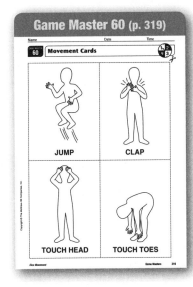

Game Master 60 (p. 319)

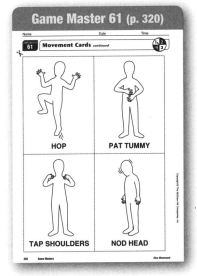

Game Master 61 (p. 320)

Differentiation Options

READINESS Students may need practice counting. Limiting how high students need to count may be helpful:

▶ Players use a die with 1, 2, and 3 dots, each on two sides.

ENRICHMENT

▶ Players roll two dot dice, each marked on two sides with 1, 2, or 3 dots. Players count the total number of dots on both dice to determine how many times to do each movement.

ELL SUPPORT Explain the meaning of *movement.* Explain that the number on the die tells the students how many times to make the movement shown on the card.

GRADES PK–K

Dice Race

Strands Number and Numeration; Data and Chance

Skill Counting; reading and writing numbers; graphing dice rolls

Materials (per group)

◆ *Dice Race* Gameboard (or Game Master 62 or 63, 1 per player)

◆ 2 dice

Players 2–5

Object of the game To fill the target column on the grid.

Games Across the Grades

Grades	PK	K	1	2	3	4	5	6
Advanced Learning								
Core Program	◆	◆						
Reteaching and Practice			◆					

NOTE: For number-writing practice, show children how to write the number in the next open box rather than just shading it.

Dice Race 1–6

Directions

Players use the gameboard (or Game Master 62) and one die.

1. Players agree on a target number from 1–6.
2. Players circle the target number on their grids.
3. Players take turns rolling one die. When the target number is rolled, that player marks the next open box above the target number. When any other number is rolled, the player does not mark the grid.
4. The player who fills the column first wins the race.

Dice Race 2–12

Directions

Players use the gameboard (or Game Master 63) and two dice. They agree on a target number from 2–12 and play as described above.

Differentiation Options

READINESS Students may need a review of counting and reading numbers through 6. Using dot patterns for support may be helpful:

▶ Draw the corresponding dot pattern below each column. To practice matching dot patterns to numerals, players can use the patterns to identify the correct column and then trace the numerals on the grid rather than just shading the boxes.

ENRICHMENT

▶ Each player chooses 2 or 3 target numbers to mark on his or her own grid.

ELL SUPPORT Point out that *columns* are positioned up and down, or vertically. Have students trace the lines around each column on the grid. Explain that the *target number* is the number the student wants to roll. When the column above the target number is filled, the player wins. Ask: *How many times do you need to roll the target number to win?*

Difference Game

Strand Operations and Computation

Skill Finding differences

Materials (per pair)

◆ For Grade 1: *Difference Game* Gameboard (optional)

◆ Everything Math Deck (number cards 1–10, 4 of each)

◆ 40 pennies

Grades 1–2

MRB
130

Players 2

Object of the game To have more pennies.

Games Across the Grades								
Grades	PK	K	1	2	3	4	5	6
Advanced Learning	◆	◆						
Core Program			◆	◆				
Reteaching and Practice								

Directions

1. One player shuffles the cards and places the deck whole-number side down.

2. Players put all of the pennies in a "bank."

3. In each round, each player draws a card from the top of the deck and takes the same number of pennies from the bank as the number shown on his or her card.

4. Players find out how many more pennies one player has by pairing as many pennies as they can.

5. The player with more pennies keeps the extra pennies. The rest go back into the bank.

Difference Game Gameboard

Example

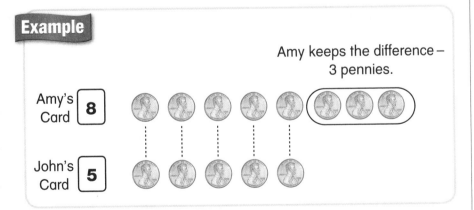

Amy keeps the difference – 3 pennies.

Amy's Card **8**

John's Card **5**

6. The game ends when there are not enough pennies to play another round. The player with more pennies wins.

Differentiation Options

READINESS Students may benefit from a review of "one more" stories. Beginning with repeated comparisons to the same number may also be helpful:

▶ Place a line of 10 pennies on the table. Each player compares his or her number of pennies to 10 and keeps the difference.

ENRICHMENT

▶ After each round, students write a number model comparing the pennies. For the above example, students would write $8 - 5 = 3$.

ELL SUPPORT Model the meaning of *difference* with 2 rows of pennies. Explain that in this game, the player who has more pennies keeps the difference, but the rest of that player's pennies go back into the bank along with the other player's pennies.

GRADES 1–2

Digit Game

Games Across the Grades									
Grades	PK	K	1	2	3	4	5	6
Advanced Learning		◆						
Core Program			◆	◆				
Reteaching and Practice					◆			

Strand Number and Numeration

Skill Comparing numbers

Materials (per pair)

◆ Everything Math Deck (number cards 0–9, 4 of each)

Players 2

Object of the game To collect more cards.

Grades 1–2

132

Directions

1. One player shuffles the deck and places it whole-number side down.

2. Each player draws two cards and uses them to make the larger possible number.

3. The player with the larger number takes all four cards.

4. The game is over when all of the cards have been used. The player with more cards wins.

Another Way to Play

Players try to make the *smaller* 2-digit number. The player who makes the greater number takes all of the cards. The player with fewer cards wins.

Advanced Version

Players draw three cards. Each player tries to make the larger 3-digit number and collect more cards.

Differentiation Options

READINESS Students may need a review of place value before playing this game. Making the tens digits a common value may be helpful:

▶ Players draw one card at the start of the game. This number will be the digit in the tens place for all numbers in the game. Each player draws one card per turn to determine the ones digit. Players write their numbers before comparing.

ENRICHMENT

▶ Players write number models for each turn.

ELL SUPPORT Ask: *When you compare two numbers, how do you know which number is larger?* (Sample answer: By comparing the values of digits in each place.) Explain that in this game, students want to create the largest number possible with their cards.

GRADE
1

Dime-Nickel-Penny Grab

Strands Number and Numeration; Data and Chance; Measurement and Reference Frames

Skill Counting and comparing collections of coins

Materials (per pair)

◆ *Coin Grab Games* Gameboard (or Game Master 64, 2 copies)

◆ 10 dimes, 8 nickels, 20 pennies

Players 2

Object of the game To have more money in at least two rounds.

Games Across the Grades								
Grades	PK	K	1	2	3	4	5	6
Advanced Learning		◆						
Core Program			◆					
Reteaching and Practice				◆				

Game Master 64 (p. 323)

Coin Grab Games Gameboard

Directions

NOTE: You may want to write ___¢ or $___.___ in the Total columns.

1. Players mix the coins and place them in a pile.

2. Player 1 grabs a handful of coins. Player 2 grabs the remaining coins.

3. Each player draws his or her coins on the Record Sheet and finds the total value.

4. Each player records both players' totals, using the ¢ or $ symbol. Each player circles the greater total.

5. Players switch roles and repeat Steps 1–4 two more times for a total of 3 rounds. The player who had more money in at least 2 rounds wins.

Differentiation Options

READINESS Students may need a review of coin values and determining the value of a coin collection. Using fewer types of coins may be helpful:

▶ Players use only nickels and pennies. (See *Nickel-Penny Grab*.)

ENRICHMENT

▶ Add 4 quarters to the coins used. (See *Quarter-Dime-Nickel-Penny Grab*.)

ELL SUPPORT Explain the meaning of **round** in this game context.

GRADES 5–6 Divisibility Dash

Games Across the Grades									
Grades	PK	K	1	2	3	4	5	6	
Advanced Learning						◆			
Core Program							◆	◆	
Reteaching and Practice									

Strand Operations and Computation

Skill Recognizing multiples; using divisibility tests

Materials (per group)

◆ For Grade 5: *Divisibility Dash* Gameboard (or Game Master 65, optional)

◆ Everything Math Deck (2 each of number cards 2, 3, 5, 6, 9, and 10)

◆ Everything Math Deck (4 each of number cards 0–9)

Players 2 or 3

Object of the game To discard all cards.

Grade 5 Grade 6
SRB 302   SRB 309

Directions

1. One player shuffles the divisor cards and places them whole-number side down. Another player shuffles the draw cards, deals 8 to each player, and places the remaining draw cards whole-number side down next to the divisor cards.

2. For each round, the top divisor card is turned whole-number side up.

3. Players take turns. For each turn, a player uses the cards in his or her hand to make 2-digit numbers that are multiples of the divisor card. Players make as many numbers as they can, but each card may be used only once.

4. The player places all the cards he or she used to make 2-digit numbers in a discard pile. The other players use the divisibility test for the divisor card to check that the numbers made are multiples of the divisor card. Any numbers that are not multiples of the divisor card must be returned to the player's hand.

5. If a player cannot make a 2-digit number that is a multiple of the divisor card, he or she must take a card from the draw pile. His or her turn is over.

6. If the draw pile or divisor cards have all been used, they can be reshuffled and put back into play.

7. The first player to discard all of his or her cards wins.

NOTE: The number cards 2, 3, 5, 6, 9, and 10 (2 of each) are the **divisor cards.**

The number cards 0–9 (4 of each) are the **draw cards.** This set of cards is called the **draw pile.**

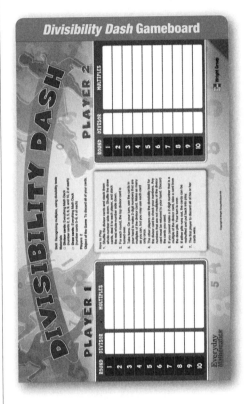

Example

Andrew's cards:

1	2	5	5	7	8

Divisor card:

3

Andrew makes 2 numbers that are multiples of 3:

1	5		5	7

He discards these 4 cards and holds the 2 and the 8 for the next round.

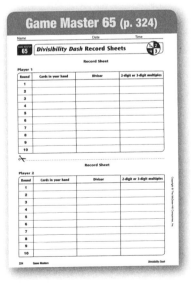

Differentiation Options

READINESS Students may need to review finding multiples of numbers before playing this game. It may be helpful to find only multiples of 2 and 5:

▶ Players use only the 2 and 5 cards in the divisor pile.

ENRICHMENT

▶ Each player begins with 9 draw cards and makes 3-digit numbers that are multiples of the divisor card.

▶ Each divisor card is multiplied by 10. For example, if a 3 is turned over, then the divisor is 30. Each player has a permanent 0 card and uses it to make 3- or 4-digit dividends. For example, a player may use 3, 2, and 4 cards to make 3,240 as a dividend. The player would discard only the 3, 2, and 4 cards.

ELL SUPPORT Discuss the meaning of *divisor.* Write the numbers 1, 2, 5, 5, 7, and 8 on the board. Say: *If the divisor is 6, what two-digit numbers that are multiples of 6 could I create with these cards?* (12 and 78, or 18 and 72)

GRADES 3–4 Division Arrays

Strand Operations and Computation

Skill Modeling division with arrays

Materials (per group)

- ◆ *Division Arrays* Gameboard (or Game Master 66)
- ◆ Everything Math Deck (number cards 6–18, 1 of each)
- ◆ 1 die
- ◆ 18 counters

Players 2–4

Object of the game To have the highest total score.

Grade 3 SRB 282
Grade 4 SRB 240

Games Across the Grades

Grades	PK	K	1	2	3	4	5	6
Advanced Learning				◆				
Core Program						◆	◆	
Reteaching and Practice								◆

Directions

1. One player shuffles the cards and places them whole-number side down.

2. Players take turns. For each turn, a player draws a number card and takes that number of counters. He or she will use those counters to make an array.

3. Next, the player rolls the die. The number on the die is the number of equal rows the player must have in his or her array.

4. The player makes the array with the counters. The player's score is the number of counters in 1 row. If there are no leftover counters, the player may double his or her score for that turn.

5. Players keep track of their own scores. The player with the highest total at the end of 5 rounds wins.

Game Master 66 (p. 325)

Division Arrays **Gameboard**

Example

Number Card	Die	Array Formed	Leftovers?	Score
10	2	• • • • • • • • • •	no	10
14	3	• • • • • • • • • • • • • •	yes	4

Differentiation Options

READINESS Students may need to review the meaning of *array.* Allowing students to choose the number of rows and columns in the array may be helpful:

▶ Players draw a card and make a rectangular array with that number of counters. Their score is the number of columns or the number of rows, whichever is smaller. For example, for 18, if they make a 1 × 18 array, their score is 1. If they make a 3 × 6 array, their score is 3.

ENRICHMENT

▶ Players predict whether they will be able to build a rectangular array with no leftovers after they roll the die. They receive 1 bonus point if their prediction is correct. If students are able to write a fact family for their array, they receive another bonus point.

ELL SUPPORT Draw several arrays on the board and label them *arrays.* In the first array, circle and label a *column.* In the second array, circle and label a *row.* Give students 12 counters each. Ask them to create an array with the 12 counters and then to record the array on paper, labeling how many counters are in each row and column.

GRADES 4–5 Division Dash

Games Across the Grades									
Grades	PK	K	1	2	3	4	5	6
Advanced Learning					♦			
Core Program						♦	♦	
Reteaching and Practice								♦

Strand Operations and Computation

Skill Dividing 2-digit by 1-digit numbers

Materials (per pair)

♦ For Grade 4: *Division Dash* Gameboard (or Game Master 67)

♦ For Grade 5: Game Master 67 (Record Sheet)

♦ Everything Math Deck (number cards 1–9, 4 of each)

Players 1 or 2

Object of the game To reach 100 in as few divisions as possible.

Grade 4   Grade 5

241   303

Directions

1. One player shuffles the cards and places them whole-number side down.

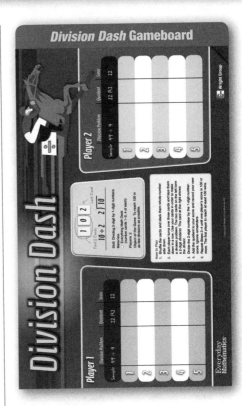

Division Dash Gameboard

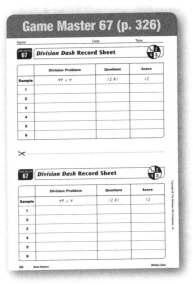

Game Master 67 (p. 326)

2. Each player turns over 3 cards and lays them down in a row. He or she uses the cards in order to generate a division problem. The two numbers on the cards on the left form a 2-digit *dividend*. The number on the right is the *divisor*. Players record their division problems.

3. Each player divides the 2-digit number by the 1-digit number. Players calculate mentally or on paper. Each player records the result. This result is the quotient.

4. Players add the quotient to their previous score and record their new score. Remainders are ignored.

5. Players repeat Steps 2–4 until one player's score is 100 or more. The first player to reach at least 100 wins. If there is only one player, he or she counts the turns it takes to reach 100 and tries to beat that score in the next game.

Example

Turn 1: Bob draws 6, 4, and 5. He divides 64 by 5. Quotient = 12 R4. Remainder is ignored. His score is 12 + 0 = 12.

64 is the dividend.   5 is the divisor.

Turn 2: Bob draws 8, 2, and 1. He divides 82 by 1. Quotient = 82. His score is 82 + 12 = 94.

Turn 3: Bob draws 5, 7, and 8. He divides 57 by 8. Quotient = 7 R1. Remainder is ignored. His score is 7 + 94 = 101. Bob has reached 100 in 3 turns and the game ends.

Quotient	Score
12 R4	12
82	94
7 R1	101

Differentiation Options

READINESS Students may need practice in using multiplication facts and parts that are easy to work with in order to divide mentally. Having just two divisors as options may also be helpful:

▶ Players draw from a separate card pile for the divisor. Only the 2 and 5 cards are in this pile.

ENRICHMENT

▶ Players draw 4 cards and make a 3-digit dividend and a 1-digit divisor greater than 2. They receive 10 bonus points if they can form a division problem with no remainder. Instead of playing to 100, they play 5 rounds, and the highest score wins.

ELL SUPPORT Model several rounds and write the resulting division problems on the board. Label the parts *dividend, divisor, quotient,* and *remainder.* Show how the quotient determines the score for each round.

GRADES 5–6

Division Top-It

Games Across the Grades								
Grades	PK	K	1	2	3	4	5	6
Advanced Learning						◆		
Core Program							◆	◆
Reteaching and Practice								

Strands Operations and Computation; Patterns, Functions, and Algebra

Skill Dividing a 2-digit number by a 1-digit number

Materials (per group)

◆ Game Master 4 (Record Sheet, optional, 1 per player)

◆ Everything Math Deck (number cards 1–9, 4 of each)

Players 2–4

Object of the game To collect the most cards.

Grade 5 **334**

Grade 6 **336**

NOTE: Players can use Game Master 4 to record their division problems and to compare quotients.

Directions

1. One player shuffles the cards and places them whole-number side down.

2. Players take turns. On each turn, a player draws 3 cards from the deck to generate a division problem.

3. The player chooses 2 cards to form the dividend and uses the remaining card as the divisor.

4. The player divides and drops any remainder.

5. The player with the largest quotient takes all of the cards. If there is a tie, the tied players each take another turn. The player with the largest quotient takes all cards from both plays.

6. The game ends when there are not enough cards for each player to have another turn.

7. The player with the most cards wins.

Advanced Version

Players use only the number cards 1–9. Each player turns over 4 cards, chooses 3 of them to form a 3-digit dividend, and uses the remaining number as the divisor.

Game Master 4 (p. 263)

Top-It Record Sheets

Differentiation Options

READINESS Students may need to review division facts. Limiting the range of divisors may be helpful:

▶ Players use 4 each of the 2, 5, and 10 cards to make a divisor pile, which they shuffle and reuse as needed. The rest of the number cards go in a dividend pile. For each turn, players turn over one divisor card and then 2 dividend cards to make a 2-digit dividend.

ENRICHMENT

▶ Players try to create 3-digit by 1-digit division problems with no remainders. Players receive a bonus point if they are able to do so. Bonus points are counted as cards at the end of the game.

ELL SUPPORT Model a round. Write the resulting number sentences on the board and label the parts *dividend, divisor, quotient,* and *remainder.*

GRADE 6 Doggone Decimal

Strand Operations and Computation

Skill Estimating products of decimals and whole numbers

Materials (per pair)

◆ *Doggone Decimal* Gameboard (or Game Master 68)

◆ Everything Math Deck (number cards 0–9, 4 of each)

◆ 4 counters

◇ 2 calculators

◇ 4 index cards labeled 0.1, 1, 10, and 100

Players 2

Object of the game To collect more number cards.

Grade 6

SRB
310

Games Across the Grades

Grades	PK	K	1	2	3	4	5	6
Advanced Learning							◆	
Core Program								◆
Reteaching and Practice								

NOTE: Point out that rounding each factor to its greatest place value can help players estimate quickly.

Also remind students that if one factor is less than 1, the product will be less than the other factor.

In Step 4, players may use the calculators for their initial computations or to check their work.

Doggone Decimal **Gameboard**

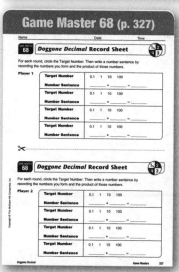

Game Master 68 (p. 327)

Directions

1. One player shuffles the number cards and deals 4 to each player.

2. The other player shuffles the index cards, places them number-side down, and turns over the top card. This card shows the **target number**—0.1, 1, 10, or 100. Both players circle the target number on their Record Sheets.

3. Using 4 number cards and 2 counters, each player forms 2 numbers. The counters are used as decimal points. Each number must have 2 digits and a decimal point.

   Players try to form 2 numbers whose product is as close as possible to the target number. The decimal point can go anywhere in a number—for example:

4. Players compute the product of their numbers on paper or with a calculator. They record their number sentences by the target number circled on their Record Sheets.

5. The player whose product is closer to the target number takes all 8 number cards.

6. Four new number cards are dealt to each player and a new target number is turned over. Players repeat Steps 3–5 with the new target number.

7. The game ends when all of the target numbers have been used.

8. The player with more number cards wins. In case of a tie, players reshuffle the index cards, turn over a target number, and play one tie-breaking round.

Example

The target number is 10.

Briana is dealt 1, 4, 8, and 8. She forms the numbers 8.8 and 1.4.

Evelyn is dealt 2, 3, 6, and 9. She forms the numbers 2.6 and 3.9.

Briana's product is 12.32. Evelyn's is 10.14.

Evelyn's product is closer to the target, 10. She wins the round and takes all 8 cards.

Differentiation Options

READINESS Students may need practice in rounding decimals to help them estimate. Limiting the number of places in the numbers may also be helpful;

▶ Players draw only 2 number cards. They make two numbers that each have 1 digit and a decimal point. They use only the target cards for 0.1, 1, and 10.

ENRICHMENT

▶ Players calculate their exact products for each round. Each player scores the difference between the product and the target number. At the end of the game, the player with the lower total score wins.

ELL SUPPORT Explain that the *target number* is the goal—the number players want to reach in each round. Distribute 2 cards and a counter to students and have them create 3 different numbers. Ask: *Which number(s) are less than 1? Less than 10? More than 10?* Explain that in this game, they will decide which numbers to make with their cards and decimal point so that their product will be close to the target number.

GRADE 2 Dollar Rummy

Strands Number and Numeration; Operations and Computation

Skill Finding complements of 100

Materials (per pair)
◆ Game Master 69 (*Dollar Rummy* Cards, 2 copies)

Players 2

Object of the game To have more $1.00 pairs of cards.

Games Across the Grades

Grades	PK	K	1	2	3	4	5	6
Advanced Learning			◆					
Core Program				◆				
Reteaching and Practice					◆			

Directions

1. One player deals 2 cards to each player. He or she puts the rest of the deck facedown between the players.

2. Players take turns. For each turn, a player turns over the top card and sets it faceup on the table.

3. The player looks for 2 cards that add up to $1.00. A player can use cards that are in his or her hand or faceup on the table.

Game Master 69 (p. 328)

Game Master 70 (p. 329)

4. If a player finds 2 cards that add up to $1.00, he or she sets them aside facedown.

5. When a player can't find any more pairs of cards that add up to $1.00, it is the other player's turn.

6. The game ends when all of the cards have been used or when neither player can make a $1.00 pair. The player with more $1.00 pairs wins.

Advanced Version

Players use two copies of the cards on Game Master 70, which have money amounts in multiples of 5¢.

Differentiation Options

READINESS Students may need to practice adding multiples of 10 or finding the total value of two money amounts. Using coins to represent amounts of money and having more choices on each turn may be helpful:

▶ Have children practice finding all matches before they play, using play coins if necessary.

▶ Players use play coins and turn over 5 cards instead of 1 to start the game. Player 1 uses coins to represent each of those amounts and the amounts on the 2 cards in his or her hand, makes all possible $1.00 combinations of these 7 cards, and replaces any cards he or she used.

ENRICHMENT Challenge students to play the game by making more difficult combinations for $1.00:

▶ On index cards, players make card pairs totaling $1.00 with amounts that do not end in 5 or 0; for example, 32¢ and 68¢. Players add these cards to the deck.

ELL SUPPORT Tell students that *rummy* card games involve finding matches. In this game, they will find matches that add up to $1.00.

 **GRADES K–1**

Domino Concentration

Strands Number and Numeration; Operations and Computation

Skill Counting; reading numerals; identifying equivalent names for numbers; writing addition facts

Materials (per group)

- For Kindergarten: Number Card Deck (number cards 1–12, 1 of each)
- For Grade 1: *Domino Concentration* Gameboard and a different-colored marker for each player (or paper and pencils)
- For Grade 1: Everything Math Deck (number cards 1–12, 1 of each)
- domino cardstock (or Game Masters 235 and 236, or 1 set of double-6 dominoes)

Players 2–5

Object of the game To collect the most card-and-domino pairs.

Games Across the Grades

Grades	PK	K	1	2	3	4	5	6
Advanced Learning		◆						
Core Program			◆	◆				
Reteaching and Practice					◆			

Directions

Advance Preparation: Select 12 dominoes, each showing a different number from 1–12, for each group.

1. Players place the 12 dominoes facedown in two equal rows. They also place number cards 1–12 number-side down in two equal rows of 6. The dominoes and cards are placed in random order.

2. Players take turns turning over 1 card and 1 domino so all players can see them.

3. If the number on the card matches the total number of dots on the domino, the player takes the card-and-domino pair and continues playing. If they do not match, the player turns them facedown in their original places.

4. Players try to remember which cards and dominoes they have seen so they can find matching pairs on their turns.

5. The game ends when no more cards and dominoes are left.

   - **For Kindergarten:** Players get one point for each pair.
   - **For Grade 1:** Players get one point for each pair *if* they can record a number sentence for the pair; for example, a player with a 3|0 domino records $3 + 0 = 3$.

6. The player with the most points wins.

Game Master 236 (p. 495)

236 Dominoes (Double-6 and Double-9)

Game Master 235 (p. 494)

235 Dominoes (Double-6)

Domino Concentration Gameboard

Domino Concentration

3+2=5   5

Number Sentences

Game Master 237 (p. 496)

237	Dominoes (Double-9)	

Differentiation Options

READINESS Students may need a review of counting dots or reading numerals. Using smaller sums or practicing with the cards faceup may be helpful:

▶ Players use two different dominoes for each sum from 2 through 7 and two number cards for each number from 2 through 7.

▶ Players spread out the number cards faceup, draw a domino card, and match it to the correct number card.

ENRICHMENT

▶ Use Game Masters 236 and 237 or a set of double-9 dominoes (one each for numbers 0–18) and the corresponding number cards.

▶ Include multiple dominoes that show different combinations forming the same total.

▶ Increase the number of dominoes and number cards in the game.

ELL SUPPORT Explain that *concentration* means that students will have to *concentrate,* or pay attention and try to remember where specific numbers are located when they do not make a match. This will help them in future rounds. Model the game with a small group of students. Ask students to share their strategies for remembering the positions of cards.

GRADES 1–2 Domino Top-It

Games Across the Grades									
Grades	PK	K	1	2	3	4	5	6	
Advanced Learning		◆							
Core Program			◆	◆					
Reteaching and Practice					◆				

Strands Number and Numeration; Operations and Computation; Patterns, Functions, and Algebra

Skill Addition; comparing sums

Materials (per group)

◆ Game Master 4 (Record Sheet, optional)

◆ Game Masters 236 and 237 (or 1 set of double-9 dominoes)

Players 2–4

Object of the game To collect the most dominoes.

Grades 1–2

MRB
122

Directions

1. One player mixes the dominoes up and turns them facedown.
2. Each player turns over a domino and says the total number of dots.
3. The player with the largest total takes both dominoes.
4. In case of a tie, each tied player turns over a new domino and calls out the total. The player with the largest total takes all of the faceup dominoes.
5. The game ends when all of the dominoes have been played. The player with the most dominoes wins.

NOTE: Players can use Game Master 4 to record and compare the total numbers of dots on their dominoes.

Differentiation Options

READINESS Students may need to review counting and counting on to find a total. Using the dominoes with fewer dots or using counters may be helpful:

▶ For each turn, a player takes one counter for each dot and counts them to find the total.

ENRICHMENT

▶ Players draw two dominoes on each turn. They record an addition number sentence and find the sum of the dots on the two dominoes. The addends in their number sentence may represent domino halves (4 addends) or domino sums (2 addends). For example, if a player draws a 3|6 and a 1|4 domino, he or she could write $3 + 6 + 1 + 4 = 14$ or $9 + 5 = 14$.

ELL SUPPORT Model a round of the game that involves a tie. Demonstrate the meanings of *largest total* and *compare* as the game is being played.

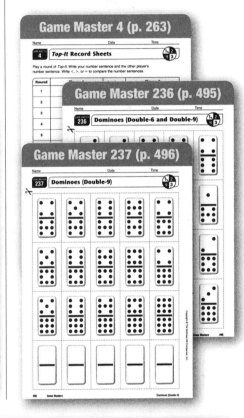

Game Master 4 (p. 263)

Game Master 236 (p. 495)

Game Master 237 (p. 496)

GRADE 2

Doubles or Nothing

Strand Operations and Computation

Skill Addition facts

Materials (per pair)
- ◆ Game Master 71 (Record Sheet, 2 copies)
- ◆ Game Master 72 (directions, optional)
- ◆ Everything Math Deck (number cards 0–9, 3 of each)
- ◆ 1 coin
- ◇ 1 calculator

Players 2

Object of the game To get the higher (or lower) Grand Total.

Games Across the Grades

Grades	PK	K	1	2	3	4	5	6
Advanced Learning			◆					
Core Program				◆				
Reteaching and Practice					◆			

NOTE: After the first game, discuss players' strategies for number placement that will increase their chance of making identical sums in each large rectangle.

NOTE: In Step 4, you may want to have students use a calculator for sums of doubles beyond 10 + 10.

Game Master 71 (p. 330)

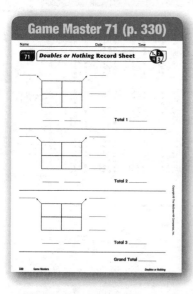

Game Master 72 (p. 331)

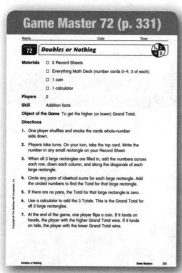

Directions

1. One player shuffles and stacks the cards whole-number side down.

2. Players take turns. For each turn, a player takes the top card and writes the number in any small rectangle on his or her Record Sheet.

3. When all 3 large rectangles are filled, each player adds the numbers across each row, down each column, and along the diagonals of each large rectangle.

4. Each player circles any pairs of identical sums for each large rectangle. He or she adds the circled numbers to find the Total for that large rectangle.

5. If there are no pairs, the Total for the large rectangle is zero.

6. Each player uses a calculator to add the 3 Totals in order to find the Grand Total for all 3 large rectangles.

7. At the end of the game, one player flips a coin. If it lands on heads, the player with the higher Grand Total wins. If it lands on tails, the player with the lower Grand Total wins.

Differentiation Options

READINESS Students may need to review strategies for addition. Using smaller numbers, dot patterns, or a Facts Table for support may be helpful:

▶ Each player uses 4 dice instead of number cards. They work in one large rectangle at a time and put one rolled die in each small rectangle to help them add.

▶ Players use an Addition/Subtraction Facts Table to find each sum and a calculator to add any sums that are doubles.

ENRICHMENT

▶ To practice extended addition facts, players treat each card as a multiple of 10 (or 100).

ELL SUPPORT Copy the Record Sheet on the board. Write three 9s and one 8 in one large rectangle and 1, 7, 3, and 2 in another large rectangle. Write 2, 3, 2, 3 in the third large rectangle so that the sum of both columns is 5. Model how to find the sums for each row, column, and diagonal. Circle pairs of identical sums. Have students find the Total for each round. Ask: *Why is this game called* Doubles or Nothing? (If you don't get pairs of identical sums, your score is 0.) *Which rectangle has the highest Total? Why? Which rectangle has the lowest Total? Why?*

GRADES 2–3

Equivalent Fractions Game

Strand Number and Numeration

Skill Recognizing fractions that are equivalent

Materials (per pair)

◆ Game Masters 73 and 74 (Fraction Cards, also available in Grade 3 Math Journal 2, Activity Sheets 5–8)

Players 2

Object of the game To collect more Fraction Cards.

Grade 3
SRB
283

Games Across the Grades

Grades	PK	K	1	2	3	4	5	6
Advanced Learning			◆					
Core Program				◆	◆			
Reteaching and Practice						◆	◆	◆

Directions

Advance Preparation: Have students write the appropriate fraction on the back of each Fraction Card from Game Masters 73 and 74.

1. One player shuffles and stacks the cards picture-side down. He or she turns over the top card and places it near the deck.

2. Players take turns. For each turn, a player turns the top card from the deck picture-side up. He or she tries to match this card with a picture-side up card on the table.

3. If the player finds a match, he or she takes the 2 matching cards. Then, if there are no cards left picture-side up, the player turns over the next card from the deck.

4. If a player cannot find a match, he or she places the card picture-side up next to the other cards. His or her turn is over.

5. If there is a match that the player didn't see, the other player can take the matching cards before his or her turn starts.

6. The game ends when all of the cards have been matched. The player with more cards wins.

NOTE: Have players record equivalent fraction pairs they make on a piece of paper; for example, $\frac{3}{6} = \frac{1}{2}$.

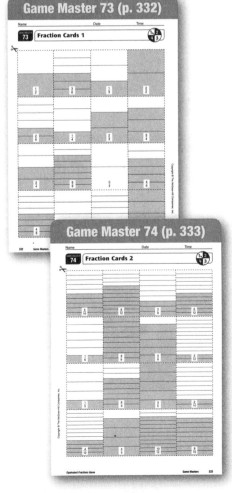

Game Master 73 (p. 332)

Game Master 74 (p. 333)

Example

The top card is turned over and put on the table. The picture shows $\frac{4}{6}$.

Player 1 turns over the $\frac{2}{3}$ card. This card matches $\frac{4}{6}$. Player 1 takes both cards. There are no cards left picture-side up. So Player 1 turns over the top card and puts it near the deck. The picture shows $\frac{6}{8}$.

Player 2 turns over the $\frac{0}{4}$ card. There is no match. This card is placed next to $\frac{6}{8}$. Player 2's turn is over.

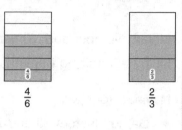

$\frac{4}{6}$ $\frac{2}{3}$

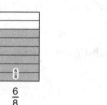

$\frac{6}{8}$ $\frac{0}{4}$

Advanced Version (recommended for Grade 3)

For each turn, a player **does not turn over** the card that he or she takes from the deck. The player tries to match the fraction with one of the picture-side up cards on the table. If the player finds a match, he or she turns the card over to check by comparing the pictures. The rest of the rules are the same as for the basic game.

Differentiation Options

READINESS Students may need a review of reading fractions or using area models to find equivalent fractions. Limiting the denominators used may be helpful:

▶ Players use only the Fraction Cards for halves and fourths.

ENRICHMENT

▶ Players use the Everything Math Deck fraction cards. They turn over four cards with fraction sides showing to start the game. They can only compare their cards side-by-side when they think they have a match.

ELL SUPPORT To ensure that students understand the meaning of *equivalent,* show them 6 cards, two of which show equivalent fractions. Model how to determine which fractions are equivalent.

GRADE 5

Estimation Squeeze

Strands Number and Numeration; Operations and Computation

Skill Estimating square roots

Materials (per pair)

◇ 1 calculator

◇ 2 pieces of scratch paper

Players 2

Object of the game To make an estimate whose square is within 0.1 of the target number.

Grade 5

SRB
304

Games Across the Grades

Grades	PK	K	1	2	3	4	5	6
Advanced Learning						◆		
Core Program							◆	
Reteaching and Practice								◆

Directions

1. Together, players choose and record a **target number** that is less than 600 and is NOT a perfect square.

2. Players take turns. For each turn, a player estimates the square root of the target number and enters the estimate on the calculator. Players may **not** use the ✓ key.

3. The player finds the square of the estimate with the calculator and records it.

Perfect Squares

1	81	289
4	100	324
9	121	361
16	144	400
25	169	441
36	196	484
49	225	529
64	256	576

▲ A **perfect square** is the square of a whole number. $1 = 1 * 1$, $64 = 8 * 8$, $400 = 20^2$ . . .

Example

A player estimates the square root of 139 to be 11.5. On a calculator, he or she will:

Press 11 $\cdot$ 5 ^ 2.

Or press 11 $\cdot$ 5 × 11 $\cdot$ 5 ENTER= .

The square of the estimate is 132.25.

4. The first player who makes an estimate whose square is within 0.1 of the target number wins. For example, if the target number is 139, the square of the estimate must be greater than 138.9 and less than 139.1.

Example

Target number: 139

	Estimate	Square of Estimate	
Nick	12	144	too large
Erin	11	121	too small
Nick	11.5	132.25	too small
Erin	11.8	139.24	too large
Nick	11.75	138.0625	too small
Erin	11.79	139.0041	between 138.9 and 139.1

Erin wins.

Differentiation Options

READINESS Students may need to review perfect squares and their square roots as benchmarks. Playing a simpler game with perfect squares may be helpful:

▶ Provide index cards showing the perfect squares from 1 to 400. For each turn, a player turns over a card, guesses the square root, and checks it with a calculator. If the player is correct, he or she keeps the card. If not, the card goes to the bottom of the deck. If the player is more than 2 away from the correct square root, he or she also loses one card from his or her hand. The player who has more cards when there are no cards left in the deck wins.

ENRICHMENT

▶ Players use number cards 1–9 and draw 3 cards to form a target number. The first card goes in the hundreds place, the second card in the tens place, and the third card in the ones place. Each player secretly records his or her estimate for the square root of the target number. Players find the squares of their estimates with a calculator. The player with the closer estimate scores the difference between the squares of the estimates. After 5 rounds, the player with the higher total score wins.

ELL SUPPORT Explain that the *target number* means the goal—the number players want to reach in each round. Make sure students understand that they will try to get close to the target (within 0.1) and that they do not have to hit the target exactly.

Exponent Ball

GRADES 5–6

Strands Number and Numeration; Data and Chance

Skill Converting exponential notation to standard notation; comparing probabilities

Materials (per pair)

- ◆ *Exponent Ball* Gameboard (or Game Master 75)
- ◆ 1 die
- ◆ 1 counter
- ◇ 1 calculator

Players 2

Object of the game To score more points.

Grade 5 **SRB** 305 Grade 6 **SRB** 311

Games Across the Grades

Grades	PK	K	1	2	3	4	5	6
Advanced Learning							◆	
Core Program							◆	◆
Reteaching and Practice								

Directions

1. Player 1 puts the ball (counter) on one of the 20-yard lines. The player will try to reach the opposite goal line, 80 yards away. A turn consists of 4 chances to advance the counter to the goal line and score.

2. The first 3 chances must be runs on the ground. To run, the player rolls the die twice. The first roll names the **base,** and the second roll names the **exponent.** For example, rolls of 5 and 4 name the number $5^4 = 625$.

3. The player calculates the value of the rolls and uses Table 1 to find how far to move the ball forward (+) or backward (–). (If a backward move should carry the ball behind the goal line, the ball is put on the goal line.)

4. If the player does not score in the first 3 chances, the player may choose to run or kick on the fourth chance. To kick, the player rolls the die once and multiplies the number by 10. The result is the distance the ball travels. (Players use Table 2.)

5. If the ball reaches the goal line on a run, the player scores 7 points. If the ball reaches the goal line on a kick, the player scores 3 points.

6. If the ball does not reach the goal line in 4 chances, the turn ends. Player 2 starts where Player 1 stopped and moves toward the opposite goal line.

7. If Player 1 scores, Player 2 puts the ball on the 20-yard line and play proceeds following Steps 2–6.

8. Players take turns. The player with more points at the end of 4 turns wins.

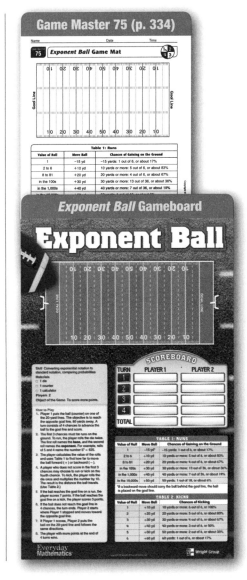

Game Master 75 (p. 334)

Exponent Ball Gameboard

Differentiation Options

READINESS Students may need to practice writing numbers in exponential notation as a product of factors. Playing without reference to the rules of football may also be helpful:

▶ Players use a piece of lined paper as a football field. The first line represents the goal line and the other lines each represent 1 yard. Both players start at the goal line, roll a base and exponent, calculate the value, and use Modified Table 1 below to determine how far they move. If a player chooses to Kick on his or her fourth chance, he or she rolls the die and uses Modified Table 2 below. The player who goes farthest in 4 tries wins.

ENRICHMENT

▶ If a player chooses to solve a problem with exponents on his or her fourth chance, he or she moves the ball an additional 20 yards.

▶ Players keep track of their dice rolls for all 4 turns. They get a 20-yard bonus for finding the prime factorization of the product of their 4 numbers. For example, if a player rolled 2^3, 4^2, 6^3, and 3^4, the prime factorization would be $2^{10} \times 3^7$.

ELL SUPPORT Discuss the meaning of the football terms *goal line, yard, yard line, kick, run,* and *touchdown* used in this game context. Model the meanings with students.

Modified Table 1: Runs		
Value of Roll	**Move Ball**	**Chances of Gaining on the Ground**
1	Back 1 yd	Back 1 yard: 1 out of 6, or about 17%
2 to 6	+1 yd	1 yard or more: 5 out of 6, or about 83%
8 to 81	+2 yd	2 yards or more: 4 out of 6, or about 67%
in the 100s	+3 yd	3 yards or more: 13 out of 36, or about 36%
in the 1,000s	+4 yd	4 yards or more: 7 out of 36, or about 19%
in the 10,000s	+5 yd	5 yards: 1 out of 18, or about 6%

Modified Table 2: Kicks		
Roll	**Move Ball**	**Chances of Kicking**
1	+1 yd	1 yd or more: 6 out of 6, or about 100%
2	+2 yd	2 yards or more: 5 out of 6, or about 83%
3	+3 yd	3 yards or more: 4 out of 6, or about 67%
4	+4 yd	4 yards or more: 3 out of 6, or 50%
5	+5 yd	5 yards or more: 2 out of 6, or about 33%
6	+6 yd	6 yards: 1 out of 6, or about 17%

GRADES 1–2

Fact Extension Game

Strand Operations and Computation

Skill Finding sums of 2-digit numbers and multiples of 10

Materials (per pair)

- ◆ *Fact Extension Game* Gameboard (or 2 sheets of paper)
- ◆ Everything Math Deck (number cards 0–9, 4 of each)
- ◆ 1 die
- ◇ 1 calculator

Players 2

Object of the game To have the higher total.

Grades 1–2

MRB 134

Games Across the Grades										
Grades	PK	K	1	2	3	4	5	6
Advanced Learning								
Core Program			◆	◆				
Reteaching and Practice					◆	◆		

Directions

1. One player shuffles the deck and places it whole-number side down.

2. Each player draws 2 cards from the deck and makes the larger 2-digit number.

3. Players take turns rolling the die and making another 2-digit number by using the number on the die in the tens place and a zero in the ones place.

4. Each player adds his or her 2 numbers and records the sum.

5. After 4 rounds, players use a calculator to find the total of the 4 sums. The player with the higher total wins.

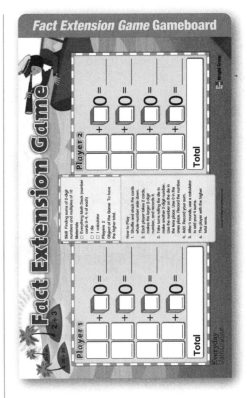

Fact Extension Game Gameboard

Example

Anna draws a 3 and a 5. She makes the number 53.
Then Anna rolls a 6. Her second number is 60.

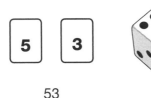

5 3

53   60

Anna finds the sum of her numbers.

53 + 60 = 113

Differentiation Options

READINESS Students may need practice with adding multiples of 10. Adding a multiple of ten to a 1-digit number may be helpful:

▶ Players begin with a 0 card, draw one card, and roll the die one time. They make a multiple of 10 with the 0 and the card they drew and add it to the number on the die. For example, a player who draws a 4 and rolls a 2 would find 40 + 2. In later games, players can use 1 die, 1 card, and 2 zeros to generate problems like 40 + 20.

ENRICHMENT

▶ Players get a bonus point for naming a related fact that helped them solve the problem. For example, if they make and solve 53 + 60, the related fact is 5 + 6 = 11.

ELL SUPPORT Explain that students will create numbers in two different ways. Model how to create the first number using 2 cards. Discuss the 2 numbers that could be created. Ask: *Which number is larger?* Explain that in this game, students want to have the higher total, so they should create the larger number. Model how to create the second number using the die. Point out that the number rolled on the die will represent the number of *tens,* not the number of *ones.* Model how to record the resulting number sentence.

GRADE 1

Fact Power Game

Games Across the Grades									
Grades	PK	K	1	2	3	4	5	6	
Advanced Learning		◆							
Core Program			◆						
Reteaching and Practice					◆	◆	◆		

Strand Operations and Computation

Skill Addition facts

Materials (per group)

◆ *Fact Power Game* Gameboard (or Game Master 76)

◆ 1 counter per player

◆ 1 die

Players 2–4

Object of the game To mark the most spaces.

Directions

1. Players place their counters on START.

2. Players take turns rolling a die and moving their counters that many spaces across the rows, following the arrows.

3. When a player lands on a space, he or she says the sum. The other player(s) check that the sum is correct. If correct, the player marks the space with his or her initial. If the player is incorrect, he or she does not mark the space and the turn is over. If a player lands on a marked space, he or she moves to the next open space.

4. A round is over when a player reaches or passes END. At that point, there will be some spaces marked and some not. Players then start again at the beginning.

5. When time is up or all of the spaces have been marked, players count their marked spaces. The player with the greatest number of marked spaces wins.

Differentiation Options

READINESS Students may need a review of strategies for addition. Limiting the facts may be helpful:

► Players use only the first 6 rows of the game mat. Increase the number of rows used as appropriate.

ENRICHMENT Challenge students to add 2-digit and 1-digit numbers:

► When a player lands on an unmarked space, he or she turns either addend into a 2-digit number by using the number from the die roll as a number of tens. For example, a player rolling 3 and landing on $1 + 9$ would generate the problem $31 + 9$ or $1 + 39$.

ELL SUPPORT Demonstrate what is meant by a *marked space.* Show what students should do if they land on a marked space or get an incorrect answer. Explain that the goal of this game is not to get to the END first, but rather to mark the most spaces.

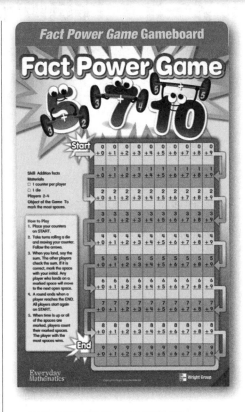

Fact Power Game Gameboard

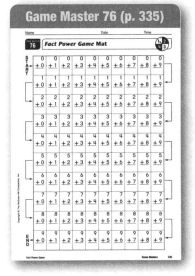

Game Master 76 (p. 335)

GRADES 3–5 Factor Bingo

Games Across the Grades

Grades	PK	K	1	2	3	4	5	6
Advanced Learning				◆				
Core Program					◆	◆	◆	
Reteaching and Practice							◆	

Strands Number and Numeration; Operations and Computation

Skill Finding factors of a number

Materials (per group)

- ◆ For Grade 3: *Factor Bingo* Gameboard (or Game Master 77, 1 per player)
- ◆ For Grades 4 and 5: Bingo grids (or Game Master 77, 1 per player) and Game Master 78 (directions, optional)
- ◆ Everything Math Deck (number cards 2–9, 4 of each)
- ◆ 12 counters per player

Players 2–4

Object of the game To cover 5 numbers in a row, a column, or a diagonal; or to cover 12 numbers anywhere on the Bingo grid.

Grade 3

SRB
285

Game Master 77 (p. 336)

Game Master 78 (p. 337)

Factor Bingo Gameboard

Directions

1. Each player chooses 25 numbers from 2 through 90 to fill in a Bingo grid. Every square must contain a different number. Players should write the numbers in random order. To keep track, players can circle the numbers they use in the list on Game Master 77.

2. One player shuffles the cards, stacks them whole-number side down, and turns over the top card. This card is the "factor."

3. Players check their Bingo grids for a number that has the card number as a factor. Players who find such a number cover that number with a counter. A player may place only 1 counter on the grid for each card that is turned over.

Example

A 5 card is turned over. The number **5** is the "factor." A player may place a counter on one number for which 5 is a factor, such as 5, 10, 15, 20, or 25.

4. Another player turns over the next card, and play continues.

5. The first player who covers 5 numbers in a row, column, or diagonal, or 12 numbers anywhere on the Bingo grid, calls out "Bingo!" and wins the game.

6. If all of the cards are used before someone wins, one player shuffles the cards and play continues.

NOTE: If players record factors and products in a table as they play, they can then use these tables to help them choose numbers for the next game. Discuss good numbers (ones that have several factors between 2 and 9) and impossible numbers (ones that do not have factors between 2 and 9).

Differentiation Options

READINESS Students may need a review of strategies for finding factors. It may be helpful to find only the factors of multiples of 5:

▶ Players fill the Bingo grid with multiples of 5 from 0 to 100. They may use a number twice.

ENRICHMENT Challenge students to identify larger factors and to develop strategies:

▶ Players use Game Master 157 (0–110 number grid) and number cards 1–20. They get Bingo for any 6 counters in a row, column, or diagonal.

▶ Have players remove the 2 and 5 cards from their decks. Players fill in new Bingo grids and discuss why they selected the numbers and locations they did.

ELL SUPPORT Explain that some numbers will help win the game and others will not. Ask: *What is an example of a number that you do not want to put on your game mat? Why would that number be a bad choice? Imagine that Maria put 12 and 13 on her game mat. Which number is a good choice? Which number is a bad choice? Why?*

GRADES 5–6 Factor Captor

Strands Number and Numeration; Operations and Computation

Skill Finding factors of a number

Materials (per pair)

◆ *Factor Captor* Gameboard (or Game Master 79 or 80)

◆ counters (48 for Grid 1; 70 for Grid 2)

◇ 2 calculators

◇ 2 pencils and 2 sheets of paper

Players 2

Object of the game To have the higher total score.

Grade 5 — SRB 306   Grade 6 — SRB 312

Games Across the Grades									
Grades	PK	K	1	2	3	4	5	6
Advanced Learning						◆		
Core Program							◆	◆
Reteaching and Practice								

F

NOTE: When players first use Grid 2 to play at the Advanced Level, suggest that they omit the last two rows.

Game Master 79 (p. 338)

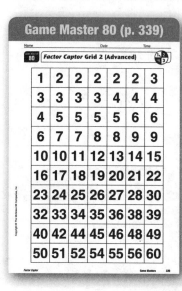
Game Master 80 (p. 339)

Directions

1. Players share Grid 1 (Beginning Level) or Grid 2 (Advanced Level.) To start the first round, Player 1 chooses a 2-digit number on the number grid, covers it with a counter, and records the number. This is Player 1's score for the round.

2. Player 2 covers all of the factors of Player 1's number. **A factor may be covered only once during a round.** Player 2 finds and records the sum of the factors. This is Player 2's score for the round.

3. If Player 2 missed any factors, Player 1 can cover them with counters and add them to his or her score.

4. For the next round, players switch roles. Player 2 chooses a number that is not covered by a counter. Player 1 covers all of the factors of that number.

5. Any number covered by a counter may not be used again.

6. The first player in a round may not cover a 1-digit number unless no other numbers are available.

7. Play continues with players trading roles after each round, until all numbers on the grid have been covered. Players then use their calculators to find their total scores. The player with the higher score wins.

Example

Round 1: James covers 27 and scores 27 points. Emma covers 1, 3, and 9, and scores $1 + 3 + 9 = 13$ points.

Round 2: Emma covers 18 and scores 18 points. James covers 2, 3, and 6, and scores $2 + 3 + 6 = 11$ points. Emma covers 9 with a counter, because 9 is also a factor of 18, and adds 9 points to her score.

Factor Captor Gameboard

Differentiation Options

READINESS Students may need a review of using divisibility rules, factor rainbows, and other strategies to find all factors of a number. Using a Multiplication/Division Facts Table may be helpful:

▶ Before playing, players use a different color to shade each of the 2-digit numbers from the *Factor Captor* Grid on a Multiplication/Division Facts Table every place they appear. They use the table as reference throughout the game.

ENRICHMENT

▶ For each number that is covered first, players make a factor tree. They get a bonus point for each correct tree.

▶ Players play on Game Master 157 (0–110 number grid).

ELL SUPPORT Explain that in this game, a player wants to score more points than his or her opponent. To score more points, it is better to choose certain numbers rather than others. Before players select a number, they should determine what factors of that number are available on the grid for their opponent to identify as part of his or her score. Discuss why it would be better to select 11 rather than 12.

GRADE 5

Factor Top-It

Strands Number and Numeration; Operations and Computation; Patterns, Functions, and Algebra

Skill Finding factors of a number

Materials (per group)
- ◆ Everything Math Deck (number cards 0–9, 4 of each)
- ◆ Game Master 4 (Record Sheet, optional, 1 per pair)
- ◇ paper and pencils

Players 2–4

Grade 5

SRB
307

Object of the game To score the most points.

Games Across the Grades

Grades	PK	K	1	2	3	4	5	6
Advanced Learning						◆		
Core Program							◆	
Reteaching and Practice								◆

Directions

1. One player shuffles and stacks the deck whole-number side down.

2. Players take turns. On each turn, a player draws 2 cards and uses them to make a 2-digit number.

NOTE: Players can use Game Master 4 to record the factors of each number, find their sum, and compare totals.

Game Master 4 (p. 263)

3. He or she records the number and all of its factors on a piece of paper and finds the sum of all of the factors. This is the player's score for that round.

4. Play continues for 5 rounds. The player with the most points wins.

Example

Find each player's score for the round.

Player 1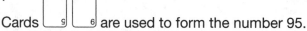

Cards ⌐5/⌐9⌐ are used to form the number 95.

Factors: 1, 5, 19, 95
Score: 1 + 5 + 19 + 95 = 120

Player 2

Cards ⌐8/⌐8⌐ are used to form the number 88.

Factors: 1, 2, 4, 8, 11, 22, 44, 88
Score: 1 + 2 + 4 + 8 + 11 + 22 + 44 + 88 = 180

Player 3

Cards ⌐2/⌐5⌐ are used to form the number 52.

Factors: 1, 2, 4, 13, 26, 52
Score: 1 + 2 + 4 + 13 + 26 + 52 = 98

Player 2 scored the most points for this round.

Differentiation Options

READINESS Students may need to review factor rainbows and other strategies for finding all of the factors of a number. Using smaller numbers may be helpful:

▶ Players place the 1 and 2 cards in a tens-place pile, and the 0, 2, and 5 cards in a ones-place pile. A player draws one card from each pile to form a 2-digit number.

ENRICHMENT

▶ Players find the prime factorization of the numbers they form and add the prime factors to find their score.

▶ Players draw 4 cards for each turn and make two 2-digit numbers. The player finds and adds the prime factors of each number to find his or her score. For 10 bonus points, a player may name the greatest common factor and least common multiple of the two numbers.

ELL SUPPORT Prior to introducing the game, demonstrate creating 2-digit numbers using the number cards and finding factors of the numbers. For example, using 3 and 6, explain that students can make 36 or 63. Together, create a list of factors for both numbers and then find the sum of each list. Ask: *Which number gave you the larger sum?*

GRADE 3 Finding Factors

Strands Number and Numeration; Operations and Computation

Skill Finding factors of a number

Materials (per pair)
- ◆ Game Master 81 (game mat and factor strip)
- ◆ 2 different-colored counters
- ◇ 2 different-colored pencils or crayons

Players 2

Object of the game To shade five products in a row, column, or diagonal.

Games Across the Grades

Grades	PK	K	1	2	3	4	5	6
Advanced Learning					◆			
Core Program						◆		
Reteaching and Practice							◆	◆	◆

Directions

1. Player 1 places a counter on one factor in the Factor Strip.

2. Player 2 places a second counter on any of the factors in the Factor Strip. (Two counters can cover the same factor.)

3. Player 2 finds the product of the two factors on the game mat. Player 2 uses his or her color to shade that space.

4. Player 1 moves **either one** of the counters to a new factor on the Factor Strip. If the product of the two covered factors has not been shaded, Player 1 shades that space with the other color.

5. Players continue taking turns moving 1 counter on the Factor Strip and shading in spaces. The first player to shade 5 spaces in a row, column, or diagonal wins.

Game Master 81 (p. 340)

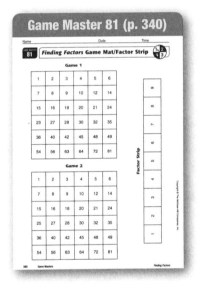

Differentiation Options

READINESS Students may need to practice multiplication facts. Using a Facts Table may be helpful:

▶ Players use a Multiplication/Division Facts Table.

▶ After two numbers are covered on the Factor Strip, players choose one of those counters to move around on subsequent turns until all possibilities are exhausted. For example, if 3 and 5 are covered in the first round, the counter covering 5 could be moved in Step 4 and in the following turns to generate all the facts with 3 as a factor. Then both counters are moved in the next round.

ENRICHMENT

▶ Each player uses scratch paper to write a family of facts for his or her two factors and their product. For example, if a player chose the factors 8 and 3, he or she would write $8 \times 3 = 24$, $3 \times 8 = 24$, $24 \div 8 = 3$, and $24 \div 3 = 8$. A player can shade a space only after he or she has correctly written a family of facts.

ELL SUPPORT Model how a winning gameboard might look. For example, shade 5 spaces in a *row, column,* and *diagonal* and label them.

GRADES 5–6 First to 100

Games Across the Grades

Grades	PK	K	1	2	3	4	5	6
Advanced Learning						◆		
Core Program							◆	◆
Reteaching and Practice								

Strands Operations and Computation; Patterns, Functions, and Algebra

Skill Variable substitution; solving equations

Materials (per group)

◆ *First to 100* Problem Cards (or Game Masters 8 and 9; also available in Grade 6 Math Journal 2, Activity Sheets 5 and 6)

◆ Game Master 82 (Record Sheet, optional)

◆ 2 dice

◇ 1 calculator

Players 2–4

Object of the game To collect 100 points.

Grade 5
308

Grade 6
313

Directions

1. One player shuffles and stacks the Problem Cards facedown.

2. Players take turns. For each turn, a player rolls 2 dice and finds the product of the numbers.

3. The player turns over the top Problem Card, substitutes the product for the variable x in the problem, and solves the problem mentally or using paper and pencil. (A player has 3 chances to use a calculator to solve difficult problems during a game.)

4. Other players check the answer with a calculator. If the answer is correct, the player wins the number of points equal to the product that was substituted for the variable x. Some Problem Cards require 2 or more answers. In order to win any points, the player must answer all parts of the problem correctly.

5. After each turn, the player puts the used Problem Card at the bottom of the card pile.

6. The first player to get at least 100 points wins.

Example

Alice rolls a 3 and a 4. The product is 12.

She turns over a Problem Card: $20 * x = ?$
She substitutes 12 for x and answers 240.
The answer is correct. Alice wins 12 points.

Differentiation Options

READINESS Students may need a review of variable substitution. Having students write simpler problems with variables may be helpful:

► Players make their own set of *First to 100* cards. Each player makes four open number sentence cards similar to the *First to 100* Problem Cards— one each for addition, subtraction, multiplication, and division. Play ends after 10 rounds. The player with the highest score wins.

ENRICHMENT

► Players make a 2-digit number from the roll of the dice and substitute this number for the variable x. The player with the highest score wins.

ELL SUPPORT If students have difficulty interpreting the text on the Problem Cards, give them the option of selecting a different card. Model and discuss the meaning of **substitute.**

NOTE: Players can use Game Master 82 to record their number models and score.

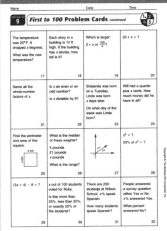

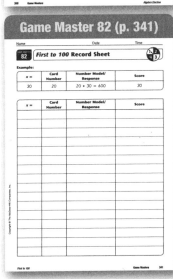

Fishing for Digits

Games Across the Grades									
Grades	PK	K	1	2	3	4	5	6
Advanced Learning				◆	◆			
Core Program						◆		
Reteaching and Practice							◆	◆

Strands Number and Numeration

Skill Place value; developing a game strategy

Materials (per player)

◆ Game Master 83 (Record Sheet; optional)

◇ 2 calculators

Players 2

Object of the game To have the larger number after 5 rounds.

Grade 4

SRB

242

NOTE: Players can use Game Master 83 to record the numbers on their calculators for each round. Players record the result of their own guesses on the "first guess" lines, and the result of the opponent's guesses on the "second guess" lines.

Depending on the ability of your students, you may want to play this game using numbers with fewer than 6 digits.

Game Master 83 (p. 342)

Directions

1. Each player secretly enters a 6-digit number into his or her calculator. Zeros may not be used.

2. Player 1 goes "fishing" for a digit in Player 2's number by naming a digit.

3. If the digit named *is* one of the digits in Player 2's number, Player 2 reports the value of the digit. Player 1 will *add* the value of that digit to his or her number, and Player 2 will *subtract* the value of that digit from his or her number.

   If the digit appears more than once in Player 2's number, Player 2 reports the largest value of that digit in the number. For example, if Player 1 names the digit 7, and Player 2's number is 987,675, then Player 2 would report the value 7,000 rather than the value 70.

4. If the digit named is *not* one of the digits in Player 2's number, Player 1 adds 0 and Player 2 subtracts 0 for that turn.

5. It is now Player 2's turn to "fish." Players reverse roles and repeat Steps 2 through 4. When each player has "fished" once, the round is over.

6. The player whose calculator displays the larger number at the end of 5 rounds wins.

Example

Player 1's calculator shows 813,296. Player 2's calculator shows 328,479.

Player 1: *Do you have the digit 4?* Player 2: *Yes, 400.*

Player 1 adds 400: 813296 $+$ 400 $\boxed{\text{ENTER}}$ 813696.

Player 2 subtracts 400: 328479 $-$ 400 $\boxed{\text{ENTER}}$ 328079.

Differentiation Options

READINESS Students may need practice identifying place values. Using place-value charts and writing down the numbers that need to be added or subtracted for each turn may be helpful:

▶ Provide place-value charts (Game Master 239) labeled from ones through hundred-thousands. Before players add or subtract a number, they can write the number in the chart.

ENRICHMENT

▶ Players choose 7- or 8-digit numbers in Step 1.

▶ To provide practice with decimal place values, players agree whether to put 2, 3, or 4 of the digits in their 6-digit secret numbers in decimal places. Both players' secret numbers should have the same number of decimal places.

ELL SUPPORT Discuss the meaning of *fishing* in this game context. Ensure that students understand the meaning of *digit* and *value.* Model how to play the game with another student and show how to complete the Record Sheet for each player.

Game Master 239 (p. 498)

GRADE 5

500

Strand Operations and Computation

Skill Adding positive and negative numbers

Materials (per pair)
- Game Master 84 (spinner and Score Sheet, 2 copies)
- 1 die
- 1 transparent spinner (or 1 paper clip and 1 pencil to use with Game Master 84)

Players 2

Object of the game To reach 500.

Games Across the Grades

Grades	PK	K	1	2	3	4	5	6
Advanced Learning						◆		
Core Program							◆	
Reteaching and Practice								◆

Directions

1. Players take turns being the "catcher" and the "batter."
2. The batter spins. The catcher tosses the die.

NOTE: To improve the players' chances of reaching 500, introduce this rule: A player who rolls two odd numbers in a row may double his or her score if it is positive, or multiply by −1 if the score is negative.

3. If the catcher rolls an odd number, the action from the spin is a "catch." If the catcher rolls an even number, the action from the spin is a "drop."

- A catch is a positive number added to the catcher's score.
- A drop is a negative number added to the catcher's score.

4. Each player uses his or her own Score Sheet to record the action from a spin, the points scored, and the score for each of his or her turns.

5. The first player to reach 500 points wins.

Game Master 84 (p. 343)

Example

Spin: Roll	Points Scored	Total Score
Grounder: catch	+ 25	25
Fly: drop	− 100	− 75
Two-bouncer: catch	+ 50	− 25

Differentiation Options

READINESS Students may need practice in adding positive and negative numbers. Using a number line and smaller numbers may be helpful:

► Change the spinner so that 2 parts are labeled 5 points, and 2 parts are labeled 10 points.

ENRICHMENT

► To provide practice subtracting positive and negative numbers, label two blank dice—one with plus and minus signs, and the other with *P* for *positive* and *N* for *negative*. The first die tells the operation, and the second die tells the sign of the value of the spin. Players who subtract a negative number from their score earn a 50-point bonus.

ELL SUPPORT Discuss the meaning of the baseball terms used, such as *fly, grounder, bounce, batter,* and *catcher.*

GRADES 5–6 Frac-Tac-Toe

Strands Number and Numeration

Skill Renaming fractions as decimals and percents

Materials (per pair)

◆ *Frac-Tac-Toe* Gameboard (or Game Master 85 and your choice of Game Masters 86–97)

◆ Everything Math Deck (number cards 0–10, 4 of each)

◆ 20 counters per player (2 different colors)

◇ 1 calculator or Table of Decimal Equivalents (optional)

Players 2

Object of the game To cover 3 spaces in a row in any direction (horizontal, vertical, or diagonal).

Grade 5 SRB 309   Grade 6 SRB 314

Games Across the Grades

Grades	PK	K	1	2	3	4	5	6
Advanced Learning						◆		
Core Program							◆	◆
Reteaching and Practice								

2-4-5-10: Decimals

Directions

Players use Game Mat 1 on the *Frac-Tac-Toe* Gameboard or Game Master 86.

1. Players separate the cards into 2 piles—a numerator pile and a denominator pile—on the gameboard or Number-Card Board. They place 2 each of the 2, 4, 5, and 10 cards in the denominator pile, and all other cards in the numerator pile.

2. Players shuffle the cards in each pile and place the piles whole-number side down in the left-hand spaces on Game Master 85, or beside the gameboard. When the numerator pile is completely used, one player reshuffles that pile and places it whole-number side down in the left-hand space. When the denominator pile is completely used, one player turns it over and places it whole-number side down in the left-hand space **without** reshuffling it.

3. Players take turns. For each turn, a player turns over the top card from each pile to form a fraction (numerator card above denominator card).

4. The player tries to match the fraction shown with one of the spaces on the game mat. If a match is found, the player covers that space with his or her counter, and the turn ends. If no match is found, the turn ends.

5. To change the fraction to a decimal, players may use a calculator or a Table of Decimal Equivalents for Fractions.

NOTE: There are three variations of *Frac-Tac-Toe* (2-4-5-10, 2-4-8, and 3-6-9) that increase in difficulty. Each variation has 4 ways to play (Decimal, Percent, Decimal Bingo, and Percent Bingo). For the decimal versions, allow students to use a Table of Decimal Equivalents, available on page 400 in the Grade 5 SRB and page 374 in the Grade 6 SRB.

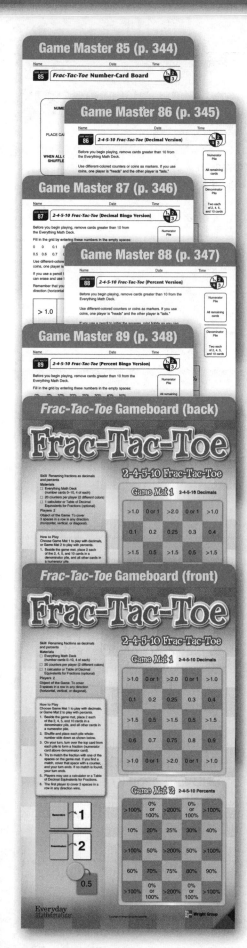

Game Master 85 (p. 344)

Game Master 86 (p. 345)

Game Master 87 (p. 346)

Game Master 88 (p. 347)

Game Master 89 (p. 348)

Frac-Tac-Toe Gameboard (back)

Frac-Tac-Toe Gameboard (front)

Example

The cards show the fraction $\frac{4}{5}$. The player may cover the 0.8 space, unless it has already been covered.

$$\frac{4}{5}$$

The cards show the fraction $\frac{0}{5}$. The player may cover one of the spaces labeled "0 or 1" that has not already been covered.

$$\frac{0}{5}$$

The cards show the fraction $\frac{4}{2}$. The player may cover any space labeled "> 1.0" or "> 1.5" that has not already been covered. The player may not cover a space labeled "> 2.0," because $\frac{4}{2}$ is equal to, but not greater than, 2.0.

$$\frac{4}{2}$$

6. The first player to cover 3 spaces in a row in any direction wins.

Another Way to Play

Players play Bingo on Game Master 87.

2-4-5-10: Percents

Players use Game Mat 2 on the *Frac-Tac-Toe* Gameboard or Game Master 88.

Alternatively, players play Bingo on Game Master 89.

2-4-8: Decimals

Players use Game Mat 3 on the *Frac-Tac-Toe* Gameboard or Game Master 90. Players use 2 each of the 2, 4, and 8 cards in the denominator pile.

Alternatively, players play Bingo on Game Master 91.

2-4-8: Percents

Players use Game Mat 4 on the *Frac-Tac-Toe* Gameboard or Game Master 92.

Alternatively, players play Bingo on Game Master 93.

3-6-9: Decimals

Players use Game Mat 5 on the *Frac-Tac-Toe* Gameboard or Game Master 94. Players use 2 each of the 3, 6, and 9 cards in the denominator pile.

Alternatively, players play Bingo on Game Master 95.

3-6-9: Percents

Players use Game Mat 6 on the *Frac-Tac-Toe* Gameboard or Game Master 96.

Alternatively, players play Bingo on Game Master 97.

Differentiation Options

READINESS Students may need to review converting fractions to decimals or percents. Limiting the denominators used may be helpful:

▶ For the *2-4-5-10* games, players use only 4s and 10s in the denominator pile.

ENRICHMENT

▶ Players add two 0s to the denominator pile as wild cards. When a 0 comes up, the player can name *any* fraction and cover the equivalent decimal or percent.

▶ For any of the decimal versions, players add one each of the numbers 12 and 20 to the denominator pile and change the middle space on the game mat to "Name the Decimal." Players can cover this space if they have a 12 or 20 in the denominator and they correctly name the decimal equivalent for the fraction.

ELL SUPPORT Explain that *three in a row* means three *adjacent* squares; not 3 counters that are in the same row but not next to one another. Show *three in a row* horizontally, vertically, and diagonally.

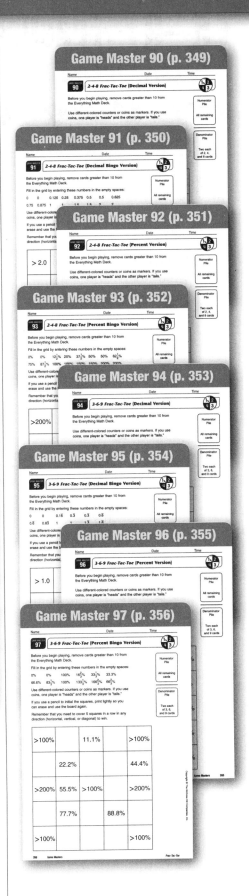

GRADES 5–6 Fraction Action, Fraction Friction

Games Across the Grades										
Grades	PK	K	1	2	3	4	5	6
Advanced Learning							◆	
Core Program							◆	◆
Reteaching and Practice								

Strands Number and Numeration; Operations and Computation

Skill Estimating sums of fractions

Materials (per group)

◆ *Fraction Action, Fraction Friction* Cards (or Game Master 98)

◇ 1 calculator (per player)

Players 2 or 3

Object of the game To collect a set of fraction cards with a sum as close as possible to 2, without going over 2, in each round.

Grade 5 · SRB 312   Grade 6 · SRB 317

Game Master 98 (p. 357)

$\frac{1}{2}$	$\frac{1}{3}$	$\frac{2}{3}$	$\frac{1}{4}$
$\frac{3}{4}$	$\frac{1}{6}$	$\frac{1}{6}$	$\frac{5}{6}$
$\frac{1}{12}$	$\frac{1}{12}$	$\frac{5}{12}$	$\frac{5}{12}$
$\frac{7}{12}$	$\frac{7}{12}$	$\frac{11}{12}$	$\frac{11}{12}$

Directions

1. One player shuffles and stacks the cards facedown.

2. Players take turns. For each player's first turn, he or she takes a card from the top of the pile and places it faceup on the table.

3. On each of the player's following turns, he or she announces one of the following:

   • **"Action"** This means that the player wants an additional card. The player believes that the sum of the fraction cards he or she already has is *not* close enough to 2 to win the hand. The player thinks that another card will bring the sum of the fractions closer to 2, without going over 2.

   • **"Friction"** This means that the player does not want an additional card. The player believes that the sum of the fraction cards he or she already has *is* close enough to 2 to win the hand. The player thinks there is a good chance that taking another card will make the sum of the fractions greater than 2.

   Once a player says "Friction," he or she cannot say "Action" on any turn after that.

4. Play continues until all players have announced "Friction" or one player has a set of cards whose sum is greater than 2. The player whose sum is closest to 2 without going over 2 wins that round. Players may check each other's sums on their calculators.

5. One player reshuffles the cards and play begins again. The first player to win 5 rounds wins the game.

Differentiation Options

READINESS Students may need practice in estimating sums of fractions and finding least common denominators. Limiting the range of denominators or using a model may be helpful:

▶ Players use multiple copies of the twelfths fraction cards.

▶ Players use fraction sticks that are divided into twelfths. For each card they draw, players shade the corresponding number of twelfths on their fraction sticks.

ENRICHMENT

▶ Players make cards showing fifths, eighths, and tenths and add them to the deck.

▶ Players use the fraction cards in the Everything Math Deck.

ELL SUPPORT Discuss the meanings of *action* and *friction* in this game context. Explain that in this game, the player who has cards with a sum that is *closest* to 2, without going over, will win the round. Model how to play a few rounds with a small group of students.

GRADES 5–6 Fraction Capture

Strands Number and Numeration, Operations and Computation

Skill Adding fractions; finding equivalent fractions

Materials (per pair)
- *Fraction Capture* Gameboard (or Game Master 99)
- Game Master 100 (Record Sheet; optional)
- 2 dice

Players 2

Object of the game To capture more squares.

Grade 6

SRB
318

Games Across the Grades									
Grades	PK	K	1	2	3	4	5	6
Advanced Learning						◆	◆	
Core Program							◆	◆
Reteaching and Practice								

Directions

1. Player 1 rolls the dice and makes a fraction with the numbers rolled. The number on either die can be the denominator. The number on the other die becomes the numerator.

Fraction Capture Gameboard

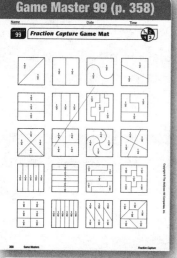

Game Master 99 (p. 358)

Name   Date   Time

99 *Fraction Capture* Game Mat

Game Master 100 (p. 359)

Name   Date   Time

100 *Fraction Capture* Record Sheet

Player 1

Round	Dice Roll	Fraction	Fraction Addition Expression
1			
2			
3			
4			
5			
6			

100 *Fraction Capture* Record Sheet

Player 2

Round	Dice Roll	Fraction	Fraction Addition Expression
1			
2			
3			
4			
5			
6			

- A fraction equal to a whole number is NOT allowed. For example, if a player rolls 3 and 6, the fraction cannot be $\frac{6}{3}$, because $\frac{6}{3}$ equals 2.

- If the two dice show the same number, the player rolls again.

2. Player 1 initials sections of one or more squares to show the fraction formed. This **claims** the sections for the player.

> **Example**
>
> - A player rolls a 4 and a 3 and makes $\frac{3}{4}$. The player claims three $\frac{1}{4}$ sections by initialing them.
>
> - Equivalent fractions can be claimed. If a player rolls a 1 and a 2 and makes $\frac{1}{2}$, the player can initial one $\frac{1}{2}$ section of a square, or two $\frac{1}{4}$ sections, or three $\frac{1}{6}$ sections.
>
> - The fraction may be split between squares. A player can show $\frac{5}{4}$ by claiming $\frac{3}{4}$ on one square and $\frac{2}{4}$ on another square.

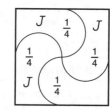 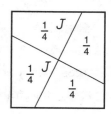

3. Players take turns. If a player cannot claim enough sections to show the fraction he or she formed, no sections can be claimed. The player's turn is over.

4. A player **captures** a square when that player has claimed sections making up **more than** $\frac{1}{2}$ of the square. If each player has initialed $\frac{1}{2}$ of a square, no one has captured that square.

5. Blocking is allowed. For example, if Player 1 initials $\frac{1}{2}$ of a square, Player 2 may initial the other half, so that no one can capture the square.

6. Play ends when all of the squares have been either captured or blocked. The player who has captured more squares wins.

Differentiation Options

READINESS Students may need practice in writing fractions. Using fraction cards may be helpful:

▶ Players use the fraction side of the Everything Math Deck cards for halves, thirds, fourths, fifths, sixths, eighths, tenths, and twelfths instead of dice to determine their fractions. If they draw a fraction card that cannot be covered on the board, they lose their turn.

ENRICHMENT

▶ Players must claim *all* of the sections to end the game. Players need to adjust their strategies to use some of their moves to claim sections that will not win squares for them.

ELL SUPPORT Ensure that students understand the meanings of *claim* and *capture.* Students may think that *claiming* more sections overall, rather than *capturing* more squares, would lead to a victory. Use the board and sample dice rolls to explain. To *claim* a section means that just one part of the square belongs to you. To *capture* a square, you have to *claim* more than half of it.

GRADE 4 — Fraction Match

Strands Number and Numeration; Operations and Computation

Skill Recognizing equivalent fractions

Materials (per group)
◆ Game Masters 101–104 (*Fraction Match* Cards)

Players 2–4

Object of the game To have the fewest cards.

Grade 4

SRB
243

Games Across the Grades

Grades	PK	K	1	2	3	4	5	6
Advanced Learning					◆			
Core Program							◆	
Reteaching and Practice								◆ ◆

Directions

1. One player shuffles the deck and deals 7 cards to each player. He or she places the remaining cards facedown.

2. The dealer turns over the top card. This is the *target card.* If a WILD card is turned over, it is returned to the deck and the dealer repeats this step until a fraction is turned over.

3. Players take turns trying to match the target card with a card from their hands. They may use:

- a card with an equivalent fraction
- a card with a like denominator
- a WILD card

Example

$\frac{2}{3}$ is the target card. It can be matched with:

- an equivalent fraction card such as $\frac{4}{6}$, $\frac{6}{9}$, or $\frac{8}{12}$;
- a like denominator card such as $\frac{0}{3}$, $\frac{1}{3}$, or $\frac{3}{3}$; or
- a WILD card. The player names any fraction (with a denominator of 2, 3, 4, 5, 6, 8, 9, 10, or 12) that is equivalent to the target card. The player can match $\frac{2}{3}$ by saying $\frac{4}{6}$, $\frac{6}{9}$, or $\frac{8}{12}$. The player may not match $\frac{2}{3}$ by saying $\frac{2}{3}$.

4. If a match is made, the player's matching card is placed on top of the pile and becomes the new target card. It is now the next player's turn. When a WILD card is played, the next player uses the fraction just stated for the new target card.

5. If no match can be made, the player takes 1 card from the deck. If the card drawn matches the target card, it may be played. If not, the player keeps the card and the turn ends.

6. The game is over when one of the players runs out of cards, when there are no cards left in the *Fraction Match* deck, or time runs out. The player with the fewest cards wins.

Differentiation Options

READINESS Students may need a review of modeling fractions or using the Equivalent Fractions Rule. Using visual models or a table may be helpful:

▶ Players use the visual models on the Everything Math Deck fraction cards that correspond to the *Fraction Match* Cards. (There will be 31 fraction cards in the new deck.)

▶ Players refer to a Table of Equivalent Fractions as they play.

ENRICHMENT

▶ Players match only equivalent fractions. When no more cards can be played, players show their cards and take turns finding a match with another player(s)' cards. Matches are discarded. Play is over when there are no more matches. The player with the fewest cards wins.

▶ Players play a card if it is an equivalent fraction or if the denominator is 1 more or 1 less than the fraction for the target card. If a player plays a fraction card with a denominator 1 more or 1 less, he or she must correctly tell whether the fraction is larger or smaller than the target number.

ELL SUPPORT Point out that *match* and *wild* have multiple meanings. Explain and model the specialized meanings of these words in the context of this game.

GRADES 5–6 Fraction Multiplication Top-It

Strands Number and Numeration; Operations and Computation

Skill Multiplying and comparing fractions

Materials (per group)
- ◆ Game Master 4 (Record Sheet, optional)
- ◆ Everything Math Deck
- ◇ 1 calculator

Players 2–4

Object of the game To collect the most cards.

Games Across the Grades

Grades	PK	K	1	2	3	4	5	6
Advanced Learning						◆		
Core Program							◆	◆
Reteaching and Practice								

Directions

1. One player shuffles and stacks the cards fraction-side down.

2. Each player turns over 2 cards and calls out the product of the fractions. Players should check each other's products with a calculator.

3. Players compare their products. The player with the greatest product takes the cards. In case of a tie, each tied player turns over 2 more cards and calls out the product. The player with the highest product takes all cards from both plays.

4. The game ends when not enough cards are left for each player to have another turn. The player with the most cards wins.

Another Way to Play

To practice multiplying fractions by whole numbers, players can turn one card fraction-side up and 1 card whole-number side up on each turn.

NOTE: Players can use Game Master 4 to record their multiplication problems and compare fractions.

Game Master 4 (p. 263)

Differentiation Options

READINESS Students may need to review area models and the meaning of fraction multiplication. Limiting the denominators used may be helpful:

▶ Players use only the cards showing halves, fourths, and eighths.

ENRICHMENT

▶ Each player draws 3 cards and multiplies 3 fractions.

▶ Players can receive up to 2 bonus points if they can name 1 or 2 fractions that are equivalent to the product of their fractions. Bonus points count as cards at the end of the game.

ELL SUPPORT Discuss the mathematical meaning of ***product*** and compare it to the other meanings.

GRADES 4–5 Fraction Of

Strand Operations and Computation

Skill Multiplying fractions and whole numbers; finding fractions of collections

Materials (per pair)

◆ *Fraction Of* Gameboard (or Game Master 105, 2 copies)

◆ *Fraction Of* Fraction Cards (or Game Masters 106 and 107)

◆ *Fraction Of* Set Cards (or Game Master 108)

Players 2

Object of the game To score more points.

Grade 4   Grade 5

SRB 244   SRB 313

Games Across the Grades

Grades	PK	K	1	2	3	4	5	6
Advanced Learning					◆			
Core Program						◆	◆	
Reteaching and Practice								◆

NOTE: For an easier version, players use only the Fraction Cards marked with a hexagon from Game Master 106.

Directions

1. One player shuffles each deck separately and places both decks number-side down.

2. Players take turns. For each turn, a player draws 1 card from each deck. He or she uses the cards to create a "fraction of" problem with a whole number solution.

   • The Fraction Card indicates what fraction of the set the player must find.

   • The Set Card offers 3 possible choices. Players must choose a set that will result in a "fraction of" problem with a whole-number solution.

Example

Player 1 draws  $\frac{1}{10}$ and [28 counters / 35 counters / 30 counters].

$\frac{1}{10}$ of 28 will *not* result in a whole-number solution.

$\frac{1}{10}$ of 35 will *not* result in a whole-number solution.

$\frac{1}{10}$ of 30 *will* result in a whole-number solution: 3 counters.

Player 1 chooses 30 counters as the set for the "fraction of" problem.

3. The player solves the "fraction of" problem and sets the 2 cards aside. The solution is the player's score for the turn.

Example

Player 2 draws | $\frac{1}{2}$ | and | 12 counters\
30 counters\
25 counters

Player 2 chooses 30 counters (to earn more points than 12 counters would), finds $\frac{1}{2}$ of 30, and earns 15 points.

4. Play continues until all of the cards in the Fraction Card pile or Set Card pile have been used. The player with more points wins.

Differentiation Options

READINESS Students may need to review how to find a fraction of a whole number. Using counters may be helpful:

▶ Instead of Set Cards, each player has 30 counters. After drawing a Fraction Card, the player uses some or all of the counters to construct an array (a set) for which they can solve the "fraction of" problem.

▶ Players use grid paper as they play. A player may draw one or more arrays for each set on a Set Card to determine whether a "fraction of" problem would result in a whole-number solution.

ENRICHMENT

▶ Players solve as many "fraction of" problems with whole-number solutions as they can on each turn. The player scores the sum of the solutions. For example, a player who drew the Fraction Card $\frac{1}{2}$ and the Set Card *5 counters, 12 counters, 20 counters* could solve $\frac{1}{2}$ of 12 (6 points) and $\frac{1}{2}$ of 20 (10 points). The player's score would be $6 + 10 = 16$ points.

ELL SUPPORT Provide students with 28 counters. Model how to find $\frac{1}{2}$ of 28. Emphasize that the answer, 14, is a whole number. Write **14** and **whole number** on the board. Explain that even though **hole** and **whole** sound the same, they have different spellings and meanings.

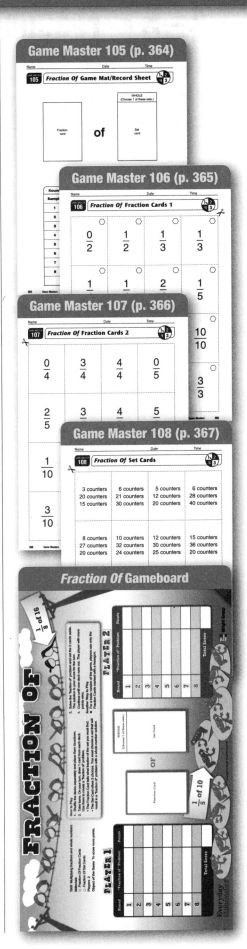

Fraction/Percent Concentration

Games Across the Grades								
Grades	PK	K	1	2	3	4	5	6
Advanced Learning								
Core Program						◆	◆	
Reteaching and Practice								◆

Strands Number and Numeration

Skill Recognizing fractions and percents that are equivalent

Materials (per group)

◆ Fraction/Decimal/Percent Card Deck (fraction and percent cards only)

◇ 1 calculator (optional)

Players 2–3

Object of the game To collect the most cards.

Grade 4   Grade 5
SRB 246   SRB 315

NOTE: Color-coding the backs of the 3 types of cards with stick-on dots may help students keep the fraction, decimal, and percent cards separate.

Directions

1. Players spread the cards out facedown in 2 separate areas—a fraction area and a percent area. Each type of cards should be arranged in the same size array.

2. Players take turns. For each turn, a player turns over a fraction card and a percent card. If the fraction and the percent are equivalent, the player keeps both cards. If the fraction and the percent are not equivalent, the player returns the cards facedown.

3. Players may use a calculator to check each other's matches.

4. The game ends when all of the cards have been taken. The player with the most cards wins.

Another Way to Play

Players use the fraction cards and the decimal cards, or the percent cards and the decimal cards.

Differentiation Options

READINESS Students may need a review of strategies for converting fractions to percents. Limiting the fractions and percents used may be helpful:

▶ Players use only the tenths cards and the equivalent percents. Add the fifths cards and their equivalent percents when students are ready.

ENRICHMENT

▶ Players receive 1 bonus point for correctly naming the decimal equivalent for each fraction/percent pair. At the end of the game, each bonus point counts as an additional card.

ELL SUPPORT To ensure that students understand the meaning of *equivalent*, model how to identify two cards that are equivalent before the game is played.

Fraction Spin

Strands Number and Numeration; Operations and Computation

Skill Estimating sums and differences of fractions

Materials (per pair)

◆ *Fraction Spin* Gameboard (or Game Masters 109 and 110)

◆ 1 transparent spinner (or a paper clip and pencil)

Players 2

Object of the game To complete 10 true sentences.

Games Across the Grades

Grades	PK	K	1	2	3	4	5	6
Advanced Learning						◆		
Core Program							◆	
Reteaching and Practice								◆

Directions

1. Each player uses a separate box on the gameboard or Record Sheet.

2. Players take turns spinning. Players may tape the transparent spinner in place over the spinner face, or use the paper clip and pencil to make a spinner.

3. Each player writes the fraction he or she spins in one of the blanks on his or her Record Sheet.

4. The first player to complete 10 true sentences wins.

Differentiation Options

READINESS Students may need to model the fractions on the spinner or model the addition and subtraction of fractions. Using easier fractions may be helpful:

► Players change the denominators on the spinner from thirds to fourths and from sixths to eighths.

ENRICHMENT

► Players add a blank for a third addend to any 3 of the addition number sentences on the gameboard or Record Sheet.

ELL SUPPORT Ask students to write 2 addition number sentences with fractions—one that has a sum less than 1 and the other with a sum greater than 1. Explain that they will create number sentences in this game. Have students analyze the spinner. Ask: *Which fractions are less than $\frac{1}{2}$? More than $\frac{1}{2}$?* Explain that students should think about the size of the fractions when they write them on the Record Sheet.

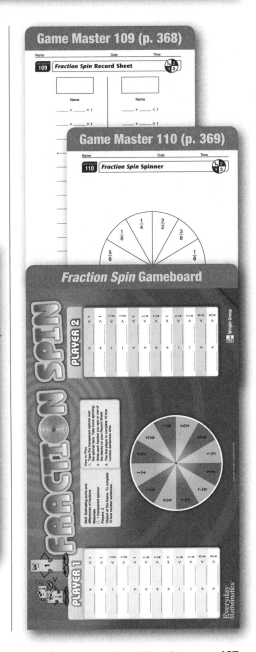

Game Master 109 (p. 368)

Game Master 110 (p. 369)

Fraction Spin Gameboard

GRADES 2–5 Fraction Top-It

Games Across the Grades

Grades	PK	K	1	2	3	4	5	6
Advanced Learning			◆					
Core Program				◆	◆	◆	◆	
Reteaching and Practice							◆	

Strands Number and Numeration; Operations and Computation

Skill Comparing fractions

Materials (per group)

◆ *Fraction Top-It* Cards

◆ Game Master 4 (Record Sheet, optional)

Players 2–4

Object of the game To collect the most cards.

Grade 3 SRB 287   Grade 4 SRB 247   Grade 5 SRB 316

NOTE: Players can use Game Master 4 to record and compare their fractions.

Game Master GM 4 (p. 263)

Name ____ Date ____ Time ____

Top-It Record Sheets

Play a round of *Top-It*. Write your number sentence and the other player's number sentence. Write <, >, or = to compare the number sentences.

Round	Player 1	>, <, =	Player 2
1			
2			
3			
4			
5			
6			

Game Master 73 (p. 332)

Fraction Cards 1

Game Master 74 (p. 333)

Fraction Cards 2

Level A (recommended for Grades 2 and 3)

Materials

◆ For Grade 2: Game Master 73 (Fraction Cards, 2 copies; also available in Grade 2 Math Journal 2, Activity Sheets 5 and 6)

◆ For Grade 3: Game Masters 73 and 74 (Fraction Cards, also available in Grade 3 Math Journal 2, Activity Sheets 5–8)

Players 2

Directions

1. One player shuffles and stacks the cards picture-side down.

2. Each player turns over a card. Players compare the shaded parts of their cards. The player with the larger fraction shaded takes both cards.

3. If the shaded parts are equal, the fractions are equivalent. Each player then turns over another card. The player with the larger fraction shaded takes all of the cards from both plays.

4. The game is over when all cards have been taken from the deck. The player with more cards wins.

Level B (recommended for Grades 2 and 3)

Materials

◆ For Grade 2: Game Master 73 (Fraction Cards, 2 copies; also available in Grade 2 Math Journal 2, Activity Sheets 5 and 6)

◆ For Grade 3: Game Masters 73 and 74 (Fraction Cards, also available in Grade 3 Math Journal 2, Activity Sheets 5–8)

Players 2

Directions

Advance Preparation: Before beginning the game, players write the fraction for the shaded part on the back of each card.

1. One player shuffles and stacks the cards picture-side down.

2. Each player takes a card **but does not turn it over.** The cards remain picture-side down.

3. Players take turns. For each turn, a player says whether he or she thinks his or her fraction is *greater than, less than,* or *equivalent to* the other player's fraction.

4. Players turn the cards over and compare the shaded parts. If the player was correct, he or she takes both cards. If the player was incorrect, the other player takes both cards.

5. The game is over when all cards have been taken from the deck. The player with more cards wins.

Level C (recommended for Grades 4 and 5)

Materials
◆ For Grades 4 and 5: Game Masters 111 and 112 (Fraction Cards, also available in Grade 4 Math Journal 2, Activity Sheets 5 and 6)

Players 2–4

Directions

Advance Preparation: Before beginning the game, players write the fraction for the shaded part on the back of each card.

1. One player shuffles and stacks the cards picture-side down.

2. One player deals the same number of cards, picture-side down, to each player:
   - If there are 2 players, 16 cards each.
   - If there are 3 players, 10 cards each.
   - If there are 4 players, 8 cards each.

3. Players spread their cards out, picture-side down, so that all of the written fractions may be seen.

4. Starting with the dealer and going in a clockwise direction, each player plays one card picture-side down.

5. Players compare the fractions. The player with the largest fraction wins the round and takes the cards. Players may check who has the largest fraction by turning over the cards and comparing the shaded parts.

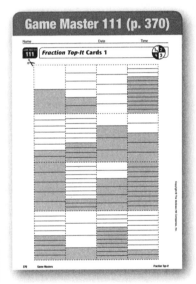

Game Master 111 (p. 370)

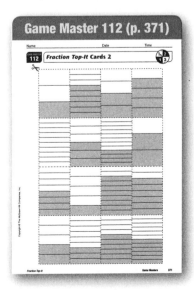

Game Master 112 (p. 371)

6. If there is a tie for the largest fraction, each tied player plays another card. The player with the largest fraction takes all of the cards from both plays.

7. The player who takes the cards starts the next round.

8. The game is over when all cards have been played. The player who has the most cards wins.

Advanced Version

Fraction Addition Top-It

Skill Adding fractions

For each turn, each player plays 2 cards and finds the sum of the fractions on the 2 cards. Players compare sums. The rest of the rules are the same as for the basic version.

Differentiation Options

READINESS Students may need to review using area models and other methods of comparing fractions. Limiting the range of denominators may be helpful:

▶ For Grade 2, players use only the halves and fourths cards. For Grades 3–5, players use only the halves, fourths, eighths, and twelfths.

ENRICHMENT

▶ Have students play in groups of 4 and order the fractions (or sums). Players score 4 points for the largest fraction and 2 points for the smallest. The player with the most points wins.

ELL SUPPORT Discuss the meaning of *top-it* in this game context. Write 4 fractions that will be used in the game on the board. Ask: *Which fraction tops all of the others—is it the largest fraction? Imagine I play a fraction card with $\frac{1}{4}$. Which fraction card would you play to top my fraction?* Introduce the game and model a round that involves a tie.

GRADES 4–6 Getting to One

Strands Operations and Computation; Patterns, Functions, and Algebra

Skill Estimation

Materials (per pair)
◆ Game Master 113 (Record Sheet, optional)
◇ 1 calculator

Players 2

Object of the game To guess a mystery number in fewer tries than the opponent.

Grade 4
SRB 248

Grade 5
SRB 318

Grade 6
SRB 321

Games Across the Grades

Grades	PK	K	1	2	3	4	5	6
Advanced Learning								
Core Program						◆	◆	◆
Reteaching and Practice								

Directions

1. Player 1 chooses a mystery number between 1 and 100.

2. Player 2 guesses the mystery number.

3. Player 1 uses a calculator to divide Player 2's guess by the mystery number. Player 1 then reads aloud the answer in the calculator display. If the answer has more than 2 decimal places, only the first 2 decimal places are read.

4. Player 2 continues to guess until the calculator result is 1. Player 2 keeps track of the number of guesses.

5. When Player 2 has guessed the mystery number, players trade roles and follow Steps 1–4 again. The player who guesses the mystery number in fewer guesses wins the round.

6. The first player to win 3 rounds wins the game.

NOTE: Players can use Game Master 113 to record their guesses, their calculator displays, and whether their results are too large or too small.

Game Master 113 (p. 372)

Example

Player 1 chooses the mystery number 65.

Player 2 guesses: 45. Player 1 keys in: 45 ÷ 65 ENTER/=.

Answer: 0.69 Too small.

Player 2 guesses: 73. Player 1 keys in 73 ÷ 65 ENTER/=.

Answer: 1.12 Too big.

Player 2 guesses: 65. Player 1 keys in: 65 ÷ 65 ENTER/=.

Answer: 1 Just right!

Advanced Version

Players use mystery numbers up to 1,000.

Differentiation Options

READINESS Before playing, students may benefit from using a given number as the divisor for each of the surrounding numbers, and drawing conclusions about the results. For example, when 10 is the divisor for each of the numbers from 1 through 20: dividends (guesses) less than 10 yield a quotient less than 1; dividends (guesses) greater than 10 yield a quotient greater than 1. Limiting the range of mystery numbers may also be helpful:

▶ Players choose a mystery number between 1 and 20. Alternatively, players choose a multiple of 5 between 1 and 100.

ENRICHMENT

▶ Players record guesses and calculator displays in a "What's My Rule?" table. Guesses are the *in* numbers and calculator displays are the *out* numbers. When players figure out the mystery number, they write a rule for the table. For example, " ÷ 46" is the rule when 46 is the mystery number.

ELL SUPPORT Discuss what is meant by ***mystery number.*** Then say: *I have chosen a mystery number between 1 and 100. You will guess what the mystery number is. We will use the calculator to give you a clue about how close each guess is to the mystery number.* Model a few guesses and write the resulting number sentences on the board. Label the guesses. Guide students to understand how the answer to the division problem can help make the next guess closer.

GRADE K

Go Forward, Back Up

Games Across the Grades									
Grades	PK	K	1	2	3	4	5	6	
Advanced Learning	◆								
Core Program		◆							
Reteaching and Practice			◆						

Strands Number and Numeration; Operations and Computation; Patterns, Functions, and Algebra

Skill Counting; addition and subtraction concepts

Materials (per pair)

◆ Game Master 114 (directions and game mat)

◆ 1 cube numbered 0–5

◆ 1 cube with 4 green sides marked "+", and 2 red sides marked "–"

◆ 2 different-colored counters

Players 2

Object of the game To reach the end of the path.

Directions

1. Players put their counters on the arrow marked "Start."

2. Players take turns rolling both cubes.

   - If a player rolls a "+," the player moves *forward* the number of spaces shown on the other cube.

   - If a player rolls a "−," he or she moves *back* the number of spaces shown on the other cube. If a player cannot go back the exact number of spaces shown on the cube, the player remains on his or her space and the turn is over.

3. The first player to reach the square marked "End" wins. Players must reach the End with an exact roll of the number cube.

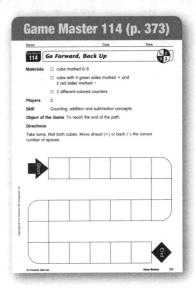

Game Master 114 (p. 373)

Differentiation Options

READINESS Students may need a review of counting dots on a die and spaces on a path with one-to-one correspondence. Using dot patterns for support may be helpful:

▶ Use dot patterns instead of numerals on the 0–5 number cube. After players roll, they count the dots aloud and then count the spaces aloud as they move their counters forward or backward.

ENRICHMENT

▶ Use a cube numbered 3–8 and a longer path. (Or have players return to the Start after reaching the End.)

▶ Before the game begins, each player shades one space on the path. If a player lands on a shaded space, on the next turn he or she moves twice as many spaces as the number rolled.

ELL SUPPORT Discuss the meanings of *go forward* and *back up.* Model a couple of turns. Ask: *What do you roll to move forward? What do you roll to back up?* Discuss the meaning of *exact roll.*

GRADES 4–6 Grab Bag

Games Across the Grades

Grades	PK	K	1	2	3	4	5	6
Advanced Learning								
Core Program						◆	◆	◆
Reteaching and Practice								

Strands Data and Chance; Patterns, Functions, and Algebra

Skill Variable substitution; calculating probabilities

Materials (per pair)

- ◆ For Grade 4: *Grab Bag* Gameboard (or Game Master 118)
- ◆ For Grade 4: *Grab Bag* Cards (or Game Masters 116 and 117)
- ◆ For Grades 5 and 6: Game Master 118 (Record Sheet, 1 per pair)
- ◆ For Grades 5 and 6: Game Masters 116 and 117 (*Grab Bag* Cards)
- ◆ Game Master 115 (directions, optional)
- ◆ 3 dice

Players 2, or 2 teams of 2

Object of the game To score more points.

Grade 4

SRB 249

NOTE: Players (or teams) should develop strategies in order to earn the most points possible when choosing the number to substitute for *x*.

NOTE: After students play a few games, you may want to encourage thoughtful use of the Record Sheet by altering the cards so some of them ask for the probability of any event other than the event labeled *y*.

Directions

1. One player shuffles the *Grab Bag* Cards and stacks them facedown.

2. Players (or teams) take turns. For each turn, a player (or team) turns over a card. Two quantities are missing from each card. They are shown with the variables *x* and *y*.

3. The player (or team) rolls the 3 dice and substitutes the numbers rolled for the variables *x* and *y* in this way:

   - Replace *x* with the number shown on 1 die.
   - Replace *y* with the sum of the numbers on the other 2 dice.

4. The player (or team) solves the problem. The opposing player (or team) checks the answer. The score for the turn is:

   - 10 points if the event is unlikely (probability less than $\frac{1}{2}$).
   - 30 points if the event is likely (probability greater than $\frac{1}{2}$).
   - 50 points if the event has a 50–50 chance (probability exactly $\frac{1}{2}$).

5. The player (or team) with the higher score after 5 rounds wins.

Example

Paul draws the card shown to the right.

He rolls 6, 1, and 4, and substitutes 1 for x and $6 + 4 = 10$ for y.

Lina's grab bag has 2 red, 2 blue, 1 pink, and 10 green ribbons. The probability of Lina picking a green ribbon is 10 out of 15, or $\frac{10}{15}$ or $\frac{2}{3}$.

Picking a green ribbon is likely (probability greater than $\frac{1}{2}$).

Paul scores 30 points.

Lina has a bag of ribbons. She has 2 red, 2 blue, x pink, and y green ribbons.

What are the chances she will pick a green ribbon without looking?

Game Master 115 (p. 374)

Game Master 116 (p. 375)

Game Master 117 (p. 376)

Game Master 118 (p. 377)

Grab Bag Gameboard

Differentiation Options

READINESS Students may need practice determining the probabilities of events and comparing these probabilities to $\frac{1}{2}$. Modeling the problems may be helpful:

▶ Players draw pictures to model the problems they generate.

ENRICHMENT

▶ A player (or team) earns 5 bonus points if they can name the probability they find on each turn as a fraction in simplest form.

ELL SUPPORT Explain the meaning of *substitute* by modeling a round. Show different ways of substituting the numbers from the dice roll and the results of the different substitutions. Discuss how different substitutions generate different results and lead to different scores.

GRADE 6

Greedy

Strand Data and Chance

Skill Using probability in a random-number situation

Materials (per group)
◆ Game Master 119 (Score Sheets)
◆ 1 die

Players 4–8 or whole class

Object of the game To have the highest total score.

Grade 6
SRB
322

Games Across the Grades

Grades	PK	K	1	2	3	4	5	6
Advanced Learning						◆	◆	◆
Core Program								◆
Reteaching and Practice								

Game Master 119 (p. 378)

Directions

1. Each player records his or her score on a separate Score Sheet.

2. To begin a round, all players stand up.

3. The group leader rolls the die twice. Each player's score is equal to the sum of the numbers rolled.

4. Before rolling the die again, the group leader asks whether any player would like to sit down. Players who sit down keep the score they have and record it as the score for that round on their Score Sheet.

5. If any players remain standing, the group leader rolls the die twice.

   • If either roll is a 2, all players standing record a score of 0 for that round and the round is over.

   • If neither roll is a 2, each player standing calculates his or her new score by adding the sum of the numbers rolled to their last score.

6. Players repeat Steps 4 and 5 until no players remain standing. The round is over.

7. The player with the largest total score after 6 rounds wins.

Differentiation Options

READINESS Students may need a review of probability in dice-rolling situations. Tracking rolls may be helpful:

▶ To help players focus on probability rather than computation, allow players to keep track of their running total on a calculator.

▶ Have one player keep a class tally of rolls. Players may refer to the tally as they make their decisions.

ENRICHMENT

▶ Have players choose different "sit" numbers that can be rolled on one die or as totals. A sit number such as a total of 6 makes the game harder, since there are many ways to roll 6.

ELL SUPPORT Discuss the meaning of *greedy.* Model a round with a small group of students. You should play the part of the greedy student and remain standing until you have a score of 0. Ask: *What happened to the greedy player?*

Grid Search

Strand Measurement and Reference Frames

Skill Deduction; developing a search strategy; navigating a coordinate grid

Materials (per pair)

◆ *Grid Search* Gameboard (or Game Master 120)

◇ 1 file folder or other divider

Players 2

Object of the game To locate the opponent's queen.

Grade 4
SRB
250

Games Across the Grades

Grades	PK	K	1	2	3	4	5	6
Advanced Learning					◆			
Core Program						◆		
Reteaching and Practice							◆	◆

Directions

Setting up the grids

Players sit so that they cannot see what the other player is doing. Each player uses Grids 1 and 2. Each player secretly decides where to place a queen and 6 knights on Grid 1. They write the letter *Q* to record the location of the queen and the letter *K* to record the location of each knight.

• The queen may be placed on any square.

• The knights may also be placed on any squares, as long as the queen and the knights can all be connected without skipping squares.

These are acceptable arrangements of the pieces:

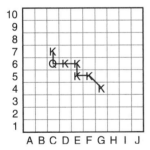

These are *not* acceptable arrangements because the pieces cannot be connected without skipping squares.

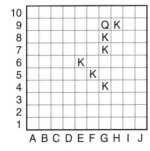

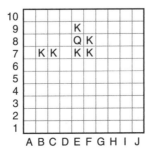

NOTE: A player hides his or her queen and knights on Grid 1. The player records the results of his or her search for the other player's queen on Grid 2.

As students play, discuss their search strategies.

Game Master 120 (p. 379)

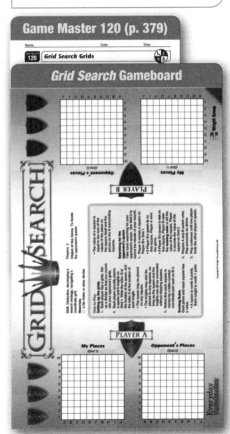

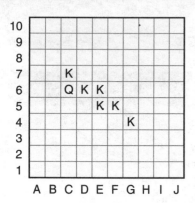

Examples of square values
for the grid above:

G-4 is worth 2: $1 + 1 = 2$

E-6 is worth 4: $1 + 1 + 1 + 1 = 4$

C-7 is worth 7: $1 + 5 + 1 = 7$

B-6 is worth 6: $5 + 1 = 6$

A-6 is worth 0.

1. Player A names a square on Player B's Grid 1. Each square is named by a letter-number coordinate pair such as B-3.

2. If Player B's queen is on that square, Player A wins the game. If Player B's queen is not on that square, Player B uses the following scoring rules to tell the value of the square:
   - Each piece and each square has a value.
   - A queen is worth 5 points. A knight is worth 1 point.
   - The value of a square is equal to the sum of the values of the piece on the square itself and the pieces on the 8 surrounding squares, including squares on a diagonal.

3. Player A records the value of the square on his or her Grid 2.

4. Players switch roles. Players should develop a search strategy that will locate the queen in as few turns as possible.

5. Play continues until one player figures out where the other player's queen is located.

Example

Suppose Player B has arranged the pieces as shown.

Player B: Grid 1

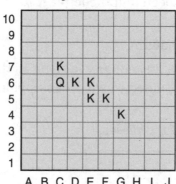

Player A: *I guess E-6.*
Player B: *You didn't find the queen, but square E-6 is worth 4 points.*

Player A: Grid 2

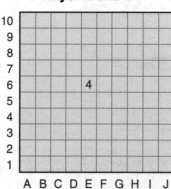

Player A writes 4 in square E-6 on his or her Grid 2.

Differentiation Options

READINESS Students may need practice in naming and locating squares on the coordinate grid and developing search strategies. Using a smaller section of the coordinate grid and fewer knights may be helpful:

▶ Players only use the section of the coordinate grid with the numbers 1–6 and the letters A–F. They hide 1 queen and 4 knights.

▶ To decrease the size of the area to be searched, the knights and queen must be placed so that no diagonal lines are necessary to connect their squares.

ENRICHMENT

▶ Players add 2 more knights, or a king whose value is 7 points.

▶ Each player hides one jester whose value is 1 point and who is not connected to the queen or any of the knights.

ELL SUPPORT Explain that the knights protect the queen so they must be placed on the board so that the queen and all of the knights are connected. Demonstrate the meaning of **connected.** Create a board and ask students to find your queen. Using a second grid on the board, model writing point values on the squares that students guess. Ask questions such as: *What does a value of 0 mean? What does a value of 2 mean? Is it possible for a square to have a value of 1? Why or why not?*

GRADE 5

Hidden Treasure

Strand Measurement and Reference Frames

Skill Plotting ordered pairs; developing a search strategy

Materials (per pair)

◆ *Hidden Treasure* Gameboard (or Game Master 121)

◇ 2 pencils

◇ 1 colored pen or pencil

◇ 1 file folder or other divider

Players 2

Object of the game To find the opponent's hidden point.

Grade 5

SRB
319

Games Across the Grades								
Grades	PK	K	1	2	3	4	5	6
Advanced Learning						◆		
Core Program							◆	
Reteaching and Practice								◆

Directions

NOTE: Each player hides a point on Grid 1 and records the other player's guesses on the same grid. Players record their guesses about their opponent's point on Grid 2.

1. Each player uses 2 grids (Grid 1 and Grid 2). Players sit so that they cannot see what the other is writing.

2. Each player secretly marks a point in color on his or her Grid 1. These are the "hidden points."

3. Player A guesses the location of Player B's hidden point by naming an ordered pair. To name (1,2), a player would say: *1 comma 2.* Player A marks the guess on his or her Grid 2.

4. If Player B's hidden point **is** at that location, Player A wins.

5. If Player B's hidden point **is not** at that location, Player B marks the guess in pencil on his or her Grid 1. Player B counts the least number of "square sides" needed to travel from the hidden point to the guessed point and tells it to Player A.

6. Player A writes the number of square sides needed to travel from the hidden point to the guessed point below the guessed point on his or her Grid 2.

7. Players switch roles and repeat Steps 3–6.

8. Play continues until one player finds the other's hidden point.

Example

Player A marks a hidden point at (2,5).   Player B marks a hidden point at (3,7).

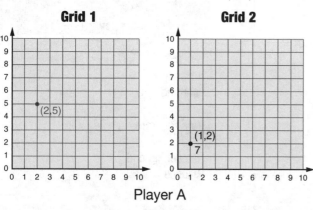

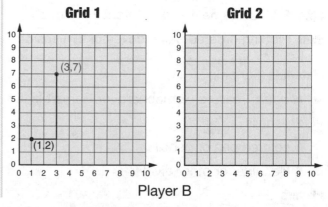

- Player A guesses that Player B's hidden point is at (1, 2) and marks it on Grid 2 in pencil.

- Player B marks the point (1, 2) in pencil on Grid 1 and tells Player A that (1, 2) is 7 units (square sides) away from the hidden point.

- Player A writes 7 next to the point (1, 2) on his or her Grid 2. Player A's turn is over, and Player B makes a guess.

Advanced Version

Students use the 4-quadrant grids on Game Master 122.

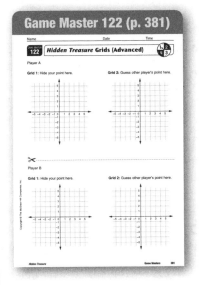

Game Master 122 (p. 381)

Differentiation Options

READINESS Students may need a review of naming ordered pairs. Making the clues more detailed may also be helpful:

▶ After Player A makes a guess, Player B tells how far the guess is from the hidden point in two parts. In the Example on the previous page, Player B might say: *Your guess is 2 units and 5 units away.* This tells Player A that he or she needs to move 2 units in one direction and 5 units in another direction to locate Player B's point.

ENRICHMENT

▶ Provide each player with two 4-quadrant grids with axes labeled from −10 to 10.

ELL SUPPORT Discuss the meaning of *hidden* and *treasure* in the context of this game. Explain that each player will select one ordered pair to represent the place the *treasure* is *hidden.* The other player will guess the location of the hidden point using clues.

Draw a grid on the board. Write an ordered pair on a piece of paper, but do not show it to the students. Ask for volunteers to guess where the hidden point is located. Label the points that students guess as well as how many units they are away from the hidden point. When students find your hidden point, show them the ordered pair on your paper.

GRADES PK–K High Low

Strand Number and Numeration

Skill Reading numbers; counting; comparing numbers

Materials (per pair)

◆ Game Masters 123–126 (number cards 0–10 with pictures)

Players 2

Object of the game To identify the high card and the low card in each pair.

Games Across the Grades

Grades	PK	K	1	2	3	4	5	6
Advanced Learning								
Core Program	◆	◆						
Reteaching and Practice		◆						

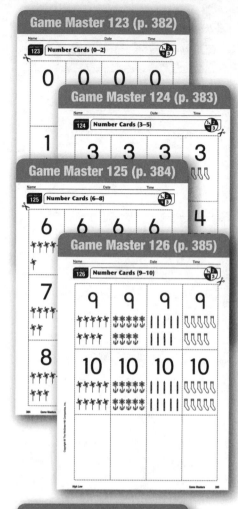

Directions

1. One player shuffles the cards and divides them evenly between the 2 players.

2. Each player stacks his or her cards facedown.

3. For each round, both players turn over their top card and read the numbers aloud.

4. Players compare numbers. The player with the higher card calls out "high," and the player with the lower card calls out "low." If there is a tie, players can call out "same" or "equal" before discarding both cards.

5. After each round, both players put their cards in a discard pile.

6. The game is over when all of the cards have been played.

Advanced Version (recommended for Grade K)

Materials (per pair)

- ◆ Game Masters 240–242 (number cards)

1. One player shuffles the cards and stacks them facedown.

2. Players take turns turning over the top card and guessing whether the next card will be a larger or smaller number.

3. After turning over the next card, the player keeps both cards if the guess was correct. If the guess was incorrect, the player returns both cards to the bottom of the deck.

4. The game ends when all of the cards have been taken.

Differentiation Options

READINESS Students may need a review of strategies for comparing numbers. Using counters may be helpful:

▶ Players model the pictures on the number cards with counters and align the counters in order to compare numbers in each round. (To aid players' counting, you may want to prepare a set of cards with dot patterns instead of pictures.)

ENRICHMENT

▶ Players play in groups of 3 or 4; the player with the highest number calls out "high," and the player with the lowest number calls out "low."

ELL SUPPORT Prior to introducing the game, draw two cards. Ask: *Are they the same? Which is larger? What are other words we can use for **larger**? (**bigger, higher, greater, more**) Which is smaller? What are other words we can use for smaller? (**lower, less**) When 2 cards are the same, what words can we use? (**tie, equal**)* Model the game with several students.

GRADES 4–6

High-Number Toss

Strands Number and Numeration

Skill Place value; exponential notation; comparing large numbers

Materials (per pair)

◆ *High-Number Toss* Gameboard (or Game Master 127)

◆ 1 die (or number cards 1–6)

Players 2

Object of the game To make the largest number possible.

Grade 4
SRB
252

Grade 5
SRB
320

Grade 6
SRB
323

Games Across the Grades

Grades	PK	K	1	2	3	4	5	6
Advanced Learning					◆			
Core Program						◆	◆	◆
Reteaching and Practice								

Directions

1. Player 1 rolls the die and writes the number on *any one* of the 4 blanks on his or her Record Sheet.

2. Player 2 then rolls the die and writes the number on *any one* of his or her blanks.

3. Players take turns rolling the die and writing the number 3 more times each.

4. Each player then uses the 4 numbers on his or her blanks to build a number.

   • The numbers on the first 3 blanks are the first 3 digits, in order.

   • The number on the fourth blank tells the number of zeros that come after the first 3 digits.

5. Each player reads his or her number aloud. The player with the larger number wins the round.

6. Players take turns starting a round. The first player to win 4 rounds wins the game.

NOTE: Students using the gameboard can write their numbers lightly above and below the place-value table in Step 4.

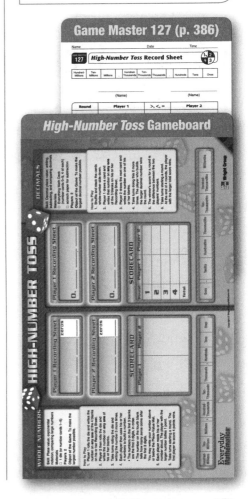

Game Master 127 (p. 386)

High-Number Toss Gameboard

Example

First three digits | Number of zeros

Player 1: <u>1</u> <u>3</u> <u>2</u> | <u>6</u> = 132,000,000 (132 million)

Player 2: <u>3</u> <u>5</u> <u>6</u> | <u>4</u> =   3,560,000 (3 million, 560 thousand)

Player 1 wins the round.

Differentiation Options

READINESS Students may need a review of reading and comparing numbers through the millions. It may also be helpful to record the numbers in a place-value chart or to begin with simpler numbers:

▶ Players use all four spaces as digits so that each number they build is in the thousands.

ENRICHMENT

▶ Players receive a bonus point if they can write their number as a 3-digit number times some power of 10.

▶ In each round, players build two numbers and find their difference. The greater difference wins the round.

ELL SUPPORT Without explaining the rules or the goal, ask students to write three blanks on a sheet of paper with a fourth blank to the side. Roll a die and guide students through Steps 1–4. Ask for volunteers to read the numbers they wrote and record them on the board. Explain that the number on the fourth blank to the side will determine the number of zeros that will follow the first three digits. Then ask: *Which number is the smallest? The largest?* Point out that the order in which the digits were written created different numbers. Explain that when students play the game, they will try to make the *largest* number.

GRADES
4–6

High-Number Toss: Decimal Version

Games Across the Grades									
Grades	PK	K	1	2	3	4	5	6
Advanced Learning					◆			
Core Program						◆	◆	◆
Reteaching and Practice								

Strands Number and Numeration; Operations and Computation

Skill Decimal place value; adding, subtracting, and comparing decimals

Materials (per pair)
- ◆ *High Number Toss* Gameboard (or Game Master 128)
- ◆ Everything Math Deck (number cards 0–9, 4 of each)

Players 2

Object of the game To make the largest decimal number possible.

Grade 5
SRB
321

Grade 6
SRB
324

Directions

1. Players shuffle and stack the cards whole-number side down.

2. Player 1 draws a card from the deck and writes that number on *any one* of the 3 blanks on his or her Record Sheet.

3. Player 2 draws the next card from the deck and writes the number on *any one* of his or her blanks.

4. Players repeat Steps 2 and 3 twice to fill in all three blanks in each number. The player who makes the larger decimal number wins the round.

5. The winner of the round scores the difference between the two players' decimal numbers. (Players subtract the smaller number from the larger number.)

NOTE: Students can record relation symbols in the space between their recording sheets on Game Master 128. Display a reminder that < means *is less than* and > means *is greater than*.

Example

Player 1: 0.<u>6</u> <u>5</u> <u>4</u>

Player 2: 0.<u>7</u> <u>5</u> <u>3</u>

Player 2 has the larger number and wins the round.

Since $0.753 - 0.654 = 0.099$, Player 2 scores 0.099 points for the round.

6. At the end of five rounds, players find their total scores. The player with the larger total score wins.

Differentiation Options

READINESS Students may need a review of using place value to compare. It may also be helpful to record the numbers in a place-value chart or to begin with simpler numbers:

▶ Players move the decimal point 1 place to the right so each number they build has ones, tenths, and hundredths.

▶ Each player draws one card, fills in the tenths, and compares. Players can progress to using the tenths and hundredths places. Players write 0s on any blanks not in use.

ENRICHMENT

▶ Students play in groups of three or more. Each player scores the difference between his or her number and the next-highest number.

▶ Players try to build a number as close to 0.5 as possible. The player with the closer number wins the round and scores the difference between his or her number and 0.5.

▶ Players use the Record Sheet for the whole-number version and draw 4 cards. They use the number in the last blank to tell how many places to move the decimal point from the right.

ELL SUPPORT Write 3 blanks followed by a decimal point on the board. Draw 3 cards. Ask students to write down the numbers that could be created with these 3 cards. Ask: *Which number is the smallest? Largest? What is the difference between the smallest and the largest?* Say: *When you play this game, you will try to make a larger decimal than your partner. Your score for a round will be the difference between two decimals.* Model a couple of rounds with a student.

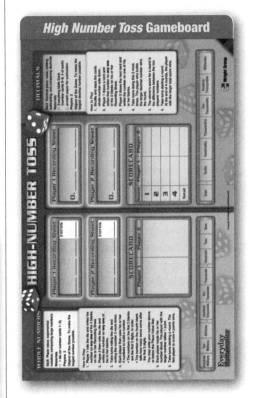

High Number Toss Gameboard

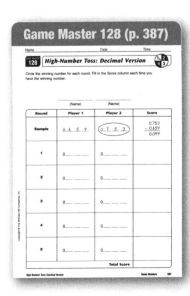

Game Master 128 (p. 387)

High Roller

Games Across the Grades

Grades	PK	K	1	2	3	4	5	6
Advanced Learning		◆						
Core Program			◆	◆	◆			
Reteaching and Practice								

Strand Number and Numeration; Operations and Computation

Skill Counting on; finding sums; comparing numbers

Materials (per pair)

- ◆ For Grade 1: *High Roller* Gameboard (or Game Masters 129 and 130)
- ◆ For other grades: Game Masters 129 (directions, optional) and 130 (Record Sheet, 1 per player)
- ◆ 2 dice
- ◆ 20 counters

Players 2–4

Object of the game To collect 10 counters.

Game Master 129 (p. 388)

Game Master 130 (p. 389)

High Roller Gameboard

NOTE: Players will need to wipe the gameboard clean after every sixth round.

Directions

1. For each turn, a player rolls 2 dice and records the numbers in the first two squares on his or her Record Sheet.

2. The player keeps the die with the larger number (the High Roller) and crosses out the smaller number.

3. The player rolls the other die again and records the number.

4. The player counts on from the High Roller to get the sum of the two dice and records the sum on the line.

5. After each player has taken a turn, players compare sums. The player with the higher sum takes a counter.

6. Players continue to take turns until one player has 10 counters. The first player to have 10 counters wins.

High Roller   Reroll this die.   High Roller   Second roll

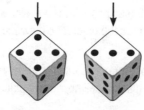  

Another Way to Play

High Roller with Subtraction

Skill Subtraction facts

The lower dice roll is subtracted from the higher dice roll. The player with the smaller difference takes a counter.

Differentiation Options

READINESS Students may need to review comparing numbers through 6 and counting on to find the total number of dots. Playing a version that involves only number comparisons may also be helpful:

▶ Each player rolls the dice once, compares the numbers, and records the larger number as his or her score.

ENRICHMENT

▶ Each player rolls two dice, keeps the High Roller, and doubles that number. He or she rolls the other die again and adds that number to the double.

▶ Players write number sentences for their scores on each turn.

ELL SUPPORT Explain that students want to get a *higher* sum than their partner and that they will get two chances to roll the dice to get the higher sum. First, they will roll two dice and keep the die with the higher number. Then they will roll the other die one more time to try to get a higher number. Model a few rounds with a small group of students. Explain that sometimes they will get a higher roll the second time around, but other times they will not.

GRADES 1–2 Hit the Target

Strand Operations and Computation

Skill Finding differences between 2-digit numbers and multiples of ten

Materials (per pair)

◆ For Grade 1: Game Master 131 (Record Sheet, 2 copies)

◆ For Grade 2: *Hit the Target* Gameboard (or Game Master 131)

◇ 1 calculator

Players 2

Object of the game To reach the target number in as few tries as possible.

Grades 1–2

MRB
136

Games Across the Grades

Grades	PK	K	1	2	3	4	5	6
Advanced Learning								
Core Program			◆	◆				
Reteaching and Practice					◆	◆		

Directions

1. Players agree on and record a 2-digit multiple of 10 as a *target number*.

2. Player 1 selects a *starting number* less than the target number and records it on Player 2's change diagram.

Game Master 131 (p. 390)

Hit the Target **Gameboard**

3. Player 2 enters the starting number into the calculator and tries to change the starting number to the target number by adding or subtracting on the calculator.

4. Player 1 records each change and its result on Player 2's change diagram.

5. When the target number is reached, players switch roles. Player 2 selects a starting number for Player 1 and fills in Player 1's change diagram as Player 1 operates the calculator.

6. The player who reaches the target number in fewer tries wins a point.

7. After 3 (or 4) rounds, the player with more points wins.

Differentiation Options

READINESS Students may need to review estimation with addition of 2-digit numbers. Using a number grid may be helpful:

▶ Players use Game Master 159 (0–110 number grid) to make their estimates for changing the starting number to the target number.

ENRICHMENT

▶ Players choose a 2-digit target number that is *not* a multiple of 10.

ELL SUPPORT Draw a change diagram on the board. Fill in 18 as the *target number,* 50 as the *starting number,* and record a *change* of −22. Explain that the *result,* 28, does not equal the target number. Try again to reach 18: $28 - 10 = 18$. Complete the change diagram. Emphasize that now the result equals the target number.

GRADES PK–K How Many More?

Games Across the Grades								
Grades	PK	K	1	2	3	4	5	6
Advanced Learning								
Core Program	◆	◆						
Reteaching and Practice			◆					

Strands Number and Numeration; Operations and Computation

Skill Counting; making 10

Materials

◆ 10 small inch cubes or blocks per player

◆ 1 inch cube or blank die marked 1, 2, 3, 1, 2, 3 (per group)

◆ 10 counters per player (Use bear counters if they are available.)

Players 2–5

Object of the game To fill the row of inch cubes or blocks with counters.

Directions

1. Each player makes a row with his or her cubes or blocks.

2. Players take turns. For each turn, a player rolls the die, takes that number of counters, and puts each counter on a block.

3. The player announces how many more counters he or she needs to fill the row. To finish filling a row, a player needs to roll an exact number.

4. You or the players decide whether the game ends when the first player's row of blocks is filled, or when all players have filled their rows.

Another Way To Play

Materials

◆ *How Many More?* Gameboard

◆ 1 cube or die marked 1, 2, 3, 1, 2, 3

◆ 10 counters per player

In this 2-player variation, each player uses counters as plates to "feed" a row of 10 dogs on the gameboard. For each die roll, a player takes that number of counters, gives each to a dog, and tells how many more dogs need to be fed.

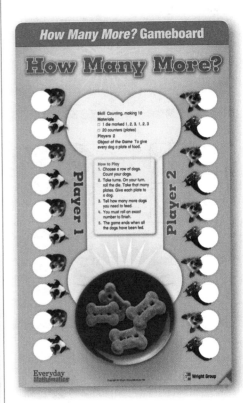

How Many More? Gameboard

Differentiation Options

READINESS Students may need practice in determining how many more are needed to make a certain total. Using smaller numbers may be helpful:

▶ Players use only 5 cubes, blocks, or dogs on the gameboard. The number of cubes, blocks, or dogs can be increased according to students' abilities.

ENRICHMENT

▶ Players use 12–15 inch cubes or blocks.

▶ Use different-colored counters. Ask students to create a pattern with the colors as they fill their rows.

ELL SUPPORT Discuss the meaning of *how many more* and *exact number* using the blocks and counters.

I

GRADE
Pre-K Itsy Bitsy Spider

Games Across the Grades								
Grades	PK	K	1	2	3	4	5	6
Advanced Learning								
Core Program	◆							
Reteaching and Practice		◆	◆					

Strand Number and Numeration

Skill Counting with one-to-one correspondence; recognizing numerals

Materials (per pair)

◆ Game Master 132 (spinner)

◆ 1 transparent spinner

◆ 2 "spiders" (different-colored counters or spider toys)

◇ 1 "spout" (egg carton without a lid or 1 ice-cube tray)

Players 1 or 2

Object of the game To reach the end of the "spout."

Directions

Advance Preparation: Write *Start* in a corner section of the egg carton or ice cube tray. Draw an arrow going up from the Start space along the long side of the carton or tray. Draw an arrow going down the other side and label the last space *End*. Make a spinner by labeling the 4-part spinner face on Game Master 132 with numbers 1–4 and taping it to the back of the transparent spinner.

> **NOTE:** Before starting the game, players can decide whether a game piece needs to land exactly on the End space to win. Players may also decide to move their game pieces up and down the spout more than once.

1. Players place the egg carton or ice-cube tray (the "spout") vertically between them. Players put their game pieces on the Start space.

2. Players take turns. For each turn, a player spins a number and moves his or her game piece that number of spaces, first up and then down the spout.

3. The first player to reach the End space wins.

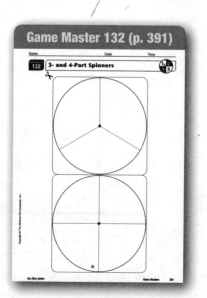

Game Master 132 (p. 391)

Name	Date	Time

132 3- and 4-Part Spinners

Itsy Bitsy Spider

Differentiation Options

READINESS Students may need practice matching numerals to the number of spaces on the spout. Using dot patterns for support or playing the game with fewer numbers may be helpful:

▶ Add the appropriate number of dots to each section of the spinner.

▶ Use Game Master 132 to create a 3-part spinner labeled 1–3.

ENRICHMENT

▶ Each player uses 2 or 3 game pieces. The game ends when all of the spiders have reached the End space.

ELL SUPPORT Play or sing the song *The Itsy Bitsy Spider.* Show images of a **water spout.** Explain that students will use an egg carton or ice tray to represent a water spout.

GRADE 6 Landmark Shark

Strand Data and Chance

Skill Finding range, mode, median, and mean

Materials (per pair)

◆ *Landmark Shark* Gameboard (or Game Master 134)

◆ *Landmark Shark* Cards (or Game Master 133): 1 each of Range, Median, and Mode cards per player

◆ Everything Math Deck

Players 2 or 3

Object of the game To score the most points by finding data landmarks.

Grade 6
SRB
325

Games Across the Grades

Grades	PK	K	1	2	3	4	5	6
Advanced Learning						◆	◆	
Core Program								◆
Reteaching and Practice								

Directions

1. For each round, the dealer shuffles the Everything Math Deck cards and deals 5 cards whole-number side down to each player.

2. Each player turns over his or her cards and puts them in order from the smallest number to the largest.

There are 3 ways to score points for the hand:

Range: The player's score is the *range* of the hand.

Game Master 134 (p. 393)

Game Master 133 (p. 392)

Landmark Shark **Gameboard**

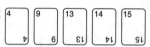

Player 1's hand:

| 1 | 4 | 6 | 8 | 12 |

Range = 12 − 1 = 11   **Points scored = 11**

Median: The player's score is the median of the 5 numbers.

Player 2's hand:

| 4 | 9 | 13 | 14 | 15 |

Median = 13   **Points scored = 13**

Mode: The player must have at least 2 cards with the same number. The player's score is found by multiplying the mode of the 5 numbers by the number of modal cards. If there is more than one mode, the player uses the mode that will produce the most points.

Player 3's hand:

| 1 | 2 | 8 | 8 | 10 |

Mode = 8   **Points scored = 2 * 8 = 16**

3. Each player decides which data landmark will yield the highest score for the hand. A player indicates his or her choice by placing 1 of the 3 *Landmark Shark* cards (Range, Median, or Mode) on the table.

4. Players can try to improve their scores by exchanging up to 3 of their cards for new cards from the deck. However, each player's *Landmark Shark* card stays the same.

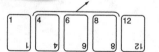 Player 1's hand:

| 1 | 4 | 6 | 8 | 12 |

| 1 | 9 | 15 |
← Exchange 3 new cards

| 1 | 1 | 9 | 12 | 15 |

Range = 12 − 1 = **11 points**

New range = 15 − 1 = **14 points scored = 14**

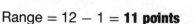

5. Players lay down their cards and record their points for the round.

6. **Bonus points:** Each player calculates the *mean* of his or her card numbers, to the nearest tenth, and adds this value to his or her score in each round.

7. The player with the highest total after 5 rounds wins.

Differentiation Options

READINESS Students may need a review of the data landmarks range, median, and mode. Playing with only 1 or 2 data landmarks may be helpful:

▶ Players use only the Median cards. They calculate bonus points by finding the mean to the nearest whole number.

ENRICHMENT

▶ Only three rounds are played. Players use each data landmark once during the three rounds.

ELL SUPPORT Select 5 cards and write the numbers on the board in order from smallest to largest. Together find the **mode, median,** and **range** of the numbers, labeling each landmark. Ask students which value is the largest. Explain that when they play *Landmark Shark,* they will choose the landmark that gives them the highest score. If students play with the option of exchanging cards or calculating the mean for bonus points, model those features of the game.

NOTE: You may wish to discuss strategies for making exchanges. For example, if a player wanted to find the median, it would be beneficial to exchange his or her 2 lowest cards. For finding the range, he or she would exchange the 3 middle cards. For finding the mode, a player would want to exchange cards that are different. For finding the mean, a player would want to exchange his or her lowest cards.

GRADE 3

Less Than You!

Strands Number and Numeration; Operations and Computation

Skills Mental addition; comparing numbers; developing a winning strategy

---

Materials (per group)

◆ Everything Math Deck (number cards 0–10, 4 of each)

Players 2

Object of the game To say *Less than you!* and have the lesser sum.

Games Across the Grades

Grades	PK	K	1	2	3	4	5	6
Advanced Learning			◆	◆				
Core Program						◆		
Reteaching and Practice							◆	

NOTE: Students will begin to make educated guesses about their opponent's hand based on the cards the opponent plays. Emphasize that the game ends as soon as a player chooses to say: *Less than you!* and advise students to refrain from saying: *Less than you!* until they are able to make an educated guess.

Directions

1. One player shuffles the cards and deals 2 cards whole-number side down (facedown) to each player. He or she stacks the remaining cards facedown.

2. Player 1 takes the top card so that he or she has 3 cards.

3. Player 1 looks at his or her cards and discards the card with the largest number faceup in a discard pile.

4. Player 1 adds the remaining two numbers mentally.

5. If Player 1 thinks that his or her sum is less than Player 2's sum, he or she says: *Less than you!*

6. Player 2 finds the sum of his or her 2 cards.

   • If Player 1's sum *is* less, Player 1 wins the game.

   • If Player 1's sum is *not* less, Player 2 wins.

7. If Player 1 thinks that his or her sum is *not* less than Player 2's sum, the turn ends. Players reverse roles and repeat Steps 2–7.

8. The game ends when one of the players says: *Less than you!*

Advanced Version

One player deals 3 cards to each player at the start of the game.

Differentiation Options

READINESS Students may need to review addition facts or use an Addition/Subtraction Facts Table. Playing with a limited range of numbers may help students develop strategies:

▶ Players use only the 0–3 number cards, 4 of each. Have them play a cooperative version in which they play by the rules but discuss their thinking and talk about their strategies as they develop them.

ENRICHMENT

▶ Players use 3 each of the number cards 0–10 and 1 each of the number cards 11–20.

ELL SUPPORT Prior to introducing the game, ask for 3 volunteers. Deal 2 cards to each person. Tell them not to show their cards to the other students. Ask the students to find the sum of their cards. Peek at the cards to determine who has the lowest sum and who has the highest sum. Ask the student with the highest sum: *Do you think you have the lowest sum? Why or why not?* Ask the other students if they think they have the lowest sum and to explain their reasoning. Ask the students to show their cards to determine who has the lowest sum. Then introduce and model the game.

GRADE **1**

Make My Design

Strand Geometry

Skill Describing geometric figures and spatial relationships in a design

Materials (per pair)

◇ 1 set of pattern blocks

◇ 1 folder

Players 2

Object of the game To create a design identical to the other player's design.

Games Across the Grades

Grades	PK	K	1	2	3	4	5	6
Advanced Learning	◆	◆						
Core Program			◆					
Reteaching and Practice				◆				

Directions

1. Player 1 chooses 6 blocks. Player 2 takes the same 6 blocks.

2. Players sit face-to-face with the folder standing between them.

3. Player 1 creates a design with the blocks.

4. Using only words, Player 1 tells Player 2 how to "Make My Design." Player 2 can ask questions about the instructions.

5. Players remove the folder and look at the two designs. Players discuss how closely the designs match.

6. Players switch roles and repeat Steps 1–5.

Differentiation Options

READINESS Students may need practice in naming shapes. Using fewer types of blocks may be helpful:

▶ Players use only 1 or 2 different shapes.

ENRICHMENT

▶ Players use more than 6 pattern blocks in each design.

ELL SUPPORT Explain to students that they need to think carefully about the words they use to describe their designs. List words on the board that they can use to describe the placement of shapes, such as **above, below, beside, left,** and **right.** Discuss and model the meanings of the words.

Pre-K
GRADE

Making Trains

Games Across the Grades									
Grades	PK	K	1	2	3	4	5	6	
Advanced Learning									
Core Program	◆								
Reteaching and Practice		◆	◆						

Strands Number and Numeration; Measurement and Reference Frames; Geometry

Skill Counting; comparing numbers; comparing lengths

Materials (per group)

◆ 1 die

◇ connecting cubes

Players 2–5

Object of the game To build a train with connecting cubes and compare its length to another train.

NOTE: For a 1-player version of the game, the player makes a new train with each roll of the die. When the player has several trains, he or she compares and describes the trains. The player can also put the trains in order from shortest to longest (from fewest cubes to most cubes).

Directions

1. One player piles the cubes between the players.
2. Players take turns rolling the die and taking that many cubes.
3. Each player connects his or her cubes to make a "train."
4. Players continue to take turns rolling the die and adding cubes to their trains.
5. Every 2 or 3 rounds, players count the cubes on their trains and compare the lengths of their trains.
6. Players may start making new trains when they can no longer count how many cubes they have in their trains.

Differentiation Options

READINESS Students may need practice in counting cubes and comparing lengths. Using fewer cubes may be helpful:

▶ Players use a die with 1, 2, and 3 dots (each on two sides), and a smaller collection of cubes.

ENRICHMENT

▶ Players determine how many cubes longer one train is than another train. Emphasize that they should line up the ends of their trains before finding the difference.

▶ Set a target length, such as 10 cubes. The first player to create a train of that length with an exact roll wins.

ELL SUPPORT Explain the meaning of *train* in this context—a *train* is formed by linking one or more things together. Tell students that they will create trains with cubes. Show them two trains of different lengths. Ask them to find how many cubes are in each train and to tell which train is longer.

Pre-K Match Up

Strand Number and Numeration

Skill Counting; associating quantities and numerals

Materials (per group)

◆ Game Master 135 (Dot Cards 1–9)

◆ Number Card Deck (cards 1–9, 1 of each)

Players 2–5

Object of the game To find all of the matching pairs of cards.

Games Across the Grades

Grades	PK	K	1	2	3	4	5	6
Advanced Learning								
Core Program	◆							
Reteaching and Practice		◆						

Directions

Advance Preparation: You may wish to laminate the dot cards or mount them on cardboard for durability.

1. One player shuffles the number cards and places them facedown in a row. Another player shuffles the dot cards and places them facedown in a second row.

2. Players take turns. For each turn, a player turns over 1 number card and 1 dot card and says the number name for each card. If the cards match, the player keeps both cards. If the cards do not match, they are turned facedown again.

3. Players take turns until all of the matching pairs are found.

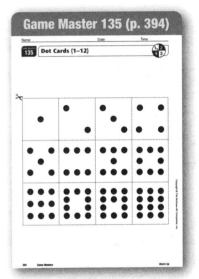

Game Master 135 (p. 394)

Differentiation Options

READINESS Students may need to review counting dots and recognizing numerals. Making a number line available, practicing with some cards faceup, or using only one type of card may be helpful:

▶ Players play with all cards (or only one set) faceup.

▶ Players match two sets of dot cards in the first game(s), and two sets of number cards in the next game(s). They progress to matching dot and number cards.

ENRICHMENT

▶ Use number cards and dot cards through 12 (Game Master 135).

ELL SUPPORT Discuss the meanings of *same* and *match* as you model how to play the game.

GRADE K

Matching Coin Game

Games Across the Grades

Grades	PK	K	1	2	3	4	5	6
Advanced Learning	◆							
Core Program		◆						
Reteaching and Practice			◆					

Strands Number and Numeration; Measurement and Reference Frames

Skill Recognizing coins; counting; comparing numbers

Materials (per group)
- ◆ Game Master 234 (or coin stickers)
- ◆ 1 inch cube
- ◆ 5 dimes, 5 nickels, and 5 pennies (per player)
- ◇ 1 muffin tin, egg carton, or other sorting tray (per player)

Players 2–5

Object of the game To collect the agreed-upon number of coins.

Game Master 234 (p. 493)

Directions

Advance Preparation: To make the money cube, use Game Master 234 or coin stickers to label an inch cube with both sides of a dime, nickel, and penny.

1. Help players agree on a goal, such as having the most dimes or the fewest pennies.
2. Players put all of the coins in a "bank" between them.
3. Players take turns rolling the money cube, finding the corresponding coin, and putting it in the sorting tray.
4. As players collect more coins, they should put each type of coin in its own section of the sorting tray.
5. After 5 rounds, players count and compare how many of each coin they have. The player who reached the agreed-upon goal wins.

Differentiation Options

READINESS Students may need practice in identifying coins. Using a money cube with only 2 coins may be helpful:

▶ Create a money cube showing just pennies and nickels, pennies and dimes, or nickels and dimes.

ENRICHMENT

▶ Create cubes that include quarters, and add 5 quarters to the bank.

ELL SUPPORT Show examples of a *penny,* a *nickel,* and a *dime.* Explain that students will be *sorting* these coins in this game. Give them a small pile of coins to sort by type. Introduce the game and model a few rounds.

GRADE Pre-K

Matching Dominoes

Strand Number and Numeration

Skill Counting dots; matching dot patterns

Materials (per group)

◆ Game Masters 235 and 236 (or 1 set of double-6 dominoes)

Players 2–5

Object of the game To make the longest possible domino "train."

Games Across the Grades								
Grades	**PK**	**K**	**1**	**2**	**3**	**4**	**5**	**6**
Advanced Learning								
Core Program	◆							
Reteaching and Practice		◆						

Directions

1. One player places all of the dominoes facedown between the players.

2. Each player takes 5 dominoes and places them faceup in front of himself or herself.

3. One player turns over a domino from the pile to be the "starter" domino. The rest of the pile is moved aside, out of play.

4. Players take turns. For each turn, a player looks at his or her dominoes and tries to match one part of any of the dominoes to one part of the "starter" domino. If a player has a match, he or she places the domino next to the correct end of the "starter" domino to begin a domino "train." If the player has no match, play moves to the next player.

5. Players continue taking turns by trying to match dominoes to either end of the growing domino train.

6. The game ends when one player has used all of his or her dominoes, or no more dominoes can be played.

> **NOTE:** To help players distinguish the two parts of dominoes, you might use color to identify the dots on one half of each domino or to emphasize the dividing line.

A domino train

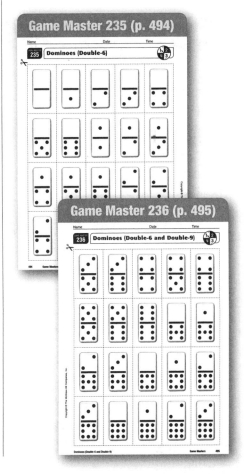

Differentiation Options

READINESS Students may need to become more familiar with dominoes. Using dominoes with fewer dots may be helpful:

► Limit the dominoes used to those with 0–4 dots.

ENRICHMENT

► Players use a set of double-9 dominoes (Game Masters 236 and 237).

► To provide practice in addition facts and renaming numbers, add this rule: Players may place a domino crosswise if the total value of the domino equals the value at the end of the domino train. For example, if the end of the train shows 5, a 2|3 domino may be placed crosswise at the end of the train. Now 2, 3, and 5 (the sum on the crosswise domino) are available for the next turn(s).

ELL SUPPORT Display a domino and emphasize the two parts. Model how to make a *domino train.*

Pre-K Matching Sets

Games Across the Grades									
Grades	PK	K	1	2	3	4	5	6	
Advanced Learning									
Core Program	◆								
Reteaching and Practice		◆							

Strand Number and Numeration

Skill Counting; matching sets of 1–5 pictures; recognizing different representations of numbers 1–5

Materials (per pair)

◆ 10 picture cards from Game Masters 136, 137, 138, and/or 139

Players 2

Object of the game To match all of the cards.

Directions

Advance Preparation: Choose Game Masters for any of these versions, listed in increasing order of difficulty:

◆ **Same pictures, same arrangement:** Game Master 136, 2 copies, *or* Game Master 137, 2 copies (Game I)

◆ **Different pictures, same arrangement:** Game Master 136 and Game Master 137 (Game I)

◆ **Same pictures, different arrangement:** Game Masters 136 and 138 *or* Game Masters 137 and 139 (Game II)

◆ **Different pictures, different arrangement:** Game Masters 136 and 139 *or* Game Masters 137 and 138 (Game II)

Remove any blank cards.

1. One player shuffles together 10 picture cards and places the 10 cards faceup in 2 rows.

2. Players take turns matching cards by the number of objects on each card. When they find a match, they say the number and remove the pair of cards from play.

3. Players continue taking turns until all cards have been matched.

Another Way to Play

Students play with the cards facedown. For each turn, a player chooses two cards and turns them over. If the cards match, he or she takes both cards. If the cards do not match, the player replaces the cards facedown.

Differentiation Options

READINESS Students may need to review counting and comparing pictures of objects. Using counters may be helpful:

▶ As a player chooses a card, he or she places a counter on top of each picture and counts aloud.

ENRICHMENT

▶ To practice addition concepts and renaming numbers, players shuffle all 4 sets of cards together and lay out half of the cards faceup. The other cards are placed in a draw pile. A player draws a card and tries to find 2 faceup cards that together have the same number of pictures as on the drawn card. If there is a match, the player takes all 3 cards and replaces the 2 faceup cards with draw cards. If there is no match, the drawn card is added to the faceup cards. Play continues until no more matches can be made.

ELL SUPPORT Discuss the meanings of *same* and *match* as you model how to play the game.

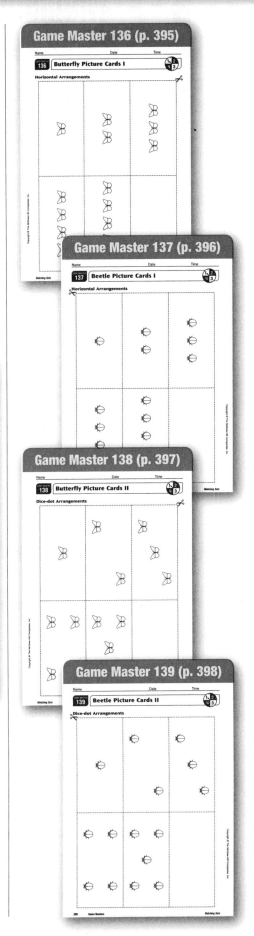

Game Master 136 (p. 395)

Game Master 137 (p. 396)

Game Master 138 (p. 397)

Game Master 139 (p. 398)

GRADE 3

Memory Addition/Subtraction

Games Across the Grades								
Grades	PK	K	1	2	3	4	5	6
Advanced Learning				◆				
Core Program					◆			
Reteaching and Practice						◆	◆	◆

Strand Operations and Computation

Skill Mental addition and subtraction; using memory keys on a calculator

Materials (per pair)

◇ 1 calculator

Players 2

Object of the game To make the number in the memory of a calculator match a target number.

Grade 3

SRB 290

Directions

1. Players agree on a target number less than 50.

2. Either player clears the calculator's memory. (See **Using the Memory Keys** below.)

3. Players take turns adding 1, 2, 3, 4, or 5 to the calculator's memory using the $\boxed{M+}$ key; or subtracting 1, 2, 3, 4, or 5 from the memory using the $\boxed{M-}$ key. They keep track of the results in their heads. A player may not use the number that was just used by the other player.

4. The goal is to make the number in memory match the target number. When it is a player's turn and he or she thinks the number in memory is the same as the target number, the player says, "same." Then he or she presses $\boxed{MR}$ or $\boxed{MRC}$ to display the number in memory.

   A player can do this before *or* after adding or subtracting a number.

5. If the number in the display matches the target number, the player who said "same" wins. If the number does not match the target number, the other player wins.

Using the Memory Keys

• Press $\boxed{AC}$ or $\boxed{MRC}$ $\boxed{MRC}$ to clear the memory.

• Press a number key and then $\boxed{M+}$ to add the number in the display to memory.

• Press a number key and then $\boxed{M-}$ to subtract the number in the display from memory.

• Press $\boxed{MR}$ or $\boxed{MRC}$ once to display the number in memory.

• Other calculators may work differently.

Example Target number: 19

Winnie presses	Display shows	Maria presses	Display shows
4 [M+]	M 4	5 [M+]	M 5
3 [M+]	M 3	1 [M+]	M 1
2 [M−]	M 2	3 [M+]	M 3
5 [M+] [MR] *or* 5 [M+] [MRC]			

Winnie says "same" after pressing 5 [M+]. Then she presses [MR] or [MRC] and the display shows the target number 19. Winnie wins. Either player presses [AC] or [MRC] [MRC] to clear the memory before starting a new game. Then, if the display shows a number that is different from 0, he or she presses [ON/C] to clear the display.

Differentiation Options

READINESS Students may need to review strategies for adding and subtracting mentally. Limiting the range of target numbers may be helpful:

▶ Players agree on a multiple of 10 as the target number.

ENRICHMENT Challenge players to use a larger target number:

▶ Players choose a target number between 50 and 100. They may add or subtract any number from 1 through 20 on each turn.

ELL SUPPORT Explain that a calculator can add and subtract numbers in two places. One place—the display—can be seen, and one—the memory—is hidden. To demonstrate how the memory works, use a drawer (or cabinet). Label the drawer "memory." Write *4 M+* on an index card, show it to students, and put it in the drawer. Ask: *What number is in the drawer or memory?* Write *5 M+* on an index card, show it to students, and put it in the drawer. Explain that [M+] tells the memory to add 5 and 4 and to "remember" it. Ask: *What is the new number in the drawer or memory?* Press [MR] to *recall* or take out what is in the memory. Open the drawer and display an index card that shows 9 to model the meaning of [MR]. Introduce the game and model how to play several rounds.

GRADES 5–6 Mixed-Number Spin

Games Across the Grades									
Grades	PK	K	1	2	3	4	5	6
Advanced Learning							◆	
Core Program							◆	◆
Reteaching and Practice								

Strand Number and Numeration; Operations and Computation

Skill Estimating sums and differences of fractions and mixed numbers; solving inequalities

Materials (per pair)

- ◆ *Mixed-Number Spin* Gameboard (or Game Master 140)
- ◆ Game Master 141 (spinner)
- ◆ 1 transparent spinner (or a paper clip and pencil)

Players 2

Object of the game To complete 10 true number sentences.

Grade 5 SRB 322   Grade 6 SRB 327

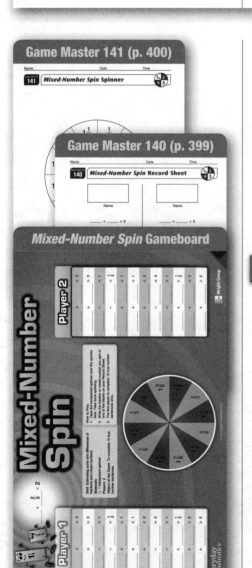

Game Master 141 (p. 400)

Game Master 140 (p. 399)

Mixed-Number Spin Gameboard

Directions

1. Each player uses one column on the gameboard or Record Sheet.

2. Players take turns spinning. Players may tape the transparent spinner in place over the spinner face, or use the paper clip and pencil to make a spinner.

3. Each player writes the fraction or mixed number that he or she spins on any one of his or her blanks.

4. The first player to complete 10 true number sentences wins.

Example

Ella has filled in 2 blanks in different sentences with 2 and $1\frac{1}{8}$.

On her next turn, Ella spins $1\frac{3}{8}$. She can write it on a line where there are 2 blanks.

Or, she can use it to form the true number sentence $1\frac{3}{8} - 1\frac{1}{8} < \frac{1}{2}$.

She cannot use it on the first line because $2 + 1\frac{3}{8}$ is not < 3.

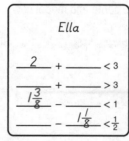

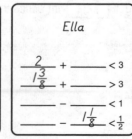

Differentiation Options

READINESS Students may need to review using benchmarks to estimate and compare sums and differences of fractions and mixed numbers. Using only addition and a few simple inequalities may be helpful:

▶ Make Record Sheets that have only 6 addition sentences. Each sentence should have two blanks for addends and then one of the following: < 3, > 3, > 1, < 1, < 2, $> \frac{1}{2}$. (Alternatively, use simpler fractions on the spinner.)

ENRICHMENT

▶ Players calculate the actual sums and differences for their 10 true number sentences. Each player adds his or her 10 results to find a total score. The player with the higher total score wins.

ELL SUPPORT Write the first sentence from the Record Sheet on the board. Direct students' attention to the numbers on the spinner. Ask students to identify pairs of numbers that will result in a true number sentence. Discuss the meaning of *true number sentence.*

GRADES
PK–2 Money Cube

Strands Number and Numeration; Measurement and Reference Frames

Skill Identifying, counting, and making exchanges with pennies, nickels, and dimes

Materials (per group)

◆ For Grades PK–K: *Money Cube* Gameboard (optional)

◆ 20 pennies, 10 nickels, and 10 dimes

◆ 1 inch cube or die, with 2 sides each marked 1¢, 5¢, and 10¢

◇ 1 calculator (optional)

Players 2–5

Object of the game To collect the most money.

Games Across the Grades								
Grades	PK	K	1	2	3	4	5	6
Advanced Learning								
Core Program	◆	◆	◆	◆				
Reteaching and Practice					◆			

Directions

1. Players put all of the coins in a "bank" between them.

2. Players take turns. For each turn, a player rolls the money cube and selects from the bank a coin (or coins) matching the value rolled. Players say the name of each coin they select.

NOTE: Students in Grades 1 and 2 may use the mats on the *Coin Exchange Games* Gameboard to play this game.

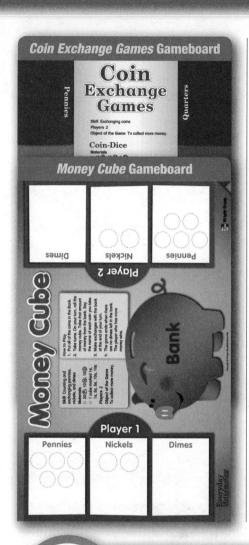

3. At the end of each turn, a player makes any possible exchanges with the bank—5 pennies for a nickel, 5 pennies and 1 nickel for a dime, 2 nickels for a dime, or 10 pennies for a dime.

4. The game ends when there are no dimes left in the bank. The player who has more money wins.

Differentiation Options

READINESS Students may need a review of coin values. Displaying coins and their values may be helpful:

► Use pictures of coins from Game Master 234 to label the money cube. Write the value on each picture or provide a reference sheet showing the coins and their values to guide players as they make exchanges.

► On the *Coin Exchange Games* gameboard, draw 5 circles for pennies and 2 circles for nickels. Players place the coins they collect in these circles to help them remember when to exchange.

ENRICHMENT

► Replace one of the 1¢ sides on the money cube with 25¢ and add 2 quarters to the bank. The game ends when there are no quarters left in the bank.

► For a game that uses quarters and dot dice, see *Coin Exchange.*

ELL SUPPORT Demonstrate the meanings of terms associated with the U.S. monetary system: *penny, nickel, dime, value,* and *bank.* Model the meaning of *trade* or *exchange.*

GRADE 2

Money Exchange Game

Games Across the Grades

Grades	PK	K	1	2	3	4	5	6
Advanced Learning			◆					
Core Program				◆				
Reteaching and Practice					◆			

Strands Number and Numeration; Measurement and Reference Frames

Skill Making exchanges with coins and bills

Materials (per pair)

◆ *Money Exchange Games* Gameboard (or Game Master 142, 1 per player)

◆ 24 pennies, 30 dimes, twenty $1 bills, and one $10 bill

◆ 1 red die

◆ 2 white dice (or 1 ten- or twelve-sided die)

Players 2

Object of the game To trade for $10.

Directions

1. Players put all of the money in a "bank" between them.

2. Players take turns rolling the dice and taking from the bank the numbers of pennies shown on the **red** die, and the number of dimes shown by the sum of the **white** dice.

3. Each player puts the coins in the correct columns on his or her Place-Value Mat.

4. Whenever possible, a player trades 10 coins or bills for a coin or bill of the next higher denomination.

5. The first player to trade for a $10 bill wins.

NOTE: For similar games, see *Paper Money Exchange* and *$1, $10, $100 Exchange*.

Game Master 142 (p. 401)

Money Exchange Games Gameboard

Differentiation Options

READINESS Students may need to review exchanges of pennies, dimes, and dollars. Removing pennies or $10 bills may simplify the game:

▶ Players use only dimes, $1 bills, and $10 bills. Players roll two dice to determine how many dimes to collect.

▶ Player use only pennies, dimes, and one $1 bill. Players take turns rolling one die and taking that number of pennies. The first player to trade for a $1 bill wins.

ENRICHMENT

▶ Players use thirty $1 bills, twenty $10 bills, twenty $100 bills, and a $1,000 bank draft (Game Master 243). Players roll 2 dice and make a 2-digit number. They collect this much money in $1 bills and $10 bills. The first player to have $1,000 wins.

▶ Players begin with a $1,000 bank draft (Game Master 243). They roll 2 dice, make a 2-digit number, and return that number of dollars to the bank. Players make exchanges as needed. The first player to put all of his or her money in the bank wins.

ELL SUPPORT Discuss terms associated with the U.S. monetary system and demonstrate the meanings of *coin* and *bill*. Discuss and model the meaning of *exchange*. Have students use coins to model different ways to make $1 and explain that the groups of coins are *equivalent* in value.

Game Master 243 (p. 502)

GRADE K

Money Grid

Games Across the Grades

Grades	PK	K	1	2	3	4	5	6
Advanced Learning	◆							
Core Program		◆						
Reteaching and Practice			◆					

Strands Number and Numeration; Measurement and Reference Frames

Skill Identifying names and values of coins; making coin exchanges

Materials (per group)

◆ Game Master 143 (game mat, 1 per player)

◆ cube marked 10¢, 5¢, 5¢, 1¢, 1¢, 1¢

◆ pennies, nickels, and dimes

Players 2–5

Object of the game To fill a game mat.

Game Master 143 (p. 402)

Directions

1. Players take turns rolling the money cube and taking a coin (or coins) from the "bank" to match the value rolled. Each player puts the coin(s) on his or her own game mat.

2. Players can take coins off their game mats to exchange for other coins of equivalent value. Players can save coins next to their mats until they collect enough to trade for a coin to place on the mat.

3. The first player to fill his or her game mat wins.

Differentiation Options

READINESS Students may need to review coin values and coin equivalencies. Playing with only 2 types of coins may be helpful:

▶ Players use a cube marked 1¢ on five sides and 5¢ on one side. (You may also want to affix a picture of a coin (Game Master 234) to each side of the cube.) Cross out the dime on the game mat, or change it to a nickel.

ENRICHMENT

▶ Add quarters and more dimes to the bank. On each game mat, add a fifth row showing 2 quarters and 2 dimes.

▶ For more practice making coin exchanges with pennies, nickels, and dimes, see *Money Cube.*

ELL SUPPORT Discuss terms associated with the U.S. monetary system and demonstrate the meanings of ***penny, nickel,*** and ***dime.*** Discuss and model the meaning of ***exchange*** or ***trade.*** Have students use coins to model different ways to make 10¢ and discuss the meaning of ***equivalent value.***

Monster Squeeze

GRADES PK–1

Strand Number and Numeration	

Skill Reading and comparing numbers

Materials (per group)

◆ *Monster Squeeze* Gameboard (or Game Master 144)

◆ 2 *Monster Squeeze* monsters (or Game Master 144)

Players 2 or more

Object of the game To guess the mystery number.

Games Across the Grades

Grades	PK	K	1	2	3	4	5	6
Advanced Learning								
Core Program	◆	◆	◆					
Reteaching and Practice				◆				

Directions

Advance Preparation: Choose an appropriate range of numbers, such as 0–10 or 0–20, for the number line.

1. Players fill in the boxes with numbers in order.

2. Player 1 places the monsters on both ends of the number line.

3. Player 1 thinks of a mystery number on the number line.

4. The other player(s) guess the mystery number.

5. If the guess is too high, Player 1 says: *Your number is too large,* and moves the right-hand monster over to cover the guess. If the guess is too low, Player 1 says: *Your number is too small,* and moves the left-hand monster over to cover the guess.

6. Players repeat Steps 4 and 5 until the correct number has been "squeezed" between the 2 monsters.

7. Players switch roles and play again.

Differentiation Options

READINESS Students may need to review the concepts of *too large, too small,* and *between.* Using a shorter number line or labels may be helpful:

▶ Write *larger, more* at the right side and *smaller, less* at the left side.

ENRICHMENT

▶ Provide clues involving addition or subtraction, such as: *My number is at least 10 more than the monster on the left.*

▶ Play mental *Monster Squeeze* with clues only, no monsters.

ELL SUPPORT Write ***too large*** on one monster and ***too small*** on the second monster. As students make guesses, explain the meaning of ***squeeze*** in this context.

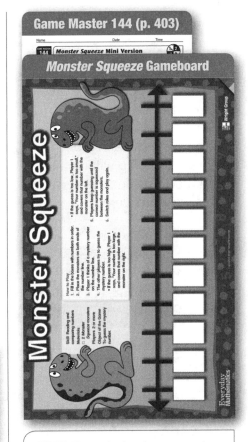

Game Master 144 (p. 403)

Monster Squeeze Mini Version

Monster Squeeze Gameboard

NOTE: The whole class can play on a number line posted on the wall. Two students use the monsters on Game Masters 145 and 146, attached to meterstick "handles". Other players take turns being the leader, who determines the mystery number.

GRADE Pre-K · More or Less

Games Across the Grades								
Grades	PK	K	1	2	3	4	5	6
Advanced Learning								
Core Program	◆							
Reteaching and Practice			◆	◆				

Strand Number and Numeration

Skill Counting; comparing numbers using *more* and *less*

Materials (per pair)
- ◆ Game Master 147 (spinner)
- ◆ Game Masters 148 and 149 (paper cookies)
- ◆ 1 transparent spinner (or a paper clip and pencil)
- ◆ 5 counters
- ◇ 1 cookie jar or other opaque container

Players 2

Object of the game To have more (or fewer) counters.

NOTE: For a non-competitive variation, use the cookie with 5 chips to keep score. The winner of each round covers one chip with a counter. Play ends when all 5 chips are covered.

Directions

Advance Preparation: To create spinners, tape a spinner face from Game Master 147 to the back of a transparent spinner, or show students how to hold the transparent spinner in place over the spinner face. Alternatively, model how to use a paper clip and pencil to spin (see the drawing on Game Master 2).

Laminate the cookies for durability, if possible.

1. Players place all of the cookies in a "cookie jar."

2. One player spins the spinner and tells whether it points to *More* or *Less*.

3. Both players close their eyes. Each takes a cookie from the jar.

4. Players count the chips on their cookies and compare numbers.

5. If the spinner is pointing to *More*, the player with more chips on his or her cookie wins the round and takes a scoring counter. If the spinner is pointing to *Less*, the player with fewer chips on his or her cookie wins the round and takes a counter.

6. One player spins the spinner again to start a new round.

7. Play continues until there are not enough cookies left in the jar for each player to take one. Players then count their scoring counters and compare totals. They can spin the spinner one last time to see whether the player with more or fewer counters wins.

Game Master 147 (p. 406)
Game Master 148 (p. 407)
Game Master 149 (p. 408)

Differentiation Options

READINESS Students may need to review comparing collections of objects. Using counters or smaller numbers may be helpful:

► Each player places one small counter, such as a unit cube, on each chip on his or her cookie. Players line up their counters in two rows to compare the number of chips.

► To compare numbers through 6, players each roll 1 die and count the dots instead of taking a cookie and counting the chips. The game ends when one player has 5 scoring counters.

ENRICHMENT

► To practice numeral recognition, players use number cards instead of cookies. For numerals only, players use the 0–11 cards in the Number Card Deck. For cards with numerals and pictures, players use the cards on Game Masters 123–126.

ELL SUPPORT Ask a student to take some cookies from the jar. Draw a picture to represent the number of cookies and label it with that number. Ask another student to take *fewer* cookies. Draw a picture to represent this number of cookies and label it with that number and the words *fewer* and *less.* Label the first picture *more.*

GRADE 3

Multiplication Bingo

Strand Operations and Computation

Skill Multiplication facts through 10 × 10

Materials (per group)

◆ *Multiplication Bingo* Gameboard (or Game Master 150)

◆ Everything Math Deck

◆ 8 counters per player

◇ Multiplication/Division Facts Table

Players 2–3

Object of the game To get 4 counters in a row, a column, or a diagonal; or 8 counters anywhere on the game mat.

Grade 3
SRB
293

Games Across the Grades

Grades	PK	K	1	2	3	4	5	6
Advanced Learning				◆				
Core Program					◆			
Reteaching and Practice							◆	◆

NOTE: Players can share a copy of Game Master 150, but each player must use his or her own grid. Players using separate Game Masters can play 4 games and record all missed facts on the back of the master.

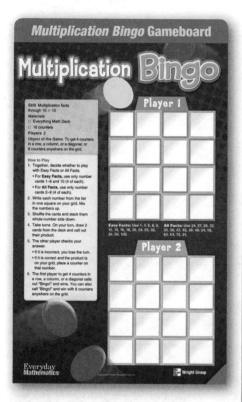

Easy Facts

Directions

1. Players use 4 each of the number cards 1–6 and 10.

2. Each player uses his or her own game mat and writes each number from the list below in one square on the grid. Players should mix up these numbers:

   1, 4, 6, 8, 9, 12, 15, 16, 18, 20, 24, 25, 30, 36, 50, 100

3. One player shuffles and stacks the cards whole-number side down.

4. Players take turns. For each turn, a player draws 2 cards from the top of the pile and calls out the product of the 2 numbers.

5. The other players check the answer. If another player disagrees with the answer, the player checks the answer on a Multiplication/Division Facts Table.

   - If the player's answer is incorrect, he or she loses the turn.

   - If the player's answer is correct *and* the product is a number on his or her game mat, the player places a counter on that number.

6. The first player to get 4 counters in a row, a column, or a diagonal calls out "Bingo!" and wins the game. A player can also call "Bingo!" and win if he or she gets 8 counters anywhere on the game mat.

7. If all of the cards are used before someone wins, one player shuffles the cards again, and play continues.

All Facts

Players use 4 each of the number cards 2–9 and this list of numbers to fill in their grids:

24, 27, 28, 32, 35, 36, 42, 45, 48, 49, 54, 56, 63, 64, 72, 81

Differentiation Options

READINESS Students may need to review multiplication facts. Limiting the products used may be helpful:

▶ Players fill their grids with multiples of 5 through 50. (They will use six of the multiples twice.) They play with 4 each of the number cards 1–10. They draw one card on each turn and multiply that number by 5. They can cover only one square for each turn.

ENRICHMENT

▶ To practice extended facts, players multiply each of the numbers in the List of Numbers by 10 and write the resulting numbers on their grids. For each turn, a player treats one of his or her cards as a number of 10s.

ELL SUPPORT Explain that *product* has multiple meanings and discuss its mathematical meaning. Introduce the game and show examples of winning boards. Label an example of a win in a *row, column, diagonal,* and with 8 counters anywhere on the game mat.

GRADES 5–6 Multiplication Bull's-Eye

Strand Operations and Computation

Skill Estimating products of 2- and 3-digit numbers

Materials (per pair)

◆ Everything Math Deck (number cards 0–9, 4 of each)

◆ 1 die

◇ 1 calculator

Players 1 or 2

Object of the game To score more points.

Grade 5 SRB 323   Grade 6 SRB 328

Games Across the Grades

Grades	PK	K	1	2	3	4	5	6
Advanced Learning						◆		
Core Program							◆	◆
Reteaching and Practice								

Directions

1. One player shuffles and stacks the cards whole-number side down.

2. Players take turns. For each turn, a player rolls the die and looks up the target range of the product in the table (shown on page 154 and in the Student Reference Books).

3. The player takes 4 cards from the top of the deck.

NOTE: For a 1-player version, a student takes 10 turns and finds his or her total score. The goal is to have a higher total score in the next game.

Number on Die	Target Range of Product
1	500 or less
2	501–1,000
3	1,001–3,000
4	3,001–5,000
5	5,001–7,000
6	more than 7,000

4. He or she uses the cards to try to form 2 numbers whose product falls within the target range. **The player may not use a calculator.**

5. The player multiplies the 2 numbers on a calculator to determine whether the product falls within the target range.

- If it does, the player has hit the bull's-eye and scores 1 point.
- If it doesn't, the player scores 0 points.
- If it is impossible to form 2 numbers whose product falls within the target range, the player scores 0 points.

6. The game ends when each player has taken 5 turns. The player with more points wins.

Example

Tom rolls a 3, so the target range of the product is from 1,001 to 3,000. He turns over the 5, 7, 9, and 2 cards.

Tom uses estimation to try to form 2 numbers whose product falls within the target range—for example, 97 and 25.

He then finds the product on the calculator: 97 * 25 = 2,425.

Since the product is between 1,001 and 3,000, Tom has hit the bull's-eye and scores 1 point.

Some other possible winning products from the 5, 7, 9, and 2 cards are: 25 * 79, 27 * 59, 9 * 257, and 2 * 579.

Differentiation Options

READINESS Students may need to review strategies for estimating products. Using smaller products as targets may be helpful:

▶ Divide each number of the target ranges by 10 to create a new table. Players draw only 3 cards to make a 2-digit and a 1-digit number.

ENRICHMENT

▶ Divide each number of the target ranges by 100 to create a new table. Players may use their 4 cards and decimal points to make any 2 numbers. Players may multiply or divide their 2 numbers to find a number that falls within the target range.

ELL SUPPORT Discuss the meaning of *bull's-eye* and *target range.* Explain that in the game of darts, a bull's-eye is the highest score. In this game, students score a bull's-eye by estimating and then calculating a product in the target range. Model how to use 4 cards to create 2 factors. Generate a list of number sentences on the board including 1-digit × 3-digit examples. Highlight the products that "land" in each of the target ranges.

GRADE 3 Multiplication Draw

Strand Operations and Computation; Patterns, Functions, and Algebra

Skill Multiplication facts; adding two-digit numbers

Materials (per group)

◆ *Multiplication Draw* Gameboard (or Game Master 151)

◆ Everything Math Deck (number cards 1–5 and 10, 4 of each)

Grade 3
SRB
296

Players 2 or 3

Object of the game To have the largest sum.

Games Across the Grades

Grades	PK	K	1	2	3	4	5	6
Advanced Learning				◆				
Core Program					◆			
Reteaching and Practice						◆	◆	

Directions

1. One player shuffles and stacks the cards whole-number side down.

2. Players take turns. For each turn, a player draws 2 cards from the deck to get 2 multiplication factors. The player records both factors and their product on his or her Record Sheet.

3. After 5 turns, each player finds the sum of his or her 5 products.

4. The player with the largest sum wins the round.

5. Players complete 3 rounds. The player who wins more rounds wins the game. If there is a tie, another round is played.

Advanced Version

Players use all number cards 1–10.

Differentiation Options

READINESS Students may need to review strategies for multiplication. Keeping one factor constant in each round may be helpful:

▶ Players use 2 as one factor in each problem in Round 1 and draw a card to find the other factor for each problem. For Round 2, students use 5 as one factor. For Round 3, they use 10 as one factor.

ENRICHMENT

▶ To practice extended multiplication facts, players treat one or both numbers they draw as a multiple of 10. For example, a player drawing 2 and 3 could generate 2×30, 20×3, or 20×30.

ELL SUPPORT Discuss and model the meaning of *draw* in this context. Write a multiplication sentence on the board and label the *factors* and *product*. Discuss the meanings of both words.

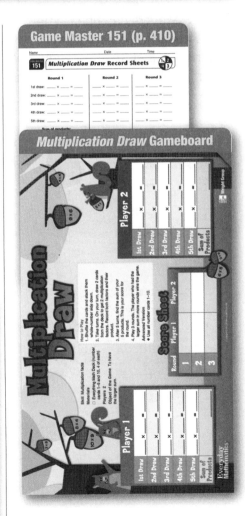

Game Master 151 (p. 410)

Multiplication Draw Gameboard

NOTE: Players will need to wipe off the gameboard's Record Tables after each round.

Multiplication Top-It

Games Across the Grades

Grades	PK	K	1	2	3	4	5	6
Advanced Learning				◆				
Core Program					◆	◆	◆	◆
Reteaching and Practice								

Strand Operations and Computation

Skill Multiplying

Materials (per group)

◆ Everything Math Deck (number cards 0–10, 4 of each)

◆ Game Master 4 (Record Sheet, optional)

Players 2–4

Object of the game To collect the most cards.

Grade 3 · SRB 297   Grade 4 · SRB 263

Grade 5 · SRB 334   Grade 6 · SRB 336

NOTE: Players can use Game Master 4 to record and compare their multiplication sentences.

Game Master 4 (p. 263)

2 Cards (recommended for Grades 3–6)

Skill Multiplication facts 0 to 10

Directions

1. One player shuffles the cards and places the deck whole-number-side down.

2. Each player turns over 2 cards and calls out the product of the numbers.

3. The player with the greatest product wins the round and takes all of the cards.

4. In case of a tie for the greatest product, each tied player turns over 2 more cards and calls out their product. The player with the greatest product takes all of the cards from both plays.

5. The game ends when there are not enough cards left for each player to have another turn. The player with the most cards wins.

3 Cards (recommended for Grades 4–6)

Skill Multiplying a 2-digit number by a 1-digit number

Players use only the number cards 1–9. Each player turns over 3 cards, forms a 2-digit number, and then multiplies the 2-digit number by the remaining number.

Differentiation Options

READINESS Students may need more practice with multiplication facts. Keeping one factor constant may be helpful:

▶ Players choose one factor to keep constant and turn over only the second factor for each round. For example, for each round, each player draws one card and multiplies that number by 5.

ENRICHMENT

▶ Players use only the number cards 1–9. Each player turns over 3 cards, forms a 2-digit number, uses the remaining card as a number of tens, and multiplies. For example, a player drawing 2, 3, and 4 could multiply 43 by 20.

ELL SUPPORT Discuss the meaning of *top-it* in this game context. Introduce the game and model a round that involves a tie. Discuss the meanings of *largest product* and *compare.*

GRADES 4–6 Multiplication Wrestling

Strand Number and Numeration; Operations and Computation; Patterns, Functions, and Algebra

Skill Using the partial-products algorithm; using the distributive property

Materials (per pair)

◆ For Grades 4 and 5: *Multiplication Wrestling* Gameboard (or Game Master 152)

◆ For Grade 6: Game Master 152 (Record Sheet)

◆ Everything Math Deck (number cards 0–9, 4 of each)

Players 2

Object of the game To get the larger product of two 2-digit numbers.

 Grade 4
253

 Grade 5
324

Games Across the Grades

Grades	PK	K	1	2	3	4	5	6
Advanced Learning					◆			
Core Program						◆	◆	◆
Reteaching and Practice								

Directions

1. Players shuffle and stack the cards whole-number side down.

2. Each player draws 4 cards and forms two 2-digit numbers. Players should form the numbers that will have the greatest possible product.

3. Players create 2 "wrestling teams" by writing each of their numbers as a sum of 10s and 1s.

NOTE: In Step 3, have students draw lines connecting the numbers that must "wrestle:"

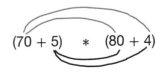

$(70 + 5) \quad * \quad (80 + 4)$

Multiplication Wrestling Gameboard

Game Master 152 (p. 411)

4. Next, each player's 2 teams wrestle. The player multiplies each member of his or her first team (for example, 70 and 5) by each member of his or her second team (for example, 80 and 4). Then the player adds the 4 products.

5. The player with the greater product wins the round and receives 1 point.

6. To begin a new round, each player draws 4 new cards and forms 2 new two-digit numbers.

7. After 3 rounds, the player with more points wins.

Example

Player 1:

Forms

75 and 84

75 * 84

Team 1	Team 2
(70 + 5)	* (80 + 4)

Products: 70 * 80 = 5,600
         70 * 4 = 280
          5 * 80 = 400
          5 * 4 =   20

(add 4 products)

Total   6,300

Player 2:

Forms

64 and 91

64 * 91

Team 1	Team 2
(60 + 4)	* (90 + 1)

Products: 60 * 90 = 5,400
         60 * 1 =   60
          4 * 90 = 360
          4 * 1 =   4

(add 4 products)

Total   5,824

Differentiation Options

READINESS Students may need a review of expanded notation for two-digit numbers, extended multiplication facts, or multidigit addition. It may also be helpful to play a few rounds with simpler numbers:

▶ In Step 2, players draw only three cards and form a 2-digit number and a 1-digit number for their factors.

▶ Players draw three cards and make one 2-digit number. They use the other card to determine what multiple of 10 to multiply by.

ENRICHMENT

▶ Players can choose to form two 2-digit numbers or one 3-digit number and one 1-digit number for their factors.

ELL SUPPORT Discuss the meaning of "wrestling." Have two teams of two students act out the wrestling match-ups. Explain that in this game, students wrestle with multiplication and try to make a product that is greater than their opponent's. Introduce the game and model a round with two students.

Mystery Change

Strands Number and Numeration; Operations and Computation

Skill Counting; modeling joining and taking-away situations; comparing sets of objects

Materials (per pair)

◆ 10 counters

◇ 1 file folder or large index card (5″ × 8″)

Players 2

Object of the game To show a group of counters that matches the other player's counters.

Games Across the Grades

Grades	PK	K	1	2	3	4	5	6
Advanced Learning								
Core Program	◆							
Reteaching and Practice		◆	◆					

Directions

Player 1 will create a "mystery" by hiding counters behind the folder. Player 2 will be a "detective" and determine how many counters are hidden.

1. Each player takes 5 counters.

2. Player 1 puts 1, 2, or 3 counters on the table for Player 2 to see. Player 1 says: *I have this many.*

3. Player 2 looks at or counts the counters.

4. Player 1 hides the counters behind a large index card or folder used as a screen between the two players.

5. Player 1 adds to or takes away from the counters behind the screen and lets Player 2 see the counters he or she is moving, while keeping the total hidden. Player 2 watches carefully.

6. When Player 1 announces that he or she is done, Player 2 uses his or her counters to show how many counters Player 1 now has behind the screen. Player 2 puts these counters behind his or her side of the screen.

7. One player removes the screen so players can check whether their numbers of counters are the same.

8. Players change roles so that Player 2 creates the mystery and Player 1 plays the detective.

Differentiation Options

READINESS Students may need to review counting forward and back, or strategies for comparing the two groups of counters. Beginning with simpler addition "mysteries" may be helpful:

► Player 1 leaves the original number of counters showing, adds some number of counters behind the screen, and then tells how many have been added. Player 2 determines the total and models it with counters. Then the players compare totals by aligning the counters with one-to-one correspondence.

ENRICHMENT

► Increase the number of counters for each player to 10.

► Instead of using counters, the "detective" writes a number sentence to show the change. Players remove the screen, and both players check the number sentence.

ELL SUPPORT Discuss and demonstrate the meanings of *mystery, detective,* and *screen* using objects, pictures, or children's literature. Model how to play the game as you discuss the meanings of *same* and *match.*

GRADES 1–6

Name That Number

Games Across the Grades									
Grades	PK	K	1	2	3	4	5	6
Advanced Learning									
Core Program			◆	◆	◆	◆	◆	◆
Reteaching and Practice									

Strands Number and Numeration; Operations and Computation; Patterns, Functions, and Algebra

Skill Naming numbers with expressions

Materials

◆ For Grade 1: Game Master 153 (Record Sheet, optional)

◆ For Grades 2–6: *Name That Number* Gameboard (or Game Master 153 or 154, optional)

◆ Everything Math Deck

Players 2–4

Object of the game To collect the most cards.

Grades 1–2 MRB 138

Grade 3 SRB 299

Grade 4 SRB 254

Grade 5 SRB 325

Grade 6 SRB 329

Grades 1–3

Directions

1. One player shuffles the deck and places 5 cards whole-number side up. He or she places the rest of the deck number-side down, turns over the top card, and lays it down next to the deck. The number on this card is the number to be named, or the **target number.**

2. Players take turns trying to name the target number by adding, subtracting, multiplying, or dividing the numbers on 2 or more of the 5 cards that are whole-number side up. A card may be used only once for each turn.

3. If the player can name the target number, he or she takes the cards that were used to name it along with the target-number card. Then he or she replaces all of the cards that were taken by drawing from the top of the deck.

4. If the player cannot name the target number, his or her turn is over. He or she turns over the top card of the deck and lays it down on the target-number pile. The number on this card is the new target number.

5. Play continues until all of the cards in the deck have been turned over. The player who has taken the most cards wins.

Example Target number: 16   **Player 1's cards:**

Some possible solutions:

7   5   8   2   10

$10 + 8 - 2 = 16$ (3 cards used)

$7 * 2 + 10 - 8 = 16$ (4 cards used)

$\frac{8}{2} + 10 + 7 - 5 = 16$ (all 5 cards used)

The player sets aside the cards used to make a solution and draws the same number of cards from the top of the deck.

Another Way to Play

To practice extended facts, players read each card as a number of tens. For example, when a 4 card is turned over, it is read as 40.

Grades 4–6

The rules are the same as for the Grades 1–3 version, except that the dealer deals 5 cards to each player instead of laying out 5 cards for all players to share. Players record their solutions on Game Master 154 and draw cards as needed after each turn.

NOTE: Students in Grades 1–3 should use Game Master 153.

For Grades 1 and 2, limit the operations used in Step 2 to addition and subtraction.

As students become proficient, challenge them to use more cards and 2 or more operations in each expression. In Grade 3, some students may be able to use negative numbers.

For further practice with computation skills and order of operations, encourage players to use any of these variations:

- The dealer turns over 2 cards and places them next to each other to make a 2-digit target number.
- Players may use 2 cards to form a fraction as part of the expression.
- Players may use 2 cards to form an exponent.
- Players may use parentheses.
- Players use polyhedral dice instead of number cards and play in groups of 4.

Differentiation Options

READINESS Students may need to review the basic operations or the order of operations. Increasing the number of cards per player, keeping the same target number, or using smaller numbers may be helpful:

▶ Players use 6 cards instead of 5.

▶ Players keep the same target number, such as 10, for each round.

▶ Players use only the 0–9 cards.

ENRICHMENT

▶ Players use at least 4 cards and 2 different operations for each solution. Players receive a bonus point if they use all 5 cards. Bonus points count as cards at the end of the game.

▶ Players must use at least 3 operations in each solution.

▶ Players may use individual digit cards in their hand as decimals or as multiples of 10. For example, if they have a 2 in their hand, they can use it as 0.2, 2, 20, and so on.

ELL SUPPORT Explain that *target number* means the goal—the number students want to reach. Select a target number and show students 5 cards. Write the 5 numbers on the board. Model one way to name the target number using the appropriate operations. Then have students try to generate another way to make the target number. Explain that typically there will be more than one way to use the cards to make the target number, but to win this game, students want to select the way that uses the *most* cards.

Nickel-Penny Grab

Strands Number and Numeration; Data and Chance; Measurement and Reference Frames

Skill Counting and comparing collections of coins

Materials (per pair)

◆ *Coin Grab Games* Gameboard (or Game Master 155, 1 per player)

◆ 8 nickels, 20 pennies

Players 2

Object of the game To have more money in at least two rounds.

Games Across the Grades

Grades	PK	K	1	2	3	4	5	6
Advanced Learning	◆	◆						
Core Program			◆					
Reteaching and Practice				◆				

Directions

1. Players mix the coins and place them in a pile.

2. Player 1 grabs a handful of coins. Player 2 grabs the remaining coins.

3. Each player draws his or her coins on the Record Sheet and finds the total value.

4. Each player records his or her total and the other player's total on the Record Sheet. Each player circles the greater total.

5. Players switch roles and repeat Steps 1–4 two more times for a total of 3 rounds. The player who had more money in at least 2 rounds wins.

> **NOTE:** Remind students to use the ¢ or $ symbol. You may want to write ___¢ or $___.___ in the Total columns of the Record Sheets.

Differentiation Options

READINESS Students may need a review of determining the value of a coin collection before playing the game. Using fewer types of coins may be helpful:

▶ Players use only pennies (see *Penny Grab*), or only nickels.

ENRICHMENT

▶ Add 10 dimes to the coins used. (See *Dime-Nickel-Penny Grab*.)

ELL SUPPORT Write the word *cent* on the board and explain that it means the value of a penny. Then write the ¢ symbol and tell students that it stands for *cent* or *cents*. Explain that students want to grab as much money as they can to win the game. Ask: *Would you rather grab 5 pennies or 5 nickels? Why?* (You may want to put the coins in a brown paper bag rather than a pile so students cannot see what they are grabbing.) Discuss the meanings of *total* and *greater*.

Number Board Games

Games Across the Grades

Grades	PK	K	1	2	3	4	5	6
Advanced Learning								
Core Program	◆	◆						
Reteaching and Practice			◆					

Strand Number and Numeration

Skill Counting with one-to-one correspondence; associating number names, quantities, and written numerals; discovering the "one more" pattern

Materials (per group)

◆ *Number Board Games* Gameboard (or Game Master 156)

◆ counters

◆ 1 die

Players 2–5

Object of the game To fill a number board.

Game Master 156 (p. 415)

Number Board Games Gameboard

Number Board Game

Directions

Advance Preparation: Provide 21 counters and one number board for each group.

1. Players take turns rolling the die, counting the dots, and finding the corresponding number on the number board.

2. The player uses counters to cover all of the circles above that number on the board.

3. If a player rolls a number that is already covered, he or she doesn't add counters to the board.

4. The game ends when all of the circles are covered.

Number Board Race

For each player, provide 21 counters and one number board. Players "race" to fill their boards by taking turns rolling the die and covering dots on their individual boards.

Differentiation Options

READINESS Students may need a review of counting and numeral recognition through 6. Providing dot patterns that are easier to match may be helpful:

▶ Replace the number board with a sheet of paper showing the appropriate dot pattern above each numeral. Have players count the dots on the die, count the corresponding set of dots on the board, and say the numeral.

▶ Draw the corresponding dot pattern below each numeral on the number board as a reference to help players match die rolls to numerals.

ENRICHMENT

▶ To provide practice in numeral recognition, cover each column of dots with a strip of paper. As they play, players refer to the numerals to decide where to place the counters. A player removes the paper strip after choosing a numeral to check.

▶ To provide practice in renaming numbers, allow players to cover either the number they rolled or any available combination equal to that number. For example, a player rolling 5 may cover 1 and 4.

ELL SUPPORT Have students use counters to represent different numbers you roll on the die. Model how to use counters to *cover* the circles above a given number on the board.

GRADES 1–3 Number-Grid Difference

Strands Operations and Computation; Patterns, Functions, and Algebra

Skill Subtracting 2-digit numbers mentally or on a number grid

Materials (per pair)

◆ For Grade 1: Game Masters 157 and 158 (Number Grid and Record Sheet)

◆ For Grades 2 and 3: *Number-Grid Difference* Gameboard (or Game Masters 157 and 158)

◆ Everything Math Deck (number cards 0–9, 4 of each)

◆ 2 counters

◇ 1 calculator (optional)

Grades 1–2 **MRB** 140 Grade 3 **SRB** 301

Players 2

Object of the game To have the lower sum.

Games Across the Grades

Grades	PK	K	1	2	3	4	5	6
Advanced Learning		◆						
Core Program			◆	◆	◆			
Reteaching and Practice						◆	◆	

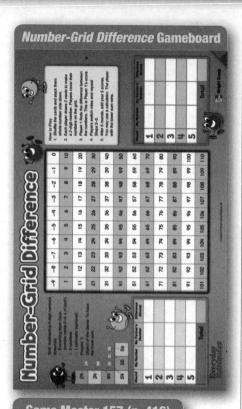

Game Master 157 (p. 416)

157 **Number Grid (–9 to 110)**

–9	–8	–7	–6	–5	–4	–3	–2	–1	0
1	2	3	4	5	6	7	8	9	10
11	12	13	14	15	16	17	18	19	20
21	22	23	24	25	26	27	28	29	30
31	32	33	34	35	36	37	38	39	40
41	42	43	44	45	46	47	48	49	50
51	52	53	54	55	56	57	58	59	60
61	62	63	64	65	66	67	68	69	70
71	72	73	74	75	76	77	78	79	80
81	82	83	84	85	86	87	88	89	90
91	92	93	94	95	96	97	98	99	100
101	102	103	104	105	106	107	108	109	110

Game Master 158 (p. 417)

158 **Number-Grid Difference Record Sheet**

Round	My Number	My Partner's Number	Difference (Score)
1			
2			
3			
4			
5			
		Total	

158 **Number-Grid Difference Record Sheet**

Round	My Number	My Partner's Number	Difference (Score)
1			
2			
3			
4			
5			
		Total	

Directions

1. One player shuffles and stacks the cards whole-number side down.

2. Each player draws 2 cards from the deck and uses them to make a 2-digit number. Each player places a counter on the grid to mark his or her number.

3. Player 1 finds the difference between the marked numbers. This difference is Player 1's score for the round.

4. Player 1 records both numbers and the difference.

5. Each player repeats Step 2, and Player 2 finds the difference. This is Player 2's score for the round.

6. Play continues for 5 rounds.

7. Each player finds the sum of his or her 5 scores. Players may use a calculator to add.

8. The player with the lower sum wins.

Differentiation Options

READINESS Students may need to review strategies for subtracting 2-digit numbers. Practicing with multiples of 10 may be helpful:

▶ In Step 2, each player draws one card and treats it as a number of tens. For example, a player drawing 2 would cover 20. For each round, players find the difference between the multiples of 10.

▶ On each player's turn, his or her partner draws two cards first, forms a 2-digit number, and places a counter over that number on the grid. The player draws only one card and treats it as a number of tens. For example, the partner's counter is on 36. The player draws a 2. The player covers 20 and finds the difference between 36 and 20.

ENRICHMENT Challenge students to subtract 3-digit numbers:

▶ Players make a 1,000 grid by adding a zero to each of the numbers in the number grid. The 2 cards drawn by each player form a 2-digit number that represents a number of tens. For example, a player drawing 2 and 7 could cover either 270 or 720.

▶ Players make a number grid for a range of 3-digit numbers—for example, 500–600. The digit in the hundreds place is fixed; in the example, it would always be 5. Players follow the directions for drawing 2 cards to identify the digits in the tens and ones places of the numbers they will cover.

ELL SUPPORT Give number cards 2 and 7 to a student. Ask: *What 2-digit number can you make with the cards?* (27 or 72) Give number cards 3 and 5 to another student. Ask: *What 2-digit number can you make?* (35 or 53) *What is the difference between the 2 numbers?* Ensure that students understand the meaning of **difference.** Then, have students make different 2-digit numbers with their cards and find the difference between them. Ask: *Which difference is smaller?*

Number-Grid Game

Strands Number and Numeration; Operations and Computation; Patterns, Functions, and Algebra

Skill Counting by 1s and 10s; navigating a number grid

Materials (per pair)

◆ For Kindergarten: Game Master 157 (Number Grid)

◆ For Grades 1–2: *Number-Grid Game* Gameboard (or Game Master 157)

◆ 1 die

◆ 1 counter per player (different colors)

Players 2 or more

Object of the game To reach 110.

Grades 1–2

MRB
142

Games Across the Grades

Grades	PK	K	1	2	3	4	5	6
Advanced Learning		◆						
Core Program			◆	◆	◆			
Reteaching and Practice								

Directions

1. Each player chooses a different-colored counter and places it on 0 on the number grid.

2. Players take turns. For each turn, a player rolls the die and uses the table to see how many spaces to move his or her counter.

Roll						
Spaces	1 or 10	2 or 20	3	4	5	6

3. The first player to reach 110 with an exact roll wins.

Advanced Versions

• Players use 2 dice. For rolls of 7 to 12, they move 7 to 12 spaces, respectively.

• Modify the table to allow a move of 3 or 30 for a roll of three, 4 or 40 for a roll of four, 5 or 50 for a roll of five, and 6 or 60 for a roll of six.

• To practice subtracting 1s and 10s, players start at 110 and move back toward 0.

Game Master 157 (p. 416)

Number-Grid Game Gameboard

Differentiation Options

READINESS Students may need more experience with the number grid. Using only part of the grid or moving only by 1s or by 10s may be helpful:

▶ Players move only the number of spaces shown on the die and play to 50.

▶ Players use a die numbered 1, 2, 1, 2, 1, 2. They move 10 for a roll of 1, and 20 for a roll of 2.

ENRICHMENT

▶ To provide practice with addition and subtraction on the number grid, add a second die that has "+" on 4 sides and "−" on 2 sides. Players roll both dice and move forward or back the number of spaces indicated. A player landing on 0 may roll again.

ELL SUPPORT Explain that students want to get to 110 as quickly as they can. So, early in the game, if they roll a 1 or a 2, they can move *10* or *20* spaces. As they get closer to 110, they may want to move 1 or 2 spaces for a roll of 1 or 2. Discuss the meaning of an *exact roll* and how this relates to the end of the game.

GRADE K — Number-Grid Grab

Games Across the Grades

Grades	PK	K	1	2	3	4	5	6
Advanced Learning	◆							
Core Program		◆						
Reteaching and Practice			◆	◆				

Strand Number and Numeration

Skill Reading and comparing numbers; recognizing 2-digit numbers as combinations of 10s and 1s

Materials (per group)

◆ Game Master 159 (number grid)

◆ 2 dice (1 marked 0, 1, 2, 3, 4, 5 and the other marked 4, 5, 6, 7, 8, 9)

◆ counters (5–10 per player, a different color for each player)

Players 2–5

Object of the game To make the largest number.

Directions

1. Players take turns. For each turn, a player rolls both dice.

2. The player makes the larger possible two-digit number with the digits rolled and places a counter on that number on the number grid. For example, if a 2 and 7 are rolled, a counter is placed on 72.

3. When all players have taken a turn, the player with the largest number for the round takes (grabs) all of the counters on the grid.

4. The game ends when one player runs out of counters or time runs out.

Game Master 159 (p. 418)

Name _____ Date _____ Time _____

159 | Number Grid (0–110)

									0
1	2	3	4	5	6	7	8	9	10
11	12	13	14	15	16	17	18	19	20
21	22	23	24	25	26	27	28	29	30
31	32	33	34	35	36	37	38	39	40
41	42	43	44	45	46	47	48	49	50
51	52	53	54	55	56	57	58	59	60
61	62	63	64	65	66	67	68	69	70
71	72	73	74	75	76	77	78	79	80
81	82	83	84	85	86	87	88	89	90
91	92	93	94	95	96	97	98	99	100
101	102	103	104	105	106	107	108	109	110

418 Game Master   Number Grid (0–110)

Differentiation Options

READINESS Students may need to review comparing 2-digit numbers. Using concrete models may be helpful:

▶ Provide craft sticks in bundles of 10 and single sticks. After rolling the dice, a player represents the two possible numbers with craft sticks. For example, a player rolling 2 and 5 would represent 25 and 52. Players use the craft sticks to compare the numbers.

ENRICHMENT

▶ To provide practice with addition on the number grid, add a die marked +20, −20, +10, −10, +1, −1 to the game. After all players have placed their counters, each player rolls the die and moves his or her counter accordingly before determining whose number is largest.

ELL SUPPORT Model how to create two-digit numbers using dice. Roll the dice. Discuss the possible two-digit numbers that can be created with the rolled numbers. Ask: *What is the larger number?* Explain that in this game, students want to create the larger possible two-digit number. Model one round of the game, discussing the meaning of *largest number.* Demonstrate the meaning of *grab* at the end of the round.

GRADES PK–K

Number-Grid Search

Strands Number and Numeration; Geometry

Skill Identifying and locating numbers on a number grid

Materials (per pair)

◆ *Number-Grid Search* Gameboard (or Game Master 159)

◆ 1 counter

◇ blindfold (optional)

Players 2

Object of the game To cover the given number without looking.

Games Across the Grades

Grades	PK	K	1	2	3	4	5	6
Advanced Learning								
Core Program	◆	◆						
Reteaching and Practice			◆					

NOTE: With stick-on notes and a Class Number Grid, the entire class can play *Number-Grid Search.* The Searcher tries to cover the given number with a stick-on note while the rest of the students take turns as the Guide.

For either version of the game, you may want to help Guides give clues by writing some key words and phrases around the grid, such as *down, to the top, up,* and *to the right.*

Directions

1. One player is the Searcher. The other player is the Guide. The Guide will name a number and then give 5 clues to help the Searcher find it.

2. The Guide says a number between 1 and 100.

3. With eyes covered or closed, the Searcher tries to place a counter on that number.

4. The Guide gives direction clues such as *the other way, up, down, near the top, to the right side,* and so on. (Note that *higher* and *lower* may be confusing. Remind students that the clues given refer to the *location* of the number, not the number itself.)

5. After the last clue, the Searcher checks to see how close he or she came to the given number. Players try to get closer to the given number in each game.

Differentiation Options

READINESS Students may need to become more familiar with the number grid. Using only part of the grid may be helpful:

▶ Players use only the numbers 1–50 on the grid.

ENRICHMENT

▶ Instead of giving direction clues, the Guide names each number the Searcher covers. Searchers use their understanding of patterns on the number grid to find the given number. The Guide may correct the Searcher with direction clues as necessary.

▶ Guides use only 4 different clues: 10 more, 10 less, 1 more, and 1 less. (The Searcher may play with his or her eyes open if the Guide keeps the target number a secret.)

ELL SUPPORT Display a number grid. Circle one number and tell students that number is the goal. Put a stick-on note somewhere on the grid. Model how to give directions, without using numbers, to move the stick-on note to the goal. As you give clues, write the words you use on the board (e.g. *down, up, right, left*). Keep track of how many clues it takes to reach the goal. Explain that the person moving the stick-on note, the Searcher, will play the game without using his or her eyes. This means that the directions will have to be very clear. Play the game again with several students. Discuss the clues given and decide whether they could be made clearer.

Number-Line Squeeze

GRADES 2–3

Strand Number and Numeration

Skill Comparing and ordering numbers

Materials (per group)

◆ Game Master 160 (directions and number lines)

◆ 2 counters

Players 2 or more

Object of the game To guess a mystery number on the number line.

Games Across the Grades

Grades	PK	K	1	2	3	4	5	6
Advanced Learning		◆	◆	◆				
Core Program				◆	◆			
Reteaching and Practice						◆		

Directions

1. Players place a counter on each end of the first number line on Game Master 160.

2. One player thinks of a mystery number on the number line.

3. The other player(s) guess the mystery number. If the guess is too high, the first player moves the right-hand counter over to cover the guess. If the guess is too low, the first player moves the left-hand counter over to cover the guess.

4. Players repeat Step 3 until the mystery number is guessed ("squeezed" between the 2 counters).

5. Players switch roles and play again.

Advanced Version

Label the second number line on Game Master 160 with more challenging numbers, such as 3-digit or negative numbers.

NOTE: The whole class can play on a class number line posted at the front of the room. Instead of counters, two students use index cards attached to meterstick "handles" to cover numbers on the line.

Game Master 160 (p. 419)

Differentiation Options

READINESS Students may need to review comparing numbers. Using a number line with fewer numbers may be helpful:

▶ Use a number line with a range of 0 to 10.

ENRICHMENT

▶ Player 1 provides clues involving addition or subtraction; for example, *My number is at least 10 more than the counter on the left.*

ELL SUPPORT Draw a number line on the board. Write **too high** and **too low** on separate stick-on notes. Write a mystery number on a piece of paper and hide it. Ask volunteers to guess the mystery number. Move the stick-on notes accordingly until students determine the mystery number. Explain the meaning of *squeeze* in this context.

Number Top-It

Games Across the Grades

Grades	PK	K	1	2	3	4	5	6
Advanced Learning			◆					
Core Program				◆	◆	◆	◆	◆
Reteaching and Practice								

Strand Number and Numeration

Skill Place value for whole numbers; comparing numbers

Materials

- ◆ For Grades 2–4: *Number Top-It* Gameboard (or Game Masters 161 and 162, 1 per pair)

- ◆ For Grade 5: Game Masters 161 and 162 (Place-Value Mat, 1 per pair)

- ◆ For Grade 6: Game Master 163 (Place-Value Mat, 1 per player)

- ◆ Game Master 4 (Record Sheet, 1 per pair; optional)

- ◆ Everything Math Deck (number cards 0–9, 4 of each)

Players 2–5

Object of the game To make the largest numbers.

Grade 3
SRB
302–304

Grade 4
SRB
255

Grade 5
SRB
326

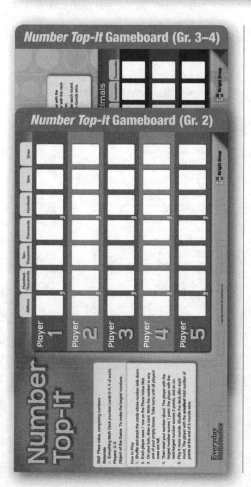

Directions

Advance Preparation: Before students begin playing, evaluate their abilities in comparing numbers to determine how many places (from 3 to 7) should be in the numbers they create. This number matches the number of turns each player has per round. If players are using fewer than 7 places, have them cross out the boxes they won't be using on the Place-Value Mat.

If students are using Game Masters and playing with more than 3 digits, they will need to cut out and tape together the parts of the Place-Value Mat before playing.

Players can use Game Master 4 to record and compare their numbers.

1. One player shuffles and stacks the cards whole-number side down.

2. Each player uses one row of boxes on the Place-Value Mat.

3. For each round, players take turns turning over the top card from the deck and placing it on (or writing the number in) any one of the empty boxes. Each player takes as many turns as there are places to fill his or her row.

4. At the end of each round, players read their numbers aloud and compare them. The player with the largest number for the round scores 1 point, the player with the next-largest number scores 2 points, and so on.

5. Players play 5 rounds per game. One player shuffles the deck after each round. The player with the **smallest** total number of points at the end of 5 rounds wins.

Differentiation Options

READINESS Students may need to review using place value to read and compare numbers. Beginning with multiples of 100 may be helpful:

▶ Players put zeros in the ones and tens columns. They draw cards to fill the remaining spaces on the game mat.

ENRICHMENT

▶ Each player makes two numbers in each round. Then each player finds the difference between his or her numbers to determine his or her score. The player with the highest score wins the round.

▶ For games with more than 2 players, players order their numbers at the end of each round.

ELL SUPPORT Discuss the meaning of *top-it* in this game context. Deal 7 cards and write each number on a separate stick-on note. Have students arrange the stick-on notes on the board to create different numbers. Ask students to create the largest and smallest possible 7-digit numbers. Record the numbers generated on the board. Discuss the meaning of *largest possible number.*

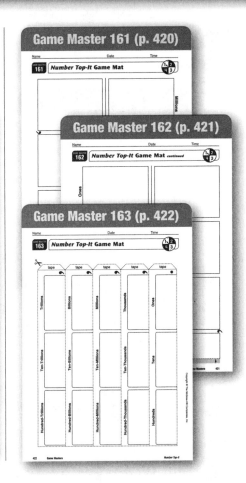

Game Master 161 (p. 420)

Game Master 162 (p. 421)

Game Master 163 (p. 422)

GRADES 3–5 Number Top-It: Decimals

Strand Number and Numeration

Skill Place value for decimals; comparing decimals

Materials

◆ For Grades 3–4: *Number Top-It* Gameboard (or Game Master 164, 1 per pair)

◆ For Grade 5: Game Master 164 (game mat, 1 per pair)

◆ Game Master 4 (Record Sheet, optional, 1 per pair)

◆ Everything Math Deck (number cards 0–9, 4 of each)

Players 2–5

Object of the game To make the largest decimal.

Grade 3
SRB
305

Grade 4
SRB
256

Grade 5
SRB
327

Games Across the Grades

Grades	PK	K	1	2	3	4	5	6
Advanced Learning				◆				
Core Program					◆	◆	◆	
Reteaching and Practice								◆

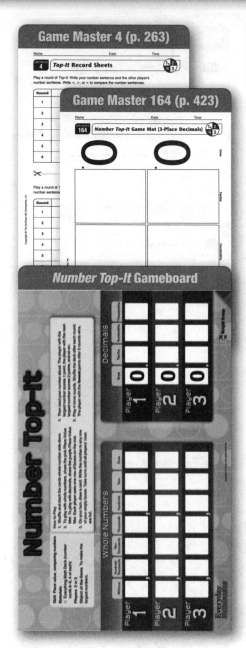

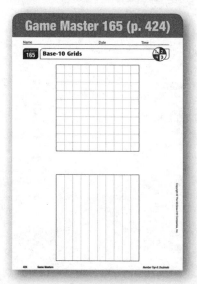

Directions

Advance Preparation: Before students begin playing, evaluate their abilities in comparing decimals to determine how many decimal places (2 or 3) should be in the numbers they create. The number of places matches the number of turns each player has per round. If players are using 2 decimal places, have them cross out the thousandths box on the Place-Value Mat.

Players can use Game Master 4 to record and compare their decimals.

1. One player shuffles and stacks the cards whole-number side down.

2. Each player uses one row of boxes on the Place-Value Mat.

3. For each round, players take turns turning over the top card from the deck and placing it on (or writing the number in) any one of the empty boxes. Each player takes as many turns as there are places to fill his or her row.

4. At the end of each round, players read their decimals aloud and compare them. The player with the largest decimal for the round scores 1 point, the player with the next-largest decimal scores 2 points, and so on.

5. Players play 5 rounds. One player shuffles the deck after each round. The player with the **smallest** total number of points at the end of 5 rounds wins.

Differentiation Options

READINESS Students may need to review reading and comparing decimal numbers. Using base-10 blocks may be helpful:

▶ Players use base-10 blocks and Game Master 165. After creating 2-place decimal numbers on their mats, each player builds his or her decimal on the base-10 grid.

ENRICHMENT

▶ Each player makes two numbers in each round. Then each player finds the difference between his or her numbers to determine his or her score. The player with the highest score wins the round.

▶ For games with more than 2 players, players order their decimals at the end of each round.

ELL SUPPORT Discuss the meaning of *top-it* in this game context. Show students 3 cards. Display a copy of the decimal place-value mat on the board and ask students to arrange the 3 numbers to create different decimals. Record the decimals on the board, and have students identify the largest and smallest possible decimals. Explain that in this game, students want to create the *largest* possible decimal, but they only get to see one digit at a time. Model several rounds with students.

GRADES 1–3 One-Dollar Exchange Games

Strands Number and Numeration; Measurement and Reference Frames

Skill Coin and bill equivalencies; counting and exchanging money

Materials (per pair)

- For Grades 1 and 2: *Exchange Games* Gameboard (or Game Master 166, 2 copies)
- For Grade 3: Game Master 167, 2 copies
- Game Master 168 (directions, optional)
- $1 bills, dimes, and pennies
- 2 dice

Players 2

Grades 1–2

MRB
144

Games Across the Grades

Grades	PK	K	1	2	3	4	5	6
Advanced Learning		◆						
Core Program			◆	◆	◆			
Reteaching and Practice						◆		

One-Dollar Exchange (Penny-Dime-Dollar Exchange)

Object of the game To make an exchange for one dollar.

Directions

1. Players put one $1 bill, 30 dimes, and 30 pennies in a "bank" between them.

2. Players take turns. For each turn, a player rolls the dice and announces the total number of dots.

3. The player who rolled takes that number of pennies from the bank and places them in the Pennies column of his or her mat.

4. Whenever possible, a player exchanges 10 pennies for 1 dime and places it in the Dimes column. When there are 10 dimes, a player exchanges them for 1 dollar.

5. The player not rolling the dice checks the accuracy of the transactions.

6. The first player to make an exchange for a dollar wins.

Game Master 166 (p. 425)

Exchange Games Gameboard

NOTE: Although the rules for *Money-Trading Game* are not shown on the gameboard, the gameboard can be used to play this game.

Game Master 167 (p. 426)

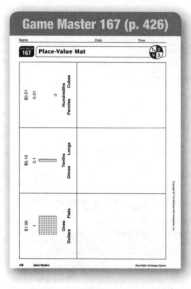

Game Master 168 (p. 427)

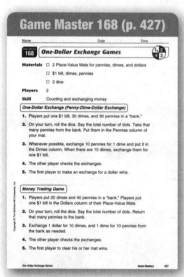

Money Trading Game

Object of the game To clear the mat.

Directions

1. Players put 20 dimes and 40 pennies in a "bank" between them. Each player puts one $1 bill in the Dollars column of his or her mat.

2. Players take turns. For each turn, a player rolls the dice and announces the total number of dots.

3. The player who rolled returns that number of pennies to the bank. A player exchanges 1 dollar for 10 dimes and 1 dime for 10 pennies from the bank as needed.

4. The player not rolling the dice checks the accuracy of the transactions.

5. The first player to clear his or her mat wins.

Differentiation Options

READINESS Students may need a review of counting money or of the possible exchanges in these games. Using only dimes and dollars may be helpful:

► Use a bank of 30 dimes and 3 dollars. Players roll one die on each turn and collect that number of dimes. The first player to get 2 dollars wins the game.

► Players draw 10 circles in the dimes and pennies columns to help them remember when to exchange.

ENRICHMENT

► Increase the bank to 9 dollar bills. Players use number cards 1–20 (four each of 1–10 and one each of 11–20). On each turn, players draw a card and take a combination of pennies and dimes equal to the total value on the card. The first player to collect 5 dollar bills wins.

ELL SUPPORT Discuss and model the meaning of *exchange* or *trade.* Have students use coins to model different ways to make 23¢. Discuss the meaning of *equivalent.* Ask: *Which way uses the fewest coins?* (2 dimes and 3 pennies). Introduce the game and model how to play several turns.

One-Dollar Game

Strands Number and Numeration; Measurement and Reference Frames

Skill Making exchanges with pennies, dimes, and dollars

Materials (per group)

◆ 1 die or inch cube, labeled 1¢, 1¢, 10¢, 10¢, 10¢, 10¢

◆ 40 pennies, 40 dimes, and 1 dollar bill

Players 2–4

Object of the game To make an exchange for a dollar.

Games Across the Grades

Grades	PK	K	1	2	3	4	5	6
Advanced Learning								
Core Program		◆						
Reteaching and Practice			◆	◆				

Directions

1. Players put the coins and dollar bill in a "bank" between them.

2. Players take turns. For each turn, a player rolls the money cube and picks up the appropriate coin from the bank.

3. When a player has 10 pennies, he or she exchanges them for 1 dime. When a player has 10 dimes, he or she exchanges them for 1 dollar.

4. The game ends when one player has a dollar bill.

> **NOTE:** For an exchange game that uses only pennies, nickels, and dimes, see *Money Cube* or *Coin-Dice.*

Differentiation Options

READINESS Students may need practice in matching coins to their values. Using pictures for support may be helpful:

▶ For the die, use a picture of the appropriate coin along with its value on each side of an inch cube.

▶ Make mats with 10 circles for pennies and 10 circles for dimes. Players can use the mats as a reminder to make exchanges when the circles are full. You may want to number the circles 1–10.

ENRICHMENT

▶ Players use a money cube labeled 25¢, 25¢, 10¢, 10¢, 10¢, and 1¢. Add 15 quarters to the bank. Players can exchange pennies for dimes, 2 dimes and 5 pennies for a quarter, and 4 quarters for a dollar bill.

ELL SUPPORT Discuss the U.S. monetary system and demonstrate the meanings of *penny, dime, dollar,* and *bank.* Discuss and model the meaning of *exchange* or *trade.* Introduce the game and model several turns.

GRADES 1–2 $1, $10, $100 Exchange Game

Games Across the Grades

Grades	PK	K	1	2	3	4	5	6
Advanced Learning		◆						
Core Program			◆	◆				
Reteaching and Practice				◆				

Strands Number and Numeration; Measurement and Reference Frames

Skill Recognizing and exchanging $1, $10, and $100 bills

Materials (per pair)

◆ For Grade 1: Game Master 169 (game mat, 1 per player) and Game Master 170 (directions, optional)

◆ For Grade 2: *Money Exchange Games* Gameboard

◆ thirty $1 bills, twenty $10 bills, one $100 bill

◆ 1 or 2 dice

Players 2

Object of the game To exchange ten $10 bills for the $100 bill.

NOTE: For $1, $10, and $100 exchanges, see *Paper Money Exchange Game.* For pennies, dimes, $1 bills, and $10 bills, see *Money Exchange Game.*

Game Master 169 (p. 428)

Money Exchange Games Gameboard

Directions

1. Players put the money in a "bank" between them.

2. Players take turns rolling the dice (or die), and taking from the bank the number of $1 bills shown on the dice (or die).

3. Whenever possible, players trade 10 bills for 1 bill of the next higher denomination. Players put the bills in the correct columns on their mats.

4. The first player to make an exchange for a $100 bill wins.

Differentiation Options

READINESS Students may need to review the possible exchanges in this game. Playing with fewer types of bills may also be helpful:

▶ Players use a bank of twenty-four $10 bills and three $100 bills. They roll one die on each turn and collect that number of $10 bills. The first player to get two $100 bills wins.

ENRICHMENT

▶ Players use a bank of one $1,000 bank draft (Game Master 243), twenty $100 bills, twenty $10 bills, and twenty $1 bills. They also use the Everything Math Deck. On each turn, a player draws a card, takes a combination of bills for the total value on the card, and makes exchanges when possible. The first player to collect a bank draft wins.

ELL SUPPORT Students may not be familiar with terms associated with the U.S. monetary system. Discuss and demonstrate the meanings of *bill, bank,* and *denomination.* Discuss and model the meaning of *exchange* or *trade.* Introduce the game and model several turns.

Ones, Tens, Hundreds Game

GRADE K

Strand Number and Numeration

Skill Counting by 10s and 1s; exchanging 1s for 10s, and 10s for 100s; recognizing numbers as combinations of 100s, 10s, and 1s

Materials (per group)

- ◆ Game Master 171 (Record Sheet, optional, 1 per player)
- ◆ 1 die marked 1, 3, 5, 10, 10, 10
- ◇ craft sticks and rubber bands (Provide 20 single sticks and 10 bundles of 10 sticks each, per player)
- ◇ 1 "big bundle" of 100 (per group)
- ◇ cups, containers, or sheets of different-colored paper for separating bundles and sticks (optional)

Players 2–5

Object of the game To make an exchange for 100.

Games Across the Grades

Grades	PK	K	1	2	3	4	5	6
Advanced Learning		◆						
Core Program			◆					
Reteaching and Practice				◆	◆			

Directions

1. Players pile all of the craft sticks between them.
2. Players take turns rolling the die and taking that number of craft sticks from the pile.
3. Players make exchanges from the pile when possible, trading 10 single sticks for a bundle of 10, and 10 bundles of 10 craft sticks for the "big bundle" of 100 craft sticks.
4. Players continue taking turns until one player makes an exchange for the "big bundle" of 100.
5. At the end of the game, players count their craft sticks. Each player records his or her number of big bundles, bundles of 10, and single sticks on Game Master 171 or a sheet of paper.

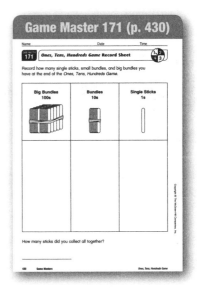
Game Master 171 (p. 430)

Differentiation Options

READINESS Students may need practice with exchanges. Counting and bundling groups of 10 may be helpful:

▶ Players begin with a bank of 100 craft sticks per player and play until the bank is empty. Then they bundle groups of 10 and lay their bundles and single sticks alongside each other to compare totals and determine which player has the most sticks.

▶ Players begin with a pile of single craft sticks (100 per player) and rubber bands. After players have collected 10 single craft sticks, they count the single sticks aloud and place a rubber band around them. When players have 10 bundles, they band them together as 100.

ENRICHMENT

▶ To provide practice with subtraction concepts and exchanges, provide a cube labeled + on 4 sides and − on 2 sides. Players roll this die along with the die from the basic version and take sticks from or return sticks to the bank accordingly. Players may need to make exchanges in order to return sticks.

ELL SUPPORT Discuss and model the meanings of *trade, bundle,* and *big bundle.* Introduce the game and model several turns.

GRADES 4–6 Over and Up Squares

Games Across the Grades									
Grades	PK	K	1	2	3	4	5	6	
Advanced Learning					◆				
Core Program						◆	◆	◆	
Reteaching and Practice									

Strand Measurement and Reference Frames

Skill Plotting ordered pairs on a coordinate grid; developing a winning strategy

Materials (per pair)

◆ For Grade 4: *Over and Up Squares* Gameboard (or Game Masters 172 and 173)

◆ For Grades 5 and 6: Game Masters 172 and 173 (directions, optional, and game mat/Record Sheet)

◆ 2 dice

◇ 2 different-colored pencils

Players 2

Object of the game To earn the higher score by connecting points on a coordinate grid.

Grade 4
SRB
257

Directions

1. Player 1 rolls 2 dice and uses the numbers to make an ordered pair. Either number can be used to name the x-coordinate (over) of the ordered pair. The other number is used to name the y-coordinate (up) of the ordered pair. After deciding which ordered pair to use, the player plots it on the grid with his or her colored pencil. (See Figure 1.)

2. Player 1 records the ordered pair and the score in his or her Record Sheet. A player earns 10 points each time an ordered pair is plotted correctly.

3. Player 2 rolls the dice and decides how to make an ordered pair. If both possible ordered pairs are already marked on the grid, the player rolls the dice again. Or, the player can change one or both of the numbers to 0.

4. Player 2 uses the other colored pencil to plot the ordered pair and records the ordered pair and score in his or her Record Sheet.

5. Players take turns rolling the dice, plotting ordered pairs on the grid, and recording the results. In a player's turn, if 2 marked grid points are next to each other on the same side of one of the grid squares, the player connects them with a line segment. Sometimes more than 1 line segment may be drawn in a single turn. (See Figure 2.) A player scores 10 points for each line segment drawn.

6. If a player draws a line segment that completes a grid square, (so that all 4 sides of the square are now drawn), that player colors in the square and earns 50 points. (See Figure 3.)

7. The player with more points after 10 rounds wins.

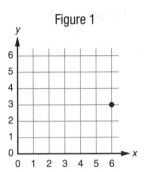

Figure 1

Player 1 rolls a 3 and a 6. The point (6,3) is marked on the grid.

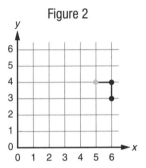

Figure 2

Player 1 marks (6,4) and scores 10 points. Player 1 draws 2 line segments and scores 20 points. The score for the round is 30 points.

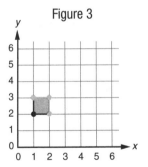

Figure 3

Player 1 marks (1,2) and scores 10 points. Player 1 draws 2 line segments and scores 20 points. The line segments complete a square. Player 1 colors in the square and scores 50 points. The score for the round is 80 points.

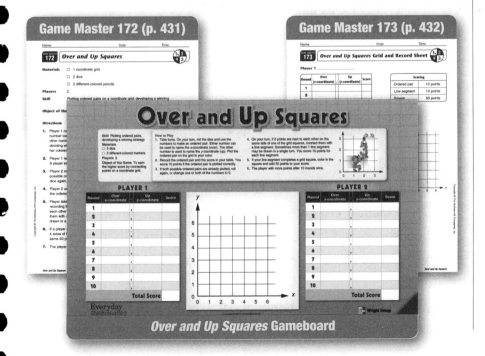

Over and Up Squares Gameboard

Game Master 174 (p. 433)

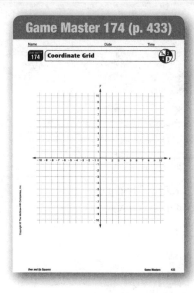

Differentiation Options

READINESS Students may need a review of naming points on a coordinate grid. Doing the tasks separately or assigning an axis to each roll of a die may also be helpful:

▶ Players do not connect the points with line segments. At the end of the game, players name the points that they plotted and get a bonus point for every segment they can draw between two adjacent points in their color.

▶ Players roll one die two times. The first roll is the *x*-coordinate and the second roll is the *y*-coordinate.

ENRICHMENT

▶ When doubles are rolled, a player can call out any ordered pair before plotting the point. If the point is plotted incorrectly, the other player scores the points.

▶ Players do not roll the dice; instead they strategically choose and name their own points.

▶ Players use a 4-quadrant grid (Game Master 174). To generate coordinates, they use two sets of 0–10 cards in black for positive numbers and two sets of 0–10 cards in blue for negative numbers.

ELL SUPPORT Draw pictures of the different ways to score and label them on the board: plotting an ordered pair (10 points), drawing a line segment (10 points), and coloring a square (50 points). Discuss the various scoring methods as well as the difference between (2,3) and (3,2). Introduce the game and model how to play until a square is shaded.

Paper Money Exchange Game

Games Across the Grades

Grades	PK	K	1	2	3	4	5	6
Advanced Learning								
Core Program		◆	◆	◆				
Reteaching and Practice					◆			

Strands Number and Numeration; Measurement and Reference Frames

Skill Recognizing and exchanging $1, $10, and $100 bills

Materials (per pair)

◆ Game Master 169 (Place-Value Mat, 1 per player)

◆ Game Master 175 (directions, optional)

◆ 1 cube marked $1 on 2 sides, $5 on 2 sides, and $10 on 2 sides

◆ twenty-three $1 bills, nineteen $10 bills, one $100 bill

Players 2

Object of the game To exchange ten $10 bills for the $100 bill.

Directions

Advance Preparation: For Kindergarten students, you may want to simplify Game Master 169 by covering up some of the text.

1. Players take turns rolling the cube and taking the correct bill (or combination of bills) from the bank. For example, a player would take five $1 bills when he or she rolls $5.

2. Players count their money after each turn.

3. When a player has ten $1 bills, he or she exchanges them for one $10 bill. When a player has ten $10 bills, he or she exchanges them for one $100 bill.

4. The first player to exchange ten $10 bills for one $100 bill wins.

Advanced Version

Materials (per pair)

◆ Game Master 169 (game mat, 1 per player)

◆ one $1,000 bank draft (Game Master 243)

◆ 1 cube marked $10 on 4 sides and $100 on 2 sides

◆ nineteen $10 bills and nineteen $100 bills

Players roll the cube and take the correct bill. They exchange ten $10 bills for one $100 bill and ten $100 bills for one $1,000 bank draft to win.

Differentiation Options

READINESS Students may need to review the exchanges possible in this game. Playing with fewer types of bills may be helpful:

▶ Players use a bank of twenty-four $10 bills and three $100 bills. Players take turns rolling one dot die and collecting that number of $10 bills. The first player to get two $100 bills wins.

ENRICHMENT

▶ Players write number sentences showing their starting amount, the amount added, and the total for each turn.

▶ After trading for the $100 bill (or the bank draft), players must roll and return all of the money to the bank to win.

ELL SUPPORT Discuss and model the meanings of *exchange, equivalent,* and *bill.* Introduce the game and model several turns.

NOTE: This game can be played on the *Money Exchange Games* gameboard. For a related exchange game, see *$1, $10, $100 Exchange Game.* For exchanges involving pennies, dimes, $1 bills, and $10 bills, see *Money Exchange Game.*

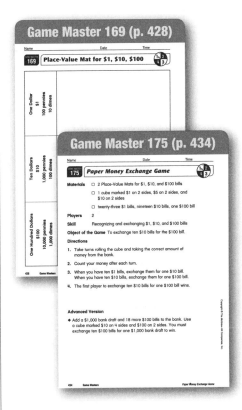

P

Pattern Cover Up

Games Across the Grades									
Grades	PK	K	1	2	3	4	5	6
Advanced Learning		◆						
Core Program			◆					
Reteaching and Practice				◆				

Strands Geometry; Patterns, Functions, and Algebra

Skill Creating patterns; identifying a missing element in a pattern

Materials (per pair)

◇ pattern blocks

◇ 1 small piece of paper for covering a pattern block

Players 2

Object of the game To identify a missing block in a pattern.

NOTE: You may want to show players how to begin by covering only the last block in the first few rounds, then the block before that, and so on until players are able to identify a missing block anywhere in the pattern.

Make sure players create patterns that repeat at least twice; for example: triangle, rhombus, pentagon, triangle, rhombus, pentagon, triangle, rhombus, pentagon.

Directions

1. Player 1 creates a pattern using pattern blocks.

2. Player 2 looks away while Player 1 covers one of the middle blocks.

3. Player 2 identifies the missing block.

4. Players switch roles. Play continues until time runs out.

Differentiation Options

READINESS Students may need to review the meaning of *pattern.* Working with simple, familiar patterns may also be helpful:

▶ Help students create a few pattern strips with simple AB or ABC patterns. Players select one of these pattern strips and use it in several games, until each player is able to identify the missing block every time.

ENRICHMENT

▶ Players cover 2 blocks in a pattern. The blocks need not be adjacent, but they cannot be identical.

▶ Players use at least 3 different blocks and create more complex patterns such as ABCC or ABBCDD.

ELL SUPPORT Discuss and model the meaning of **pattern** using pattern blocks. Have a volunteer use the blocks to create a repeating pattern on the board or overhead projector. Ensure that students know the names of the blocks. Ask students to close their eyes. Remove or erase one of the blocks. Have students open their eyes and ask: *Which block is missing? How do you know? What does* **missing** *mean?*

GRADE 1

Penny-Dice Game

Strands Number and Numeration; Measurement and Reference Frames

Skill Counting pennies; comparing quantities

Materials (per pair)

- Game Master 176 (directions, optional)
- 1 die
- 20 pennies

Players 2

Object of the game To have more (or fewer) pennies.

Games Across the Grades

Grades	PK	K	1	2	3	4	5	6
Advanced Learning	◆	◆						
Core Program			◆					
Reteaching and Practice				◆				

Directions

1. Players take turns. For each turn, a player rolls the die and takes as many pennies as indicated on the die.

2. The players continue taking turns until all of the pennies have been picked up. To pick up the last pennies, the number on the die must match the number of remaining pennies.

3. The player with more pennies wins, or players can flip a penny to determine who wins. If the penny lands on heads, the player with more pennies wins. If the penny lands on tails, the player with fewer pennies wins.

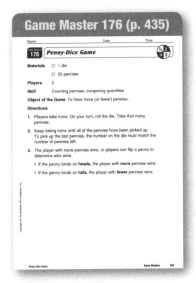

Game Master 176 (p. 435)

Differentiation Options

READINESS Students may need to review matching pennies to die rolls and comparing groups of pennies. Providing larger visuals may be helpful:

▶ Use stickers or markers to make large images of dice faces so that players can place a penny on each dot.

ENRICHMENT

▶ To practice exchanging pennies for nickels, players use a bank of 50 pennies and 10 nickels. When the game ends, players exchange as many pennies for nickels as they can before comparing their totals.

▶ For a game with pennies, nickels, and dimes, see *Coin-Dice.*

ELL SUPPORT Explain that for the last roll, the number of pennies picked up must *match* the number on the die. If there isn't an exact match, no pennies are picked up and the other player rolls. Model this situation and discuss the meaning of *exact match.*

K–2 Penny Exchange Games
GRADES

Games Across the Grades								
Grades	PK	K	1	2	3	4	5	6
Advanced Learning		◆						
Core Program			◆	◆	◆			
Reteaching and Practice					◆			

Strands Number and Numeration; Measurement and Reference Frames

Skill Making exchanges with pennies, nickels, and dimes

Materials (per pair)

◆ Game Master 177 (directions, optional)

◆ 1 die

◆ pennies, nickels, and dimes

Players 2

Object of the game To collect more nickels (or dimes).

NOTE: For another game about exchanging 5 objects, see *The Raft Game.*

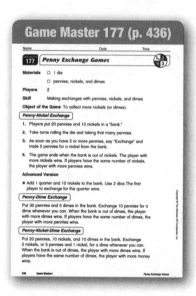

Game Master 177 (p. 436)

Penny-Nickel Exchange (recommended for Grades K–2)

Directions

1. Players put 20 pennies and 10 nickels in a "bank."

2. Players take turns rolling the die and collecting that number of pennies from the bank.

3. As soon as a player has 5 or more pennies, he or she says "Exchange" and trades 5 pennies for a nickel from the bank.

4. The game ends when the bank is out of nickels. The player with more nickels wins. If players have the same number of nickels, the player with more pennies wins.

Another Way to Play

Players add 10 nickels to the bank and use 2 dice.

Advanced Version

Players add 1 quarter and 10 nickels to the bank. The first player to exchange for the quarter wins.

Penny-Dime Exchange (recommended for Grades K–2)

Players use 30 pennies and 5 dimes. The rules are the same as for *Penny-Nickel Exchange,* except that players exchange 10 pennies for a dime as soon as they have 10 or more pennies. When the bank is out of dimes, the player with more dimes wins. If players have the same number of dimes, the player with more pennies wins.

Penny-Nickel-Dime Exchange (recommended for Grades 1–2)

Players use 20 pennies, 10 nickels, and 10 dimes. The rules are the same as for *Penny-Nickel Exchange,* except that players also exchange 2 nickels, or 5 pennies and 1 nickel, for a dime whenever possible. When the bank is out of dimes, the player with more dimes wins. If players have the same number of dimes, the player with the greater amount of money wins.

Another Way to Play

Players use a larger bank and 2 polyhedral dice.

Differentiation Options

READINESS Students may need a review of the exchanges possible in these games. You may want to make a poster showing the exchanges. Making all of the exchanges at the end of the game may also be helpful:

▶ Players use a bank of 50 pennies. Instead of making exchanges during the game, students play until all of the pennies are gone. At the end of the game, players count their pennies, exchange the pennies for nickels, and then recalculate their totals.

ENRICHMENT

▶ Players use 20 pennies, 10 nickels, 10 dimes, and 10 quarters. The rules are the same as for *Penny-Nickel-Dime Exchange,* except that players also exchange 2 dimes and 1 nickel, or 2 dimes and 5 pennies, for a quarter. When the bank is out of quarters, the player with more quarters wins. If players have the same number of quarters, the player with the greater amount of money wins.

▶ For a game that includes dollar bills, see *One-Dollar Exchange.*

ELL SUPPORT Discuss the U.S. monetary system and demonstrate the meanings of **penny, nickel,** and **bank.** Discuss and model the meaning of **exchange** or **trade.** Explain that students can exchange 5 pennies for a nickel because both are worth 5¢. Introduce the game and model several turns.

Penny Grab

GRADE 1

Games Across the Grades

Grades	PK	K	1	2	3	4	5	6
Advanced Learning	◆	◆						
Core Program				◆				
Reteaching and Practice				◆				

Strands Number and Numeration; Measurement and Reference Frames

Skill Counting and comparing groups of pennies

Materials (per pair)
- *Coin Grab Games* Gameboard (or Game Master 178)
- 40 pennies

Players 2

Object of the game To have more money in at least two rounds.

NOTE: Encourage players to estimate before counting.

Remind students to use the ¢ symbol. You may want to write ___ ¢ in the Total columns of the Record Sheets.

Game Master 178 (p. 437)

Directions

1. Players place the pennies in a pile between them.

2. Each player grabs a handful of pennies. (Alternatively, Player 1 grabs a handful, and Player 2 grabs all of the remaining pennies.)

3. Each player draws his or her pennies on the Record Sheet and finds the total value.

4. Each player records his or her total and the other player's total on the Record Sheet. Each player circles the greater total.

5. Players switch roles and repeat Steps 1–4 two more times for a total of 3 rounds. The player who had more money in at least 2 rounds wins.

Differentiation Options

READINESS Students may need a review of counting and comparing groups of pennies. Using a smaller number of pennies may be helpful:

▶ Use only 20 pennies. To determine who has more pennies, players can line up their pennies in two rows, one below the other, and compare. (Also see *Difference Game*.)

ENRICHMENT

▶ Add 8 nickels to the coins used. (See *Nickel-Penny Grab*.)

▶ Players write a subtraction number model to represent the difference between their penny totals.

ELL SUPPORT Put the pennies in a paper bag. After Player 1 grabs a handful of pennies, give the pennies left in the bag to Player 2. Ask: *How many pennies did each player get? Which player has* **more** *pennies? Which player has the* **greater** *total value?*

GRADES 1–2 Penny Plate

Strands Operations and Computation; Patterns, Functions, and Algebra

Skill Sum-equals-ten facts

Materials (per pair)

◆ *Penny Plate* Gameboard (or Game Master 179)

◆ 10 (or more) pennies

◇ 1 plate

Grades 1–2

MRB 146

Players 2

Object of the game To get 5 points.

Games Across the Grades

Grades	PK	K	1	2	3	4	5	6
Advanced Learning		◆						
Core Program				◆	◆			
Reteaching and Practice						◆		

Directions

1. Player 1 turns the plate upside down, hides some of the pennies under the plate, and puts the rest on top of the plate.

2. Player 2 counts the pennies on top of the plate and figures out how many pennies are hidden under the plate.

> **NOTE:** Model how to use the language of addition to describe the placement of the pennies; for example: *I see 6 pennies. 6 plus what number is 10?*

3. If the number is correct, Player 2 gets a point.

4. Players trade roles and repeat Steps 1–3.

5. Players tally their points. The first player to get 5 points wins.

Another Way to Play

One player hides some of the pennies without counting them and puts the rest on top of the plate. Players work together to guess how many pennies are under the plate. If their guess is correct, they get a team point. The team plays 10 rounds. The goal is to improve the team score in each round.

Advanced Version

Increase the total number of pennies as players become proficient, until players are using a total of 20 pennies.

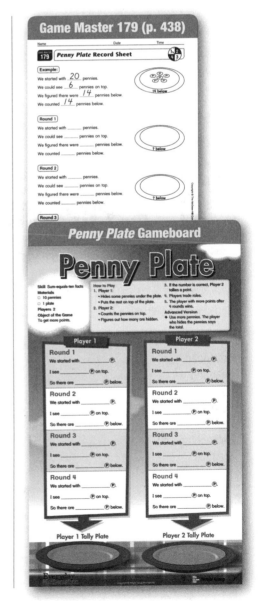

Differentiation Options

READINESS Students may need a review of counting on and other strategies for finding a missing part. Modeling the problems may be helpful:

▶ Provide counters or a second set of pennies. Players draw circles on a sheet of paper to represent the total number of pennies, cover one circle for each penny they see on top of the plate, and count the uncovered circles to find the number of hidden pennies. (Alternatively, draw circles on top of the plate to represent the total. The pennies on top of the plate are placed in the circles, and players count the empty circles.)

ENRICHMENT

▶ The player hiding the pennies can choose between 10 and 20 pennies and report the total number as ____ *more than 10 pennies.*

▶ Players use 10 dimes instead of 10 pennies and determine the amount of money hidden under the plate.

ELL SUPPORT Model how to play the game. Say: *I have 10 pennies.* Count them aloud with students. Say: *I will **hide** some pennies under the plate. This means you will not be able to see them.* Place some pennies under the plate. Say: *You will have to figure out how many pennies I hid under the plate. I will give you a clue. I will put the rest of the pennies on top of the plate.* Discuss how students are to use the pennies on top of the plate to figure out how many are under the plate.

GRADE 6

Percent/Sector Match Up

Games Across the Grades									
Grades	PK	K	1	2	3	4	5	6
Advanced Learning							◆	
Core Program								◆
Reteaching and Practice								

Strands Number and Numeration

Skill Matching percents to shaded sectors

Materials (per pair)
◆ Game Master 180 (Percent/Sector Tiles)

Players 2 or 3

Object of the game To collect the most tiles by matching percents to shaded sectors.

Directions

Advance Preparation: Have students write the percent symbol (%) on the back of each percent tile.

1. One player shuffles the tiles and places them facedown in a 6-row-by-4-column array. The backs of the 12 percent tiles should have the percent symbol (%) showing. The backs of the sector tiles are blank.

2. Players take turns. For each turn, a player turns over a percent tile and a sector tile. If the tiles match, the player keeps both tiles. If the tiles do not match, the player replaces the tiles facedown.

3. Play continues until all tiles have been matched. The player with the most tiles wins.

Another Way to Play

If the selected percent tile and sector tile add up to 100%, the player keeps the tiles. The game ends when all of the tiles are matched. (You will need to remove the 100% tiles.) The player with the most tiles wins.

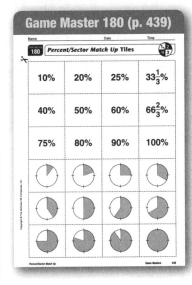

Game Master 180 (p. 439)

Differentiation Options

READINESS Students may need practice with sector models for benchmark percents. Using fewer tiles may be helpful:

▶ Players use only the percent and sector tiles for 25%, 50%, 75% and 100%. Gradually add the other tiles closest to these benchmarks.

▶ Players play with the tiles faceup. For this game, you may want to write the correct percents on the backs of a set of sector tiles so players can check their matches.

ENRICHMENT

▶ Players receive a bonus point if they can name the equivalent fraction and decimal for each match they make. Each bonus point counts as 1 tile at the end of the game.

ELL SUPPORT Ensure that students understand the meaning of *equivalent*. Prior to playing the game, show the students 6 tiles (two of the tiles should be equivalent). Ask students to identify "matches" that are equivalent. Discuss the meaning of *match* in this context. Discuss the meaning of *percent tile* and *sector tile*.

GRADES 2–3 Pick-a-Coin

Games Across the Grades

Grades	PK	K	1	2	3	4	5	6
Advanced Learning		◆						
Core Program				◆	◆			
Reteaching and Practice					◆			

Strands Operations and Computation; Measurement and Reference Frames

Skill Finding the value of coin collections; adding dollar and coin values on a calculator; using place value for decimals; using dollars-and-cents notation

Materials (per group)

◆ For Grade 2: *Pick-a-Coin* Gameboard (or Game Master 181)

◆ For Grade 3: Game Master 181 (Record Tables)

◆ 1 die

◆ 1 calculator (per player)

Players 2 or 3

Object of the game To make the largest dollar-and-cents amount.

Grade 3
SRB
306

Game Master 181 (p. 440)

Pick-a-Coin Gameboard

Directions

1. Each player uses his or her own Record Table.

2. Players take turns. For each turn, a player rolls the die 5 times. He or she records each number rolled in any cell on one line of his or her record table.

3. With a calculator, the player finds and records the total for that turn.

4. After 4 turns, each player uses a calculator to add the 4 totals. The player with the largest sum wins.

Example

On his first turn, Brian rolled 4, 2, 4, 6, and 1. He filled in his Record Table like this.

Brian	Ⓟ	Ⓝ	Ⓓ	Ⓠ	$1	**Total**
1st turn	2	1	4	4	6	$ 7.47
2nd turn						$__.__
3rd turn						$__.__
4th turn						$__.__
					Grand Total	$__.__

Differentiation Options

READINESS Students may need to review determining the value of a group of like coins. Modeling each group of coins or limiting the game to coins of lesser value may be helpful:

▶ Provide coins and bills. Players model each group of like coins and write the total value in the appropriate cell of the table.

▶ Each player crosses out the columns for quarters and bills on the table and fills in numbers of pennies, nickels, and dimes only.

ENRICHMENT

▶ Players use an 8-sided die to generate greater numbers. They record a number sentence using dollars-and-cents notation to calculate the total for their combination.

ELL SUPPORT Copy the *Pick-a-Coin* Record Table on the board. Review the meaning of each column heading. Complete the first row using the numbers that Brian rolled (2, 1, 4, 4, and 6). Explain that Brian could have written these numbers in the table in different ways. Ask the students to use coins to model the value ($7.47) that Brian recorded in the table. Ask students to rearrange the same 5 numbers and record an example in the second row. Ask students to model this arrangement using coins. Ask: *Which arrangement is worth more?* Introduce the game and model how to record the rolls and calculate the total using a calculator.

GRADES PK—K

Plus or Minus Game

Strands Operations and Computation; Patterns, Functions, and Algebra

Skill Adding and subtracting 0 to 3 items; recognizing the + and − symbols; exploring the difference between addition and subtraction

Materials (per pair)

◆ *Plus or Minus* Gameboard (or Game Master 182)

◆ 1 die marked +1, +2, +3, −1, −2, 0

◆ 32 counters

Players 2

Object of the game To cover a game mat.

Games Across the Grades

Grades	PK	K	1	2	3	4	5	6
Advanced Learning								
Core Program	◆	◆						
Reteaching and Practice			◆	◆				

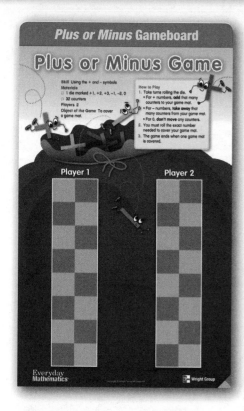

Directions

1. Players take turns rolling the die. A player who rolls:
   - a + number **adds** that many counters to his or her game mat.
   - a − number **removes** that many counters from his or her mat (unless there are not enough counters on the mat).
   - 0 makes no move.
2. The game ends when one player has covered his or her game mat with an exact roll.

Another Way to Play

Plus or Minus Steps

Plus or Minus Steps is a game that includes physical movement. For this variation, mark starting and ending lines on opposite sides of an outdoor area, hallway, or large classroom rug; or use a large walk-on number line. You may also want to use a large cube for the die. Players begin at the starting line (or at 0 on the number line). They take turns rolling the cube and taking the correct number of steps forward (+) or backward (−) until a player reaches the ending line. Remind students to take regular steps. Alternatively, vary the steps for each round; for example, players hop or take baby steps.

Differentiation Options

READINESS Students may need to review matching numerals to corresponding numbers of spaces on the game mat. Playing on a smaller board or using dot patterns for support may be helpful:

▶ Players use only 10 squares on the game mat.

▶ Provide cards instead of a die, with the corresponding number of dots on each card. Mark the top of each card with a red − or a green + to match the possibilities of the die.

ENRICHMENT

▶ Players write number sentences for each move. For example, a player who rolls +2 on his or her first turn would write $0 + 2 = 2$. The first addend is the number of counters already on the board.

ELL SUPPORT Discuss and model the meanings of *plus, add, minus,* and *remove* using counters on the game mat. Ask: *Why don't you make a move when you roll a 0?*

Pocket-Billiards Game

GRADE 4

Strand Geometry

Skill Finding lines of reflection

Materials (per pair)

◆ Game Master 183 (billiards table; also available in Grade 4 Math Journal 2, Activity Sheet 8)

◇ 1 transparent mirror

Players 2

Object of the game To get the higher score by reflecting the ball into one of the pockets.

Games Across the Grades

Grades	PK	K	1	2	3	4	5	6
Advanced Learning					◆			
Core Program						◆		
Reteaching and Practice							◆	

Directions

1. Players practice the game first by choosing a ball (1, 2, 3, or 4) and a pocket (A, B, C, D, E, or F) on Game Master 183. Players look through the mirror and move it around until they reflect the ball into the pocket.

2. Players take turns. For each turn, a player says which ball and which pocket he or she has picked; for example, *Ball 2 to go into Pocket D.*

3. The player tries to get the ball into the pocket by placing the transparent mirror on the billiard table **without looking through the mirror.**

4. After a player has placed the mirror on the master, both players look through the mirror to check whether the ball has gone into the pocket.

5. If a ball goes into the pocket, the player scores 1 point.

6. The player with the higher total score after 5 rounds wins.

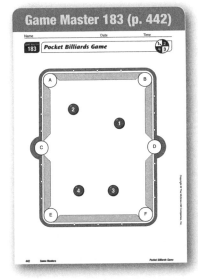

Game Master 183 (p. 442)

Differentiation Options

READINESS Students may need a review of the effects of reflection and the use of a transparent mirror. Allowing more attempts on each turn may be helpful:

▶ For each turn, a player has 3 chances to sink a ball into a pocket. A player scores 5 points if he or she is successful on the first try, 3 points on the second try, and 1 point on the third try.

ENRICHMENT

▶ If a player successfully puts a ball into a pocket, he or she may draw a ball anywhere else on the billiards table, and try to put that ball into the same pocket. If the player is successful, he or she receives a bonus point.

ELL SUPPORT Show students images of the game of billiards and explain how it is played. Discuss terminology related to the game, including *pocket* and *ball.* Explain that students will play a game similar to billiards, but will use mirrors and *reflection* to play. Introduce the game and model the meaning of *reflection* using the transparent mirror.

GRADES 5–6 **Polygon Capture**

Strand Geometry

Skill Identifying properties of polygons

Materials (per group)

◆ 1 set of *Polygon Capture* Pieces (or Game Master 184; also available in Grade 5 Math Journal 1, Activity Sheet 3)

◆ 1 set of *Polygon Capture* Property Cards (or Game Master 185; also available in Grade 5 Math Journal 1, Activity Sheet 4)

Players 2, or 2 teams of 2

Object of the game To collect more polygons.

Grade 5
SRB
328

Grade 6
SRB
330

Games Across the Grades

Grades	PK	K	1	2	3	4	5	6
Advanced Learning							◆	
Core Program							◆	◆
Reteaching and Practice								

Directions

Advance Preparation: Have players write the word *Sides* or *Angles* on the back of each Property Card according to what the card describes.

1. One player spreads out the polygons between players. A second player shuffles the Property Cards and sorts them sentence-side down into *Angles* and *Sides* piles.

2. Players take turns. For each turn, a player draws the top Property Card from each pile.

3. The player takes all of the polygons that have **both** of the properties shown on the Property Cards in the player's hand.

   If there are no polygons with both properties, the player draws one additional Property Card—either an *Angle*- or a *Side*-card. He or she looks for polygons that have this new property and one of the properties already drawn. The player takes any polygons that have both properties.

4. At the end of a turn, the player discards the Property Cards. If the player has not captured a polygon that he or she could have taken, the other player may name and capture it.

5. When all of the Property Cards in either pile have been drawn, one player shuffles *all* of the Property Cards and sorts them sentence-side down into *Angles* and *Sides* piles. Play continues.

6. The game ends when there are fewer than 3 polygons left.

7. The player who has captured more polygons wins.

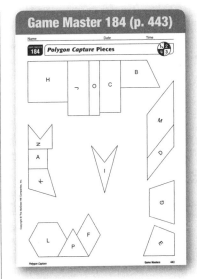

Game Master 184 (p. 443)

Game Master 185 (p. 444)

> **Example**
>
> Liz has these Property Cards: *All angles are right angles,* and *All sides are the same length.* She can take all of the squares (Polygons A and H). Liz has "captured" these polygons.

Differentiation Options

READINESS Students may need to review the meanings of key terms, such as *parallel* or *right angle,* on the Property Cards. Drawing shapes with a Geometry Template or working with a list of polygon properties instead of drawing cards may also be helpful:

▶ Players use only the Property Cards. They draw 1 Property Card and use their Geometry Templates to draw a shape with that property. They receive 1 point if they correctly draw a shape. The player with more points wins.

▶ Players use only the Polygon Capture Pieces. Before beginning, they work together to make a list of polygon properties. On each turn, a player turns over the top piece and wins the piece if he or she can name a property of the polygon. The player receives a bonus point if he or she can name a second property. For scoring, bonus points count as pieces.

ENRICHMENT

▶ Players shuffle together 2 complete sets of Property Cards. They do *not* separate them into *Sides* and *Angles* piles. On each turn, a player takes 2 Property Cards and tries to draw a polygon with both properties. If a matching polygon is drawn, the player earns a point. After all of the cards have been used, the player with the most points wins.

▶ Once during the game, each player may call a "Free Turn" and declare one "angle" and one "side" property. The player collects 1 Polygon Capture Piece with both properties.

ELL SUPPORT Ensure that students understand the meaning of **property** in this mathematical context. Discuss the meanings of some of the expressions used on the property cards, such as **at least one, one or more,** and **opposite sides.** Model how to play a few turns, emphasizing that students should capture *all* of the polygons that match the selected properties.

GRADE 4

Polygon Pair-Up

Strand Geometry

Skill Identifying properties of polygons

Materials (per group)

◆ *Polygon Pair-Up* Gameboard (optional)

◆ *Polygon Pair-Up* Polygon Cards (or Game Master 186)

◆ *Polygon Pair-Up* Property Cards (or Game Master 187)

◇ paper and pencils for sketching

Players 2, or 2 teams of 2

Object of the game To collect more cards by matching polygons with their properties.

Grade 4

SRB

258

Games Across the Grades

Grades	PK	K	1	2	3	4	5	6
Advanced Learning					◆			
Core Program						◆		
Reteaching and Practice							◆	

Directions

1. One player shuffles the Polygon Cards and the Property Cards and places the two decks side by side and facedown.

2. Players take turns. For each turn, a player places one card from each deck faceup, below the decks.

3. If the player can match a Polygon Card with a Property Card, he or she says "Match!" and takes those 2 cards. His or her turn is over. (A player may make only 1 match and take 2 cards per turn.)

4. If a player is not able to make a match, the player says "Done!" The turn is over. All of the cards that are faceup remain faceup for the next player.

5. At the start of a turn, a player may notice a match. If the player says "Steal!" he or she can take the matching cards before taking his or her turn.

6. A player may use a WILD card to make a match during any turn.

   • To use a WILD Property Card, a player picks any faceup Polygon Card. If he or she names a property to match that Polygon Card, he or she takes both cards.

   • To use a WILD Polygon Card, a player picks any faceup Property Card. If he or she sketches a polygon that matches that Property Card, he or she takes both cards.

7. The game is over when all of the cards have been turned over and no more matches can be made. The player (or team) with more cards wins.

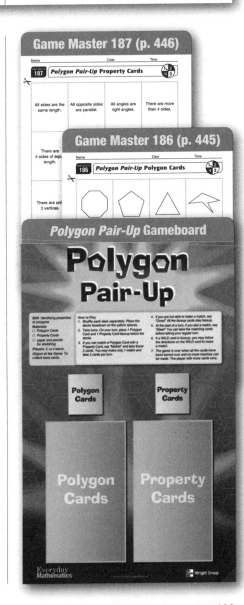

Differentiation Options

READINESS Students may need to review the meanings of key terms on the Property Cards. Using a Geometry Template or describing polygons may be helpful:

▶ Players draw 1 Property Card and use their Geometry Templates to draw a shape with that property. They receive 3 points the first time an appropriate shape is drawn and 1 point if the shape is correct but has been drawn in a previous turn.

▶ Players make a list of polygon properties. Only Polygon Cards are used. For each turn, a player turns over a Polygon Card and names one of its properties to win the card. The player gets a bonus point if he or she can name a second property. For scoring, bonus points count as cards.

ENRICHMENT Challenge players to identify more than one property of a polygon or to make multiple matches to a single card:

▶ Each partnership uses 2 sets of Property Cards. On each turn, players turn over 2 Property Cards and 1 Polygon Card. They can use 1 or 2 Property Cards to make a match. The player who collects more cards wins.

▶ Players use WILD Property Cards to name any property and to collect all faceup Polygon Cards with that property. They use WILD Polygon Cards to name any polygon and to collect all matching Property Cards.

ELL SUPPORT Ensure that students understand the meaning of *property* in this context. Display several Polygon Cards and Property Cards. Model how to find a match. Use pictures and gestures to discuss the meanings of some of the terms used on the Property Cards, such as *only 1 pair,* and *pairs of sides.* Introduce the game and model a few turns. Show how a *steal* works.

GRADE 4

Product Pile-Up

Strand Operations and Computation

Skill Multiplication facts through 10×10

Materials (per group)

◆ 2 Everything Math Decks (number cards 1–10, 8 of each)

Players 3–5

Object of the game To have no cards left.

Grade 4

SRB
259

Directions

1. The dealer shuffles the cards and deals 12 cards to each player. The dealer places the rest of the deck whole-number side down.

2. The player to the left of the dealer begins. This player selects 2 of his or her cards, places them whole-number side up on the table, multiplies the numbers, and says the product.

3. Play continues with each player selecting and playing 2 cards with a product *greater than* the previous player's product.

Example

Joe plays 3 and 6 and says: *3 times 6 equals 18.*

The next player, Rachel, looks at her hand to find 2 cards with a product higher than 18. She plays 5 and 4 and says: *5 times 4 equals 20.*

4. If a player is not able to play 2 cards with a greater product, the player must draw 2 cards from the deck. These 2 cards are added to the player's hand. If the player is now able to make a greater product, the 2 cards are played, and play continues.

5. If after drawing the 2 cards a player still cannot make a play, the player says "Pass." If *all* of the other players say "Pass," the last player who was able to lay down 2 cards may select 2 cards to make *any* product, and play continues.

6. If a player states an incorrect product, he or she must take back the 2 cards, draw 2 cards from the deck, and say "Pass."

7. The first player to run out of cards wins. If the deck runs out first, the player with the fewest cards wins.

Differentiation Options

READINESS Students may need to review strategies for multiplication. Keeping one factor constant or using various tools may be helpful:

▶ Instead of 2 cards, players use 1 card. For each round, players select one factor by which everyone must multiply a card from his or her hand.

▶ Players use facts tables, counters, or calculators to find products.

ENRICHMENT

▶ Players make an extended fact by treating one card on each turn as a number of 10s.

ELL SUPPORT Write *3, 4, 5, 7, 8,* and *10* on the board. Ask volunteers to select two numbers, multiply them, and find the product. Write the resulting number sentences on the board. Discuss which product is the largest. Introduce the game and model how to play with a few students. Make sure students understand the meaning of **pass.**

GRADE 1
Quarter-Dime-Nickel-Penny Grab

Games Across the Grades

Grades	PK	K	1	2	3	4	5	6
Advanced Learning		◆						
Core Program			◆					
Reteaching and Practice				◆				

Strands Number and Numeration; Data and Chance; Measurement and Reference Frames

Skill Counting and comparing collections of coins

Materials (per pair)

- *Coin Grab Games* Gameboard (or Game Master 188, 2 copies)
- 4 quarters, 10 dimes, 8 nickels, 20 pennies

Players 2

Object of the game To have more money in at least two rounds.

NOTE: Remind students to use the ¢ or $ symbol. You may want to write ___¢ or $___.___ in the Total columns of the Record Sheets.

Directions

1. Players mix the coins together in a pile.
2. Player 1 grabs a handful of coins. Player 2 grabs the remaining coins.
3. Each player draws his or her coins on a Record Sheet, finds their total value, and records both players' totals. Each player circles the greater total.
4. Players switch roles and repeat Steps 1–3 two more times for a total of 3 rounds. The player who had more money in at least 2 rounds wins.

Game Master 188 (p. 447)

Coin Grab Games Gameboard

Differentiation Options

READINESS Students may need a review of determining the value of a coin collection. Using fewer types of coins may be helpful:

▶ Players use only dimes, nickels, and pennies. (See *Dime-Nickel-Penny Grab*.)

ENRICHMENT

▶ To earn a bonus point, a player finds the difference between the two players' totals. At the end of the game, bonus points are counted as rounds won. The player who won the most rounds wins.

ELL SUPPORT Write *dollar* on the board and explain that it has the same value as 100 cents, 20 nickels, 10 dimes, or 4 quarters. Write the $ symbol and read it aloud. Have students write and read aloud various amounts of money using the $ symbol.

Racing Cars

Strand Number and Numeration

Skill Counting with one-to-one correspondence

Materials (per group)

◆ *Racing Cars* Gameboard (or Game Masters 189 and 190)

◆ 1 dot die

◆ 2–5 cardstock racing cars (or Game Master 189, or counters)

Players 2–5

Object of the game To cross the finish line.

Games Across the Grades

Grades	PK	K	1	2	3	4	5	6
Advanced Learning								
Core Program	◆	◆						
Reteaching and Practice			◆					

Directions

Advance Preparation: For the racetrack, you can use the *Racing Cars* Gameboard, which accommodates 2 players, or cut and tape together the tracks from Game Masters 189 and 190. You can lengthen the track by making additional copies of the middle track sections. The track is designed for 2 players (1 lane per player), but you can tape additional Game Masters next to each other to have more than 2 players use the same track. If possible, laminate or mount the track and cars on cardboard for durability.

1. Each player chooses a lane and places his or her car on Start. Each player's car must stay in his or her chosen lane.

2. Players take turns. For each turn, a player rolls the die and moves his or her race car that number of spaces.

3. The game ends when all of the cars have crossed the finish line.

Another Way to Play

Small groups can play *Kid Race*. In this game, players use a life-size racetrack created from masking tape, carpet squares, or papers on the floor. One player acts as the car for each lane. Players take turns rolling the die and moving along the track until all players have crossed the finish line.

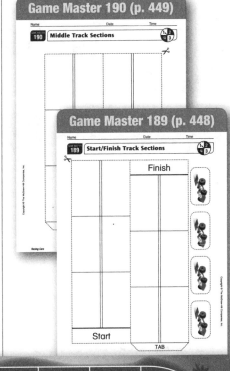

Racing Cars Gameboard

Differentiation Options

READINESS Students may need to review counting through 6. Using smaller numbers or counters may be helpful:

▶ Players use a die that has two sides each with 1 dot, 2 dots, and 3 dots.

▶ Before moving the car, a player takes the number of counters rolled and places them on the track in front of the car.

ENRICHMENT

▶ Provide number cards or a die with numerals instead of the dot die.

ELL SUPPORT Show students a picture of a racetrack with Start and Finish lines. Explain that students will roll the die and move their cars along the track the number of spaces shown on the die. Model how to play.

GRADE K — The Raft Game

Games Across the Grades									
Grades	PK	K	1	2	3	4	5	6	
Advanced Learning	◆								
Core Program		◆							
Reteaching and Practice		◆							

Strand Number and Numeration

Skill Counting by 5s; exploring equivalent names for numbers; making exchanges

Materials

◆ 1 die per group

◆ 1 counter or toy animal per player

◇ at least 10 planks, 3 rafts, and 15 beans per pair

Players 2–6

Object of the game To collect as many rafts as possible.

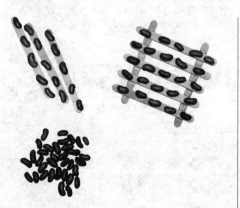

Directions

Advance Preparation: A few days before introducing the game, have students make planks and rafts. They glue (or draw) 5 beans on each craft stick to make planks, and then glue 5 planks together to make rafts. You will need at least 31 craft sticks and 125 beans (optional) to make at least 10 planks and 3 rafts for each pair of children who will play at the same time.

1. Players take turns rolling the die and counting out that number of beans.

2. When a player collects 5 beans, he or she trades them for 1 plank.

3. When a player collects 5 planks, he or she trades them for 1 raft.

4. When a player collects a raft, he or she can place a counter (or toy animal) on it and "float" it across a pretend river.

5. Players collect as many rafts as time allows.

> **NOTE:** To help players determine when to exchange 5 beans for a plank, have them place their beans in a row below a plank. To determine when to exchange 5 planks for a raft, players can position planks alongside a raft with one-to-one correspondence.

Differentiation Options

READINESS Students may need to review matching groups of objects in order to make exchanges. Removing the rafts from the game may also be helpful:

▶ Players exchange 5 beans for 1 plank and collect as many planks as time allows.

ENRICHMENT

▶ To practice numeral recognition, players use a die with the numbers 1–6 instead of a dot die.

ELL SUPPORT Discuss and model the meanings of *plank, raft, trade, equivalent,* and *exchange.* Use pictures of planks and rafts to support this discussion.

GRADE K

Read My Mind

Strands Geometry; Patterns, Functions, and Algebra

Skill Using attributes to describe objects and to select an object from a collection

Materials (per group)

◇ 1 set of attribute blocks

Players 2–5

Object of the game To find the mystery block.

Games Across the Grades								
Grades	PK	K	1	2	3	4	5	6
Advanced Learning		◆						
Core Program			◆					
Reteaching and Practice				◆				

Directions

1. Players spread out the set of attribute blocks.

2. One player secretly chooses a mystery block. This block remains among the others on the table.

3. The other players take turns asking *yes* or *no* questions about the mystery block; for example: *Is it red? Is it small? Is it the large, blue triangle?*

4. After a player asks a question, he or she removes attribute blocks according to the answer. For example, if the answer to *Is it red?* is *Yes,* the player who asked the question removes all of the blocks except the red blocks.

5. Players continue asking questions and removing blocks until only the mystery block remains or a player guesses the correct block.

Differentiation Options

READINESS Students may need to review identifying attributes of blocks. Using blocks with fewer attributes may be helpful:

▶ Use blocks with only 3 different attributes. Eliminate color, size, shape, or thickness as a varying attribute. Or, you may want to eliminate both thickness and size; start with only different colors and shapes and later add each of the other 2 attributes.

ENRICHMENT

▶ Players ask questions that involve 2 attributes; for example: *Is it small and red?*

ELL SUPPORT Using a set of attribute blocks, discuss different words that describe the various colors, shapes, thicknesses, and sizes. Write each word on the board next to a picture representing its meaning. As you model with a student the process of asking questions and removing blocks, highlight and discuss the meanings of ***attribute, mystery block,*** and ***remove.***

GRADES 3–4 Robot Game

Games Across the Grades									
Grades	PK	K	1	2	3	4	5	6	
Advanced Learning				◆					
Core Program					◆	◆			
Reteaching and Practice							◆	◆	

Strands Measurement and Reference Frames; Geometry

Skill Exploring rotations and angles

Materials (per pair)

◆ Game Master 191 (directions, optional)

◇ sheet of paper with an arrow

Players 2

Object of the game To reach the destination.

Directions

1. One player is the Controller and the other player is the Robot. The Robot stands on the piece of paper and faces the direction that the arrow is pointing.

2. The Controller picks a destination and gives the Robot "turn-and-move" directions, one at a time. The Controller gives the approximate measure of each turn and the number of steps. Each turn may be given as a fraction of a full turn or as a degree measure. The Controller gives directions until the Robot reaches the destination.

Example

The Controller says: *Make a half-turn. Go forward 5 steps.* The Robot moves accordingly. Then the Controller says: *Now turn clockwise a quarter-turn (90 degrees). Go back 3 steps.* The Robot follows the directions.

3. Players change roles and play again.

Another Way To Play

The Controller does not choose a destination. Instead, he or she gives 3 "turn-and-move" direction pairs and then says to the Robot, *Tell where you are.* The robot tells where he or she is in relation to the starting position; for example, a quarter-turn clockwise and about one step to the right of the starting position.

Differentiation Options

READINESS Students may need to review types of turns and degree measures; you may want to help them make a chart. Continuing to use the piece of paper with the arrow may also be helpful:

▶ After each successful completion of a direction, the Controller moves the piece of paper with the arrow to the Robot's new location.

ENRICHMENT

▶ The Controller gives directions that include at least 4 turns and 4 different angle measures.

ELL SUPPORT Show students a picture of a robot. Explain that a **robot** is a machine that does what it is told. A **controller** tells a robot what to do; for example, a controller can tell a robot to walk or turn. Have a volunteer pretend to be a robot. Explain that you will give directions to the robot so that he or she reaches a destination you select. Discuss the meaning of **destination.** As you give directions and the robot responds, discuss the meanings of **turn, angle, distance,** and **direction.**

NOTE: Have the Controller give one "turn-and-move" direction at a time and wait until the Robot completes it before giving the next direction.

Game Master 191 (p. 450)

Rock, Paper, Scissors

Strand Data and Chance

Skill Organizing data in a tally chart

Materials (per pair)

◆ Game Master 192 (Record Sheet)

Players 2

Object of the game To make the winning hand sign.

Game Master 192 (p. 451)

Directions

1. Three objects—a rock, a piece of paper, and scissors—are represented by the following hand signs:

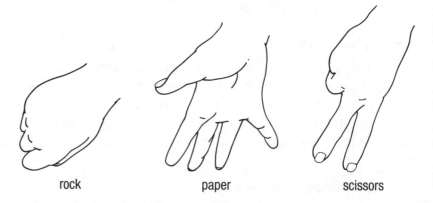

rock   paper   scissors

2. Players make one of the hand signs behind their backs.

3. One player counts to 3, and then both players show their hands. The following rules determine which player wins the round:

   • **Scissors and paper:** Scissors wins because scissors can cut paper.

   • **Paper and rock:** Paper wins because paper can be wrapped around a rock.

   • **Rock and scissors:** Rock wins because it can blunt the scissors (make them less sharp).

   • If both players choose the same hand sign, it is a tie.

4. Players play 20 rounds. After each round, each player makes a mark in his or her tally chart to indicate either the winning sign or that the round ended in a tie.

Differentiation Options

READINESS Students may need to review making and counting tally marks. Making the tallies at the end of the game may be helpful:

▶ Players place counters instead of tallies in the columns of the table. At the end of the game, they make a tally mark for each counter to complete the tally chart. Show how tally marks are made in groups of 5.

ENRICHMENT

▶ Before copying Game Master 192, draw a line horizontally across each chart to make a row for "predictions." Explain to students that they should first predict how many times the winning sign will be in each category. Remind them that the total for their predictions should be 20. It might be helpful to provide students with 20 counters so that they can partition them into categories to help with their predictions. At the end of the game, players discuss how their predictions compare to the actual outcomes.

ELL SUPPORT Explain that sometimes people use *signs* to communicate or stand for something. Model some hand signs such as *come, stop,* and *silence,* and ask students to guess their meanings. Explain that they will play a game that uses hand signs to represent three objects—a rock, a piece of paper, and scissors. Model the signs and how to play the game. Have a volunteer complete a tally chart on the board to record how often each hand sign won.

Roll to 100

Strand Operations and Computation

Skill Mental addition; developing a winning game strategy

Materials (per group)

◆ Game Master 193 (Record Sheet)

◆ 2 dice

Players 2–4

Object of the game To score at least 100.

Grade 3

SRB
307

Games Across the Grades

Grades	PK	K	1	2	3	4	5	6
Advanced Learning			◆	◆				
Core Program					◆			
Reteaching and Practice						◆		

Directions

1. Players take turns rolling the dice any number of times.

2. Players mentally add all of the numbers they rolled and enter the totals as their scores for Turn 1.

Game Master 193 (p. 452)

3. If a player rolls a 1 at any time, his or her turn is over and 0 is entered as the score for Turn 1.

4. After the first turn, players start with their scores from the previous turn and mentally add on all of the numbers they roll. They enter their final sum as the score for this turn.

5. After the first turn, if players roll a 1 at any time, their turn is over and the score they enter is the same as the score for the previous turn.

6. The first player to score 100 or more wins.

Differentiation Options

READINESS Students may need to review strategies for mental addition. Using only 1-digit addends may be helpful:

▶ Players roll 1 die repeatedly on each turn.

ENRICHMENT

▶ Instead of adding the total on the dice for each roll, players add 10 times the total on the dice. For example, if a player rolls a 2 and a 3, he or she adds 50 to the score. The first player to reach 1,000 wins.

ELL SUPPORT Introduce the game and model how to play with two students. Make sure players understand how to fill in the Record Sheet. Emphasize that the students do *not* want to roll a 1 at any time and that every time they roll the dice, they take a risk that a 1 will be rolled.

GRADE 1

Rolling for 50

Games Across the Grades

Grades	PK	K	1	2	3	4	5	6
Advanced Learning	◆	◆						
Core Program			◆					
Reteaching and Practice				◆				

Strand Number and Numeration

Skill Using a number grid; counting forward and backward by 1s

Materials (per pair)

◆ *Rolling for 50* Gameboard (or Game Master 194)

◆ 1 die

◆ 2 counters

Players 2

Object of the game To reach 50.

Directions

1. Players put their counters on 0 on the game mat.

2. Players take turns rolling the die and using the table to see how many spaces and which direction to move.

3. The first player to reach 50 wins.

Game Master 194 (p. 453)

Differentiation Options

READINESS Students may need to explore the number grid with your guidance or review counting forward and backward. Counting in only one direction may be helpful:

▶ Players start at 0 and move their markers *only forward* the number of spaces shown on the die. When they are proficient at moving forward, players start at 50 and move their markers *only backward* the number of spaces on the die.

ENRICHMENT

▶ On the gameboard or Game Master 159, players can pick any number through 110 as the goal. Players may also choose to multiply some of the moves in the table by 10.

ELL SUPPORT Explain that each player will start at 0 and move his or her counter for each turn. The goal is to reach 50 first. Ask: *How many spaces will you move when it is your turn?* Explain that players will roll a die and look at the table to figure out how many spaces to move. Sometimes they will move forward and sometimes backward. With a student, model how to play.

GRADES 4–5 Rugs and Fences

Strand Measurement and Reference Frames

Skill Calculating area and perimeter

Materials (per pair)

◆ For Grade 4: *Rugs and Fences* Gameboard (or Game Master 195)

◆ For Grade 5: Game Master 195 (Record Sheet)

◆ Polygon Deck A, B, or C (or Game Master 196, 197, or 198)

◆ Area and Perimeter Cards (or Game Master 199)

Players 2

Object of the game To score more points.

Grade 4

SRB
260

Games Across the Grades

Grades	PK	K	1	2	3	4	5	6
Advanced Learning				◆	◆			
Core Program						◆	◆	
Reteaching and Practice								◆

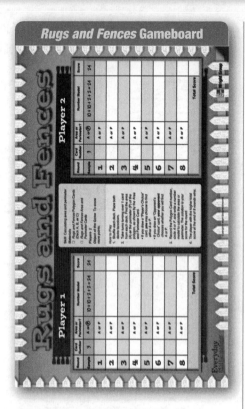

Rugs and Fences Gameboard

Game Master 195 (p. 454)

Directions

Advance Preparation: Before playing the game, choose one of the Polygon Decks based on students' abilities and experiences finding perimeter and area. The Polygon Decks provide practice in these skills:

- **Deck A:** Counting unit squares and sides of squares to find the area and perimeter of rectangles.
- **Deck B:** Using formulas to find the area and perimeter of rectangles, triangles, and parallelograms.
- **Deck C:** Using combinations of formulas to find the area and perimeter of irregular shapes.

When using Decks B and C, students should assume that sides that appear to be the same length are the same length and angles that appear to be right angles are right angles.

Solutions for each Polygon Deck:

Polygon Deck A			Polygon Deck B			Polygon Deck C		
Card	A	P	Card	A	P	Card	A	P
1	48	28	17	35	24	33	48	28
2	40	26	18	36	26	34	22	20
3	20	24	19	14	18	35	48	36
4	16	20	20	60	32	36	17	20
5	27	24	21	64	32	37	28	28
6	49	28	22	8	18	38	40	36
7	56	30	23	36	24	39	28	32
8	9	20	24	54	30	40	24	24
9	24	20	25	48	32	41	23	26
10	72	34	26	6	12	42	28	32
11	42	26	27	54	36	43	86	54
12	63	32	28	192	64	44	48	32
13	25	20	29	32	26	45	22	30
14	16	16	30	64	36	46	48	52
15	28	22	31	20	25	47	60	32
16	18	18	32	216	66	48	160	70

1. Players shuffle both decks and place them facedown side by side.
2. Players take turns drawing 1 card from each deck and placing them faceup. Players find the area (A) *or* the perimeter (P) of the polygon, as directed by the Area and Perimeter Card.

- If a "Player's Choice" card is drawn, the *player* may choose to find either the area or the perimeter.
- If an "Opponent's Choice" card is drawn, the *opposing player* chooses whether the area or the perimeter will be found.

3. The player records the Polygon Card number, circles A (area) or P (perimeter), and writes a number model to calculate the area or perimeter. The solution is the player's score for the round.

4. The player with the higher total score at the end of 8 rounds wins.

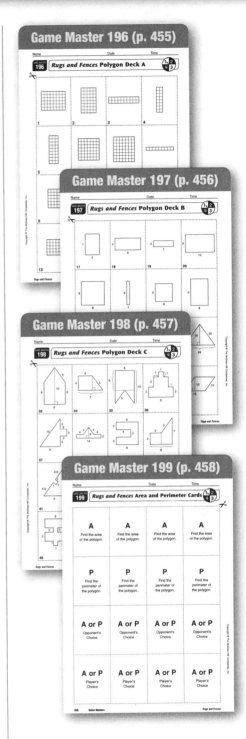

Game Master 196 (p. 455)

Game Master 197 (p. 456)

Game Master 198 (p. 457)

Game Master 199 (p. 458)

Example

Amy draws the 2 cards shown here. She may choose to calculate the area or the perimeter.

- Amy counts unit squares to find the area.
  Area = 20 square units
- Amy counts unit lengths around the polygon to find the perimeter.
  Perimeter = 24 units

Amy records card number 3 and circles P on her Record Sheet. She writes the number model $10 + 10 + 2 + 2 = 24$, and earns 24 points.

Parker draws the 2 cards shown here.

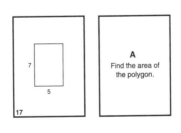

He finds the area of the polygon by using the formula $A = b * h.$ He records card number 17 and circles A on his Record Sheet. He writes the number model $5 * 7 = 35$, and earns 35 points.

Another Way to Play

Players combine 2 or 3 Polygon Decks.

Differentiation Options

READINESS Students may need to review strategies and formulas for finding perimeter or area. Calculating only area or perimeter throughout the game or having players make their own cards may also be helpful:

▶ Players use only Deck A and choose to calculate either area or perimeter on every turn.

▶ Players make their own version of Deck A by outlining rectangles on quarter-sheets of grid paper.

ENRICHMENT

▶ Players calculate both the area and the perimeter for each polygon. Their score is the combined total. The "A or P" cards become "double" cards; if the player is correct, his or her score is doubled.

▶ A player can earn 10 bonus points by drawing on grid paper a different polygon that has the same perimeter or area as their polygon.

ELL SUPPORT Draw a polygon from the Polygon Decks on the board. To help students understand the *"Player's Choice"* and *"Opponent's Choice"* cards, ask students to predict whether the area or perimeter of the polygon is larger and to explain their thinking. Find the area and perimeter of the polygon and discuss predictions. Model how to complete the Record Sheet.

GRADES 5–6

Scientific Notation Toss

Games Across the Grades									
Grades	PK	K	1	2	3	4	5	6
Advanced Learning						◆		
Core Program							◆	◆
Reteaching and Practice								

Strand Number and Numeration

Skill Converting from scientific notation to standard notation; comparing and ordering numbers

Materials (per pair)

◆ Game Master 200 (Record Sheets, 2 copies)

◆ 2 dice

Players 2

Object of the game To create the largest number written in scientific notation.

Grade 5   Grade 6
SRB 329   SRB 331

Directions

1. Each player rolls both dice 3 times. The player uses each roll of 2 dice to write an expression in scientific notation. One of the numbers is used to name a power of 10. The other number is used to multiply that power of 10: $\square * 10^{\square}$.

Game Master 200 (p. 459)

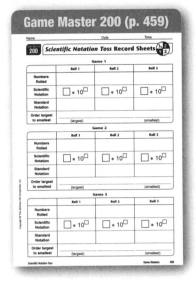

Example

A 5 and a 4 are rolled.

Either $\boxed{4} * 10^{\boxed{5}}$ or $\boxed{5} * 10^{\boxed{4}}$ can be written for Roll 1.

2. Players convert their numbers from scientific notation to standard notation. Then each player orders his or her numbers from largest to smallest.

3. Players compare lists. The player who has the largest number wins. In case of a tie, they roll a fourth time.

Example

Ann rolls:	2 and 4	5 and 3	1 and 6
writes:	$2 * 10^4$	$3 * 10^5$	$1 * 10^6$
	$= 2 * 10,000$	$= 3 * 100,000$	$= 1 * 1,000,000$
	$= 20,000$	$= 300,000$	$= 1,000,000$

orders: 1,000,000; 300,000; 20,000

Keith rolls:	5 and 5	2 and 1	4 and 3
writes:	$5 * 10^5$	$1 * 10^2$	$3 * 10^4$
	$= 5 * 100,000$	$= 1 * 100$	$= 3 * 10,000$
	$= 500,000$	$= 100$	$= 30,000$

orders: 500,000; 30,000; 100

Ann's largest number is greater than Keith's largest number. Ann wins.

Advanced Version

Players use 2 twelve-sided dice or 4 six-sided dice. If players use 4 dice, they should first add the results on pairs of dice. A dice roll of 11 and 9 generates either $9 * 10^{11}$ or $11 * 10^9$.

Differentiation Options

READINESS Students may need to review the meaning of scientific notation. Using organizing tools may be helpful:

▶ Provide $\square * 10^{\square}$ templates for players to fill in as they roll the dice, and place-value charts through the ten-millions place to use as they write the numbers in standard notation.

ENRICHMENT

▶ Players roll four dice and use two numbers as powers of 10 and two numbers to multiply the powers of 10. For example, if a player rolls 3, 4, 6 and 2, he or she could write $3 * 4 * 10^6 * 10^2$ or $6 * 2 * 10^3 * 10^4$.

ELL SUPPORT Write $5 * 10^6$ and $6 * 10^5$ on the board. Discuss which number is larger. Explain that students will play a game in which they roll two dice. They will use the two numbers they roll to create a number written in scientific notation. Write $\square * 10^{\square}$ on the board. Roll two dice and ask a volunteer to fill in the boxes with the numbers rolled. Ask: *Could you create a larger number with these dice rolls? Why or why not?* Introduce the game and model how to play.

GRADE 4 — Seega

Games Across the Grades									
Grades	PK	K	1	2	3	4	5	6	
Advanced Learning					◆				
Core Program						◆			
Reteaching and Practice							◆	◆	

Strand Data and Chance

Skill Developing a winning game strategy

Materials (per pair)
- ◆ Game Master 201 (game mat)
- ◆ 6 counters (3 each of 2 colors)

Players 2

Object of the game To place 3 counters in a straight line horizontally, vertically, or diagonally.

Grade 4
SRB
309

Player 1

Player 2

Directions

1. Each player takes 3 counters of the same color. Players place their counters on opposite ends of the game mat.

2. Players take turns moving one of their counters 1 or 2 squares.

- A counter can be moved to any open square that is next to it. Diagonal moves are allowed.

- A counter can be moved two squares in any one direction to an open square. Diagonal moves are allowed, but a change in direction during the move is *not* allowed. Jumping over another counter is also *not* allowed.

> **NOTE:** This is a version of a traditional Egyptian game that is popular among young Egyptians today.

Example

Moves allowed:

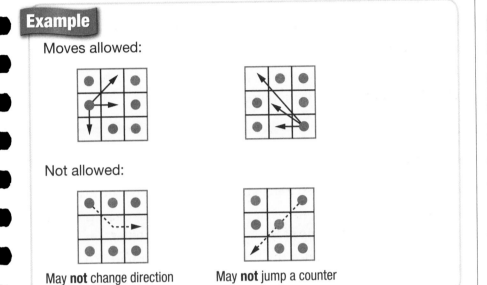

Not allowed:

May **not** change direction   May **not** jump a counter

Game Master 201 (p. 460)

3. The first player to get his or her counters in a straight line wins. The line may be horizontal, vertical, or diagonal, but it may not be the player's starting line.

Differentiation Options

READINESS Students may need to see moves that are and are not allowed before playing the game. Adding another rule may also be helpful:

▶ Model appropriate horizontal, vertical, and diagonal moves. Then model moves that are *not* allowed.

▶ Once during a game, a player's counter may jump over any other counter.

ENRICHMENT

▶ Players use a 4-by-4 gameboard and 4 counters each.

ELL SUPPORT Introduce the game. Draw examples of moves that are allowed and are not allowed on the board. Show examples of winning boards including *horizontal,* *vertical,* and *diagonal* wins.

GRADE
3

Shading Shapes

Games Across the Grades								
Grades	PK	K	1	2	3	4	5	6
Advanced Learning				◆				
Core Program					◆			
Reteaching and Practice						◆	◆	

Strand Geometry

Skill Identifying quadrangles; exploring quadrangle properties

Materials (per pair)

◆ *Shading Shapes* Gameboard (or Game Masters 202 and 203)

◇ 2 different colors of markers (or pencils)

Players 2

Object of the game To claim more quadrangles.

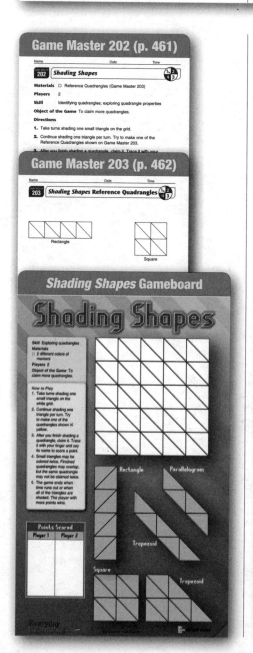

Game Master 202 (p. 461)

Game Master 203 (p. 462)

Shading Shapes Gameboard

Directions

1. Players take turns shading one small triangle on the grid.

2. In the following turns, each player shades one more triangle in order to make one of the reference quadrangles.

3. When a player shades the final triangle of a reference quadrangle, that player claims the quadrangle by tracing it with a finger and saying its name. The player scores a point and that quadrangle is no longer available.

4. Finished quadrangles may overlap each other (the same small triangle may be shaded twice), but a player cannot shade exactly the same quadrangle once it has been claimed.

5. The game ends when time runs out or when all of the triangles are shaded. The player with more points wins.

Differentiation Options

READINESS Students may need to study and describe the reference shapes before playing. Allow players to focus on one or two types of quadrangles:

▶ Players may shade and identify the same reference shape more than once. To score a point the second time a shape is drawn, the player must identify the shape on the grid that is the same as the shape he or she drew.

ENRICHMENT

▶ Players shade and identify *any* shapes made up of at least 4, but no more than 8 triangles. You may want to list polygons players may choose.

ELL SUPPORT Shade the reference quadrangles on a sample grid. Explain that students will shade triangles in order to create these shapes. As you name each shape, point to the example on your grid. Emphasize that students will shade only one triangle per turn. Model how to play. Demonstrate the meaning of *claiming a quadrangle* while you play.

GRADES 1–2

Shaker Addition Top-It

Strands Number and Numeration; Operations and Computation

Skill Addition facts; comparing numbers

Materials (per group)

◆ Game Master 204 (Record Sheet, optional, 1 per player)

◆ 2 six-sided dice (or 2 polyhedral dice)

◆ counters for scoring

Players 2–5

Object of the game To collect the most counters.

Games Across the Grades

Grades	PK	K	1	2	3	4	5	6
Advanced Learning		◆						
Core Program			◆	◆				
Reteaching and Practice						◆	◆	

Directions

1. For each round, players take turns rolling the dice, adding the numbers, and stating the sum.

2. Saying the wrong sum disqualifies a player for that round. A disqualified player may still check others' responses.

3. The player with the highest sum for each round takes a counter from the pile. If there is a tie, the tied players each take a counter.

4. The player with the most counters at the end of a given time period wins.

NOTE: Players can use Game Master 204 to record their addition facts.

Game Master 204 (p. 463)

Differentiation Options

READINESS Students may need to review strategies for addition and for recalling facts. Keeping one addend constant may be helpful:

▶ Players choose one addend, such as 5, to use throughout the game. A player rolls one die on each turn to generate a second addend.

ENRICHMENT

▶ For each round, players sit in a circle. They agree on a number as their target sum. One after another, they roll a die. The group works together to find the cumulative total after each roll until the total passes the target sum set before play began.

ELL SUPPORT Explain that *Top-It* is an expression that means "beat that." For example, a sum of 12 "tops" a sum of 8. Introduce the game. Explain that in this game, students want to roll the *highest sum;* discuss the meaning of this term. Model a few turns with a small group and explain what to do in case of a tie.

GRADE Pre-K · Shape Concentration

Games Across the Grades									
Grades	PK	K	1	2	3	4	5	6	
Advanced Learning									
Core Program	◆								
Reteaching and Practice		◆	◆						

Strands Geometry; Patterns, Functions, and Algebra

Skill Identifying and naming basic geometric shapes; recognizing and matching attributes of geometric shapes

Materials (per group)

◆ Game Masters 205–207 (shape cards, 2 copies of each)

Players 2–4

Object of the game To collect the most cards.

Game Master 205 (p. 464)

Game Master 206 (p. 465)

Game Master 207 (p. 466)

Directions

1. Players select 4 matching pairs of Shape Cards: 2 identical triangles, 2 identical squares, 2 identical circles, and 2 identical rectangles.

2. One player shuffles these cards and places them facedown in 2 rows.

3. Players take turns turning over 2 cards at a time.

   - If the shapes on the cards match, the player names the shapes. If the shapes are correctly identified, the player keeps both cards. If he or she is incorrect, the cards are replaced facedown. The player's turn is over.

   - If the cards do not match, the player replaces the cards facedown and his or her turn is over.

4. Play continues until all of the cards have been matched.

Differentiation Options

READINESS Students may need to review attributes of the shapes on the cards. A practice round may be helpful:

▶ Players practice with all of the cards faceup. They talk about the attributes they use to make their matches.

ENRICHMENT

▶ Create cards for other shapes, such as ovals and rhombuses (diamonds), and add them to the deck.

ELL SUPPORT Explain that *concentration* means the students will have to pay attention and try to remember where specific shapes are located. Remembering will help them in future turns. Model how to play the game with several students. Discuss the meaning of *match* in this context.

2—3 Soccer Spin

Strand Data and Chance

Skill Predicting outcomes of events

Materials (per pair)

◆ Game Masters 208 and 209 (3 spinners and game mat)

◆ 1 counter

◆ 1 transparent spinner (or a paper clip and pencil)

Players 2

Object of the game To test the prediction made at the beginning of the game.

Games Across the Grades

Grades	PK	K	1	2	3	4	5	6
Advanced Learning			◆					
Core Program				◆	◆			
Reteaching and Practice						◆	◆	◆

Directions

1. Players agree on one spinner face to use for the round. Players may hold or tape the transparent spinner in place over the spinner face, or use a paper clip and pencil to make a spinner.

2. Each player chooses a team to cheer for, **Checks** or **Stripes.** (Players can cheer for the same team.) They look at their spinner choice and predict which team will win the game.

3. The game begins with the counter in the center of the field.

4. Players take turns spinning and moving the counter one space toward the goal that comes up on the spinner.

5. The game is over when the counter reaches a goal.

6. Players compare and discuss the results of their predictions.

7. Players play two more rounds using the other spinners.

Game Master 208 (p. 467)

Game Master 209 (p. 468)

Differentiation Options

READINESS Students may need to review probability concepts and predicting the outcomes of events. Tallying the results of each spin may be helpful:

▶ Players use each spinner for one game and tally the results of each spin.

ENRICHMENT

▶ Players design spinners to match a given prediction.

ELL SUPPORT Discuss the meaning of *prediction* using sports contexts. Ask: *What information can you use to predict whether a team will win? When we use a spinner, how can we predict where the spinner will land?* Introduce the game. Explain that the counter will move one space closer to the goal that matches the section that the spinner lands on. Analyze the spinner with students and model how to make a prediction about which team will win.

GRADE 6

Solution Search

Games Across the Grades									
Grades	PK	K	1	2	3	4	5	6	
Advanced Learning								◆	
Core Program								◆	
Reteaching and Practice									

Strands Operations and Computation; Patterns, Functions, and Algebra

Skill Identifying a solution to an inequality

Materials (per group)

◆ *Solution Search* Cards (or Game Master 210)

◆ Everything Math Deck

Players 3 or 4

Object of the game To discard all cards.

Grade 6

SRB
332

Game Master 210 (p. 469)

Name	Date	Time

210 | Solution Search **Cards**

$q + 2 > 20$	$m < 3.5$	$y^2 < 5$	$6 < x$
$q + 2 > 20$	$m < 3.5$	$y^2 < 5$	$6 < x$
$q + 2 > 20$	$m < 3.5$	$y^2 < 5$	$x > 9$
$b < 6$	$5 \neq s$	$100 / k > 25$	$(9 \cdot z) + 2 > 65$
$b < 6$	$5 \neq s$	$100 / k > 25$	$(9 \cdot z) + 2 > 65$
$b < 6$	$5 \neq s$	$100 / k > 25$	$(9 \cdot z) + 2 > 65$
$49 \leq p^2$	$r / 2 \geq 5$	$w - 3 < 2$	$-2 + a \geq 5$
$49 \leq p^2$	$r / 2 \geq 5$	$w - 3 < 2$	$-2 + a \geq 5$
$49 \leq p^2$	$r / 2 \geq 5$	$w - 3 < 2$	$-2 + a \geq 5$
$\sqrt{25} \leq t$	$10 < 50 / d$	$c + 7 \leq 14$	$81 > f^2$
$\sqrt{25} \leq t$	$10 < 50 / d$	$c + 7 \leq 14$	$81 > f^2$
$\sqrt{25} \leq t$	$10 < 50 / d$	$c + 7 \leq 14$	$81 > f^2$

Solution Search | Game Masters 469

Directions

1. One player shuffles and stacks the *Solution Search* Cards facedown.

2. A second player shuffles the number cards, deals 8 cards to each player, and stacks the rest whole-number side down.

3. Player 1 begins the first round by turning over the top *Solution Search* Card. He or she discards any one of his or her number cards that is a solution of the inequality. If Player 1 does not have a card that shows a solution, he or she draws number cards until a solution card is drawn, and then discards that card.

4. Play continues in a clockwise direction, with each player discarding a number card that shows a solution of the inequality on the faceup *Solution Search* Card. The round is over when each player has had a turn.

5. The player who takes the last turn in a round begins the next round. Players follow Steps 3 and 4 to play another round.

6. When all of the *Solution Search* Cards have been used, one player turns the pile facedown and, without shuffling, takes the next card. When no more number cards remain, another player shuffles the discard pile and places it whole-number side down. Play continues.

7. The first player to discard all of his or her cards wins.

Another Way to Play

Twos and 7s are special cards. Twos are WILD, and a player may assign any value to the 2 card. The value of the 7 card is always 7. However, if a player plays the 7 card, the next player loses his or her turn.

Differentiation Options

READINESS Students may benefit from a review of representing inequalities on number lines. Using inequalities with only the four basic operations may also be helpful:

▶ Players make their own set of *Solution Search* Cards. Each player makes four inequality cards—one each for addition, subtraction, multiplication, and division. The missing number for each card must be between 1 and 20.

ENRICHMENT

▶ Players multiply or divide one of the numbers on the *Solution Search* Card by 10, and they may use a product or quotient of two number cards as a solution.

ELL SUPPORT Write an inequality from a *Solution Search* Card on the board. Have students list examples of solutions of the inequality. Introduce the game and model how to play with 3 students. Emphasize that students should test each card as a solution before drawing another card.

GRADES

PK—K Spin a Number

Strand Number and Numeration

Skill Counting and reading numbers 1–10

Materials (per group)

◆ *Spin a Number* Gameboard (or Game Master 211)

◆ 1 transparent spinner (or a paper clip and pencil)

◆ 1 counter per player

Players 2–5

Object of the game To reach the End.

Games Across the Grades

Grades	PK	K	1	2	3	4	5	6
Advanced Learning								
Core Program	◆	◆						
Reteaching and Practice			◆					

Directions

Advance Preparation: Tape the transparent spinner in place over the spinner face. Alternatively, players may use the paper clip and pencil to make a spinner. (See the picture on Game Master 2.)

1. Each player puts a counter on the arrow marked "Start."

2. Players take turns spinning and moving that number of spaces on the path.

3. The game ends when one player reaches the space marked "End."

NOTE: The path on Game Master 211 is approximately half as long as the gameboard path. Use Game Master 211 for a shorter game.

Game Master 211 (p. 470)

Spin a Number Gameboard

Another Way to Play

A player must roll an exact number to reach the End.

Differentiation Options

READINESS Students may need to review numeral recognition and counting through 10. Using smaller numbers may be helpful:

▶ Change the numbers on the spinner so that each number from 1–5 appears twice. (You may also want to shorten the path.)

ENRICHMENT

▶ Change the spinner to show higher numbers. Players must reach the end and then return to the beginning of the path to win.

▶ Mark 1 and 3 on the spinner with a minus (−) sign to indicate that players should go back that many spaces. Mark the other numbers with a plus (+) sign.

ELL SUPPORT With a student, model how to play. Ask: *How many spaces will you move when it is your turn?* Check that students understand that they will spin a spinner and move the number of spaces shown on the spinner. For Another Way to Play, show what it means to *roll an exact number.*

Spinning for Money

Games Across the Grades								
Grades	PK	K	1	2	3	4	5	6
Advanced Learning		◆	◆					
Core Program				◆	◆			
Reteaching and Practice						◆		

Strands Measurement and Reference Frames

Skill Exchanging coins and dollar bills

Materials (per group)

◆ *Spinning for Money* Gameboard (or Game Master 212)

◆ 7 pennies, 5 nickels, 5 dimes, 4 quarters, and one $1 bill per player

◆ 1 transparent spinner (or a paper clip and pencil)

Players 2–4

Object of the game To exchange for a $1 bill.

Directions

1. Players put all of the money in a "bank" between them.

2. Players take turns spinning the spinner and taking the coins shown from the bank.

3. Whenever possible, players exchange coins for fewer coins, a single coin, or a bill of the same value.

4. The first player to exchange for a $1 bill wins.

Differentiation Options

READINESS Students may need to review coin values and exchanges. Making all of the exchanges at once may also be helpful:

▶ Each player puts 15 pennies, 10 nickels, 10 dimes, and 4 quarters in the bank. They do not make exchanges during the game. Instead, they calculate and record their total at the end of 5 spins and then exchange their coins for the fewest possible coins. Then they calculate and record their total again. The player with the most money wins.

ENRICHMENT

▶ To include mixed coin combinations, players draw 2 pennies, 2 nickels, and 2 dimes anywhere on the spinner. For example, they add a penny and a nickel to the section with 2 dimes.

ELL SUPPORT Discuss the words *bank* and *exchange.* Explain that *bank* has many different meanings. For example, it may refer to a container, usually with a slot in the top, for keeping money at home; or to a building where money is saved. Model exchanging coins. Ask students to identify examples of coin exchanges. With a student, model how to play.

Game Master 212 (p. 471)

212 *Spinning for Money* Spinner

Spinning for Money Gameboard

GRADE 3

Spinning to Win

Strand Data and Chance

Skill Using chance data to develop a winning game strategy

Materials (per group)
- ◆ Game Master 213 (directions and spinner face)
- ◆ 50 counters
- ◆ 1 transparent spinner (or a paper clip and pencil)

Players 2–4

Object of the game To collect the most counters.

Grade 3

SRB

309

Games Across the Grades								
Grades	PK	K	1	2	3	4	5	6
Advanced Learning			◆	◆				
Core Program					◆			
Reteaching and Practice						◆		

NOTE: Players may hold or tape the transparent spinner in place over the spinner face, or use a paper clip and pencil to make a spinner.

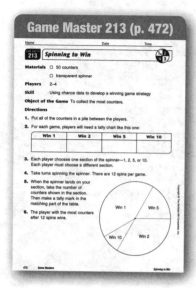

Game Master 213 (p. 472)

Name _____ Date _____ Time _____

213 | **Spinning to Win**

Materials ☐ 50 counters
☐ transparent spinner

Players 2–4

Skill Using chance data to develop a winning game strategy

Object of the Game To collect the most counters.

Directions

1. Put all of the counters in a pile between the players.

2. For each game, players will need a tally chart like this one:

Win 1	Win 2	Win 5	Win 10

3. Each player chooses one section of the spinner—1, 2, 5, or 10. Each player must choose a different section.

4. Take turns spinning the spinner. There are 12 spins per game.

5. When the spinner lands on your section, take the number of counters shown in the section. Then make a tally mark in the matching part of the table.

6. The player with the most counters after 12 spins wins.

472   Game Masters   Spinning to Win

Directions

1. One player puts all of the counters in a pile between the players.

2. For each game, players use this tally chart on Game Master 213:

Win 1	Win 2	Win 5	Win 10

3. Each player claims one section of the spinner—1, 2, 5, or 10. Each player must choose a different section.

4. Players take turns spinning the spinner. In all, there are 12 spins per game.

5. When the spinner lands on a section claimed by a player, the player who chose that section takes the number of counters shown. The player makes a tally mark in the table to show the result of that spin and to keep track of the number of spins.

6. The player with the most counters after 12 spins wins.

Differentiation Options

READINESS Students may need to review making and comparing tally marks. Encouraging students to think explicitly about probability may also be helpful:

▶ After choosing a section, each player predicts how many times (in 12 spins) that section will be spun. Have players share their predictions and make a joint prediction about who will win the most counters. At the end of the game, players discuss how their predictions compare to their results.

ENRICHMENT

▶ Players cooperate to design a spinner showing wins of 1–5 counters. Their goal is to make their spinner as fair as possible. Make sure students understand that in this instance, "fair" does not mean an equal chance of *spinning,* but rather an equal chance of *winning.* After 12 spins, players compare their numbers of counters and use the tally table to redesign the spinner if necessary. Suggest that they record their thinking as they make adjustments to the spinner.

ELL SUPPORT Show students the spinner. Explain that the pointer will land on one of the sections. Discuss which section the pointer is most likely to land on and which section it is least likely to land on. Make sure students understand that even though it is least likely to land on *Win 10,* if it does, the player takes the greatest possible number of counters. Introduce the game and model how to complete the tally chart.

Spoon Scramble

GRADES 5–6

Strand Number and Numeration; Operations and Computation

Skill Multiplying fractions, decimals, and percents

Materials (per group)

◆ For Grade 5: *Spoon Scramble* Card Deck A (or Game Master 214)

◆ For Grade 6: *Spoon Scramble* Card Deck B or C (or Game Master 215 or 216)

◇ 3 spoons

Players 4

Object of the game To avoid getting all of the letters in the word *SPOONS*.

Grade 5 SRB 330 Grade 6 SRB 333

Games Across the Grades

Grades	PK	K	1	2	3	4	5	6
Advanced Learning							◆	
Core Program							◆	◆
Reteaching and Practice								

Directions

1. Players sit in a circle and put the spoons in the center.

2. The dealer shuffles the deck and deals 4 cards number-side down to each player.

3. Players look at their cards. If a player has 4 cards of equal value, he or she goes on to Step 5. Otherwise, each player chooses a card to pass, number-side down, to the player on his or her left.

4. Each player picks up the new card and repeats Step 3. The passing of the cards should proceed quickly.

5. As soon as a player has 4 cards of equal value, the player places the cards number-side up on the table and grabs a spoon.

6. The other players then try to grab one of the 2 remaining spoons. The player left without a spoon is assigned a letter from the word *SPOONS*, starting with the first letter. Players then check the values on the 4 faceup cards. If a player incorrectly claimed to have 4 cards of equal value, that player receives a letter instead of the player left without a spoon.

7. A new round begins. Players put the spoons back in the center of the table, return their cards to the dealer, and repeat Steps 2–6.

8. Play continues until 3 players have each gotten all of the letters in the word *SPOONS*. The player who does not have all of the letters wins.

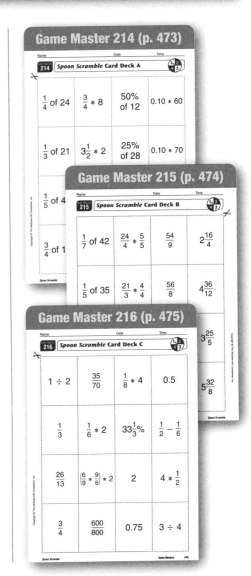

Other Ways to Play

- For 3 players, eliminate one set of 4 equivalent *Spoon Scramble* cards and use only 2 spoons.

- Players can make their own deck of *Spoon Scramble* cards. Each player writes 4 computation problems that have equivalent answers on 4 index cards. (Players need to verify that the sets of cards have different values.) All players should use the same writing tool and write the expression in the same place on each card. Have groups trade their sets of cards so players cannot look for their own set as they play.

Differentiation Options

READINESS Students may need to review identifying equivalent names for numbers and using the operations on the cards. Making name-collection boxes may be helpful:

▶ Each player makes a name-collection box for either a fraction or a whole number and then makes a set of *Spoon Scramble* cards using four expressions from their name-collection boxes.

ENRICHMENT

▶ Each player makes a set of cards for a mixed number. The set includes a fraction name, a decimal name, a percent name, and an addition or subtraction number sentence.

ELL SUPPORT Ask students if they have ever played musical chairs. Discuss how the game is played. Explain that *Spoon Scramble* is played with spoons and is similar to musical chairs. In musical chairs, a person grabs a chair when the music stops, but in this game, students will grab a spoon when someone shows that they have 4 cards of equal value. Point out that there will be 4 players, but only 3 spoons. Players will "scramble" to grab a spoon. The player who doesn't grab a spoon will be assigned a letter. In this game, players do *not* want to get letters. With 3 volunteers, model how to play.

Spreadsheet Scramble

Strand Operations and Computation

Skill Adding positive and negative numbers

Materials (per pair)

◆ *Spreadsheet Scramble* Gameboard (or Game Master 217)

Players 2

Object of the game To score more points.

Grade 6
SRB
334

Games Across the Grades

Grades	PK	K	1	2	3	4	5	6
Advanced Learning							◆	
Core Program								◆
Reteaching and Practice								

Directions

1. Player 1 uses the positive numbers 1, 2, 3, 4, 5, and 6. Player 2 uses the negative numbers −1, −2, −3, −4, −5, and −6.

2. Player 1 begins the game. Players take turns writing one of their numbers in a cell within the 3-by-4 rectangle outlined on the spreadsheet. Once a player has written a number, it cannot be used again.

3. After all 12 numbers have been used, players fill in Total cells F2, F3, and F4 by adding across each row. For example, F2 = B2 + C2 + D2 + E2. Players fill in Total cells B5, C5, D5, and E5 by adding down each column. For example C5 = C2 + C3 + C4.

4. Seven cells show row and column totals: F2, F3, F4, B5, C5, D5, and E5. Player 1 gets one point for each cell that has a positive total. Player 2 gets one point for each cell that has a negative total. Neither player gets a point for a cell that has 0. The player with more points wins.

Example

Player 1 gets 1 point each for cells F3, F4, and C5.

Player 2 gets 1 point each for F2 and E5.

Player 1 wins the game, 3 points to 2 points.

	A	B	C	D	E	F
1						Total
2		−1	−6	3	−5	−9
3		4	2	−4	6	+8
4		−3	5	1	−2	+1
5	Total	0	+1	0	−1	

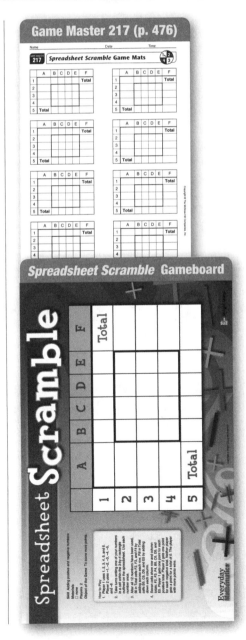

Game Master 217 (p. 476)

Spreadsheet Scramble Gameboard

Differentiation Options

READINESS Students may need to review number-line models for adding positive and negative numbers. Using color-coded numbers, a calculator, and simpler numbers may also be helpful:

▶ Each player writes in a different color. One player enters all 6 of his or her numbers, and then the other player enters his or hers. Players take turns being the first player in a round. At the end of a round, they use a calculator to find the totals.

▶ Player 1 uses 5, 5, 5, 10, 10, and 10. Player 2 uses −5, −5, −5, −10, −10, and −10.

ENRICHMENT

▶ Each player gets twelve number cards (two each of the digits 4–9). Players shuffle their cards. For each turn, a player draws two cards, makes a 2-digit number, and writes the 2-digit number (positive or negative according to the player's assignment) in the spreadsheet.

▶ Before finding the totals, each player chooses two cells to multiply by 10. Players can write their choices down secretly at the same time so that neither player has an advantage. When players find totals, the numbers in those cells are multiplied by 10.

ELL SUPPORT Show students a spreadsheet. Point out *columns, rows,* and *cells.* Tell students that there are multiple meanings for *cell.* Explain the meaning of *cell* in this mathematical context and how cells are read; for example, F2 and not 2F. Introduce the game, model how to play it with a student, and discuss game strategies.

GRADE 4 — Sprouts

Games Across the Grades									
Grades	PK	K	1	2	3	4	5	6
Advanced Learning					◆			
Core Program						◆		
Reteaching and Practice							◆	◆

Strand Geometry

Skill Drawing line segments, curves, and points; developing a winning game strategy

Materials (per pair)

◇ paper and pencil

Players 2

Object of the game To draw the last connecting line segment or curve.

Grade 4
SRB
313

Directions

1. One player draws 3 dots that are widely spaced apart.

2. Players take turns drawing a line segment or curve connecting any two dots. Players may also join a dot to itself.

3. A player completes his or her turn by drawing another dot anywhere on the new line or curve.

4. Players must follow these rules when drawing the connectors:

   - No line (or curve) may cross itself.

   - No line (or curve) may cross any other line (or curve) that has been drawn.

   - No line (or curve) may be drawn through a dot.

   - A dot can have no more that 3 lines (or curves) coming from it. A good way to keep track of this is to draw a box around any dot that has 3 lines (or curves) coming from it. (See the example.)

5. The last player who is able to draw a connecting line (or curve) wins.

NOTE: As players progress, they can begin the game with more dots.

Example

Sample play (for an incomplete game)

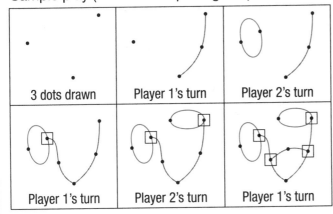

3 dots drawn	Player 1's turn	Player 2's turn
Player 1's turn	Player 2's turn	Player 1's turn

Differentiation Options

READINESS Students may need help in developing winning strategies. Adding the following rule may be helpful:

▶ Once during the game, a player may end his or her turn by drawing a point that does *not* lie on the line (or curve) he or she drew.

ENRICHMENT

▶ On each turn, a player must begin from the dot his or her partner drew.

ELL SUPPORT As you introduce and model the game, draw pictures on the board to represent each rule. Discuss and model the meanings of *lines* and *curves* as well as *crossing a line.*

GRADES 4–5 Subtraction Target Practice

Games Across the Grades									
Grades	PK	K	1	2	3	4	5	6	
Advanced Learning				◆	◆				
Core Program						◆	◆		
Reteaching and Practice								◆	

Strand Operations and Computation

Skill 2- and 3-digit subtraction

Materials (per group)
- ◆ Everything Math Deck (number cards 0–9, 4 of each)
- ◇ 1 calculator per player
- ◇ scratch paper

Players 1 or more

Object of the game To get as close as possible to 0, without going below it.

Grade 4 · SRB 262   Grade 5 · SRB 331

NOTE: For a 1-player game, the player finds his or her score for the first game, and then tries to get closer to 0 in each subsequent game.

Directions

1. One player shuffles and stacks the cards whole-number side down. Each player writes 250 on scratch paper.

2. Each player takes 5 turns. For Turn 1, each player turns over the top 2 cards and makes a 2-digit number. (The digits can be in either order.) Each player subtracts his or her 2-digit number from 250 on scratch paper and then checks the answer on a calculator.

3. For Turns 2–5, each player takes 2 cards and makes a 2-digit number. Each player subtracts this number from the result obtained in the previous subtraction and checks the answer on a calculator.

4. The player with a final result that is closest to 0, without going below 0, wins. If the final results for all players are below 0, no one wins.

Example

Turn 1: Draw 4 and 5. Subtract 45 or 54. $250 - 45 = 205$

Turn 2: Draw 0 and 6. Subtract 6 or 60. $205 - 60 = 145$

Turn 3: Draw 4 and 1. Subtract 41 or 14. $145 - 41 = 104$

Turn 4: Draw 3 and 2. Subtract 32 or 23. $104 - 23 = 81$

Turn 5: Draw 6 and 8. Subtract 68 or 86. $81 - 68 = 13$

Another Way to Play

Each player starts at 100 instead of 250.

Advanced Version

To practice decimal subtraction, players start at 20 and use a penny or a counter as a decimal point in the numbers they make. Each number should have one digit in the ones place and one digit in the tenths place.

Differentiation Options

READINESS Students may need to review regrouping in subtraction. Subtracting only multiples of 10 or 1-digit numbers may be helpful:

▶ Players turn over one card on each turn. They choose to subtract that number or that many tens from their total. For example, a player who turns over a 3 may subtract either 3 or 30.

ENRICHMENT

▶ Players draw two cards and either subtract a 2-digit number that they make with the cards or subtract the sum of the two cards from their total.

ELL SUPPORT Explain to students that in this game, the *target* is the number that they want to reach, which is 0 or very close to 0. If they end with a number below 0, they will lose. Explain that players will start at 250 and subtract five 2-digit numbers to reach the target. Write 250 at the top of two columns on the board. Label one column *Subtract larger 2-digit number* and the other column *Subtract smaller 2-digit number*. Draw two cards and model making the two 2-digit numbers. Record the subtraction sentences in each column. Repeat four more times. Ask: *Which column is closer to 0 without going below 0? Do you always want to subtract the larger number? Why or why not?*

Subtraction Top-It

Strand Number and Numeration; Operations and Computation

Skill Subtraction

Materials (per group)

◆ Everything Math Deck

Players 2–4

Object of the game To collect the most cards.

Grades 1–2

MRB 148

Grade 3

SRB 310

Grade 4

SRB 263

Grade 5
SRB 333

Games Across the Grades

Grades	PK	K	1	2	3	4	5	6
Advanced Learning		◆						
Core Program			◆	◆	◆	◆	◆	
Reteaching and Practice								◆

NOTE: Players can use Game Master 4 to record and compare their numbers.

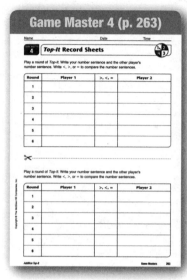

Game Master 4 (p. 263)

Subtraction Facts 0 to 10 (recommended for Grades 1–2)

Directions

1. Players use 4 each of the cards numbered 0–10. One player shuffles and stacks the cards whole-number side down.
2. Each player turns over 2 cards and subtracts the smaller number from the larger number.
3. The player with the largest difference wins the round and takes all of the cards.
4. In case of a tie for the largest difference, each tied player turns over 2 more cards and calls out the difference of the numbers. The player with the largest difference then takes all of the cards from both plays.
5. The game ends when not enough cards are left for each player to have another turn. The player with the most cards wins.

Another Way to Play

Players use dominoes instead of cards. (See *Domino Top-It.*)

Subtraction Facts 0–20 (recommended for Grade 3)

Directions

Players use the entire Everything Math Deck.

Another Way to Play

Players use a regular six-sided die and a polyhedral die with numbers 1–20. They roll both dice and subtract the smaller number from the larger one.

Three Cards (recommended for Grades 4–5)

Directions

Players use 4 each of the cards numbered 1–10. Each player turns over 3 cards, finds the sum of any 2 of the numbers, and then finds the difference between the sum and the third number. (Players always subtract the smaller number from the larger one.) The player with the largest difference takes all of the cards.

Advanced Version

Players use two polyhedral dice with numbers 1–20. They roll both dice and subtract the smaller number from the larger one.

Subtracting 2-Digit Numbers (recommended for Grades 4–5)

Directions

Players use 4 each of the number cards 1–9. Each player turns over 4 cards, forms two 2-digit numbers, and finds their difference. Players should carefully consider how they form their numbers. For example, 75 − 24 has a greater difference than 57 − 42 or 74 − 25.

Differentiation Options

READINESS Students may need to review strategies for subtraction. Limiting the range of subtrahends may be helpful:

▶ Players choose one number to subtract throughout the game. A player draws one card and subtracts the constant from the number on the card. For example, if 2 is the constant and a player draws an 8, the problem is 8 − 2.

ENRICHMENT

▶ Just before subtracting, players draw one extra card and use it as a digit in one of the numbers they formed.

ELL SUPPORT Explain that *Top-It* is an expression meaning "beat that." For example, a card showing 14 "tops" a card showing 13. If necessary, discuss the meaning of *difference.* Introduce the game and model how to play, explaining what to do in case of a tie.

GRADE 4 Sz'kwa

Strand Geometry

Skill Identifying intersections; developing a winning game strategy

Materials (per pair)

◆ Game Master 218 (game mat)

◆ 40 counters (20 each of two different colors)

Players 2

Object of the game To capture more counters.

Grade 4

SRB
310

Games Across the Grades								
Grades	PK	K	1	2	3	4	5	6
Advanced Learning					◆			
Core Program							◆	
Reteaching and Practice							◆	◆

NOTE: This is a Chinese children's game. Its name means "the game of four directions." In China, the game mat is often marked in the dirt or gravel; pebbles, nuts, or shells are used as counters.

Game Master 218 (p. 477)

Directions

1. Each player takes 20 counters of the same color.

2. The game mat has 21 places called "intersections," where lines and/or curves meet. Players take turns placing one counter on any intersection that is not already covered by a counter.

3. A counter is captured when all of the intersections around it are covered by the opponent's counters (See Figure 1.) A group of counters is captured in the same way. (See Figures 2 and 3.) The captured counters are removed from the mat and kept by the opponent.

Figure 1

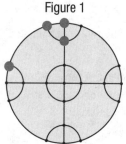

A gray counter is captured.

Figure 2

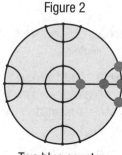

Two blue counters are captured.

Figure 3

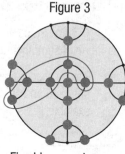

Five blue counters are captured.

4. Play continues until players run out of counters or until there is no place left on the mat to put a counter without it being captured. The player who holds more captured counters wins.

Differentiation Options

READINESS Students may need help in developing winning strategies. Adding a rule or using a smaller game mat may also be helpful:

▶ Once during the game, each player can call "switch" after the opponent has made a play, and switch one of their placed counters with the one the opponent just played.

▶ Players fold the game mat in half and use only the 14 intersections showing.

ENRICHMENT

▶ One time during the game, each player can call "take back" after the opponent has made a play. The opponent must remove their counter for that turn. The player who made the call then takes their next turn.

ELL SUPPORT As you introduce how to play the game, discuss and model the meanings of *intersection*, *capture*, and *surround*.

GRADE 3

Target 50

Strands Number and Numeration; Operations and Computation

Skill Identifying place values for whole numbers; adding, subtracting, and making exchanges with base-10 blocks

Materials (per pair)
- ◆ *Target 50* Gameboard (or Game Masters 219 and 220, 2 copies of each)
- ◆ Everything Math Deck (number cards 0–9, 4 of each)
- ◇ base-10 blocks: 30 longs and 35 cubes

Players 2

Object of the game To have 5 longs on the Place-Value Mat.

Grade 3
SRB
312

Games Across the Grades

Grades	PK	K	1	2	3	4	5	6
Advanced Learning			◆	◆				
Core Program					◆			
Reteaching and Practice						◆		

Directions

1. One player shuffles and stacks the cards whole-number side down.

2. Players take turns. For each turn, a player turns over 2 cards. The player may use either card as a 1-digit number or use both cards to make a 2-digit number.

3. The player uses base-10 blocks to model his or her number. On the first turn, the player places these blocks **on** the mat. On the following turns, the player places these blocks **below** the mat.

4. The player makes one of the following choices:
   - **Addition:** The player can add all of the blocks below the mat to the blocks already on the mat.
   - **Subtraction:** The player can subtract blocks equal in value to the blocks below the mat from the blocks already on the mat. If a player decides to subtract, he or she may have to make exchanges on the Place-Value Mat first. (Players may not choose to subtract if the value of the blocks below the mat is greater than the value of the blocks on the mat.) The player clears away the subtracted blocks and the blocks beneath the mat.

5. Players can make exchanges on their Place-Value Mats at any time.

6. Play continues until the blocks on one player's mat have a value of exactly 50 (5 longs). That player wins the game.

NOTE: Players can use Game Master 220 to record the numbers they made for each turn and the total value of the blocks on their place-value mats.

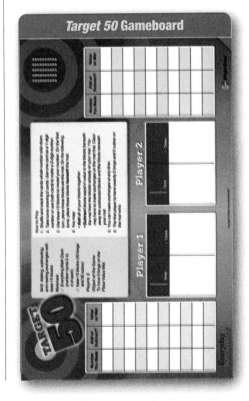

Target 50 **Gameboard**

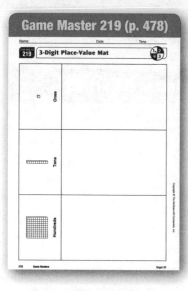

Game Master 219 (p. 478)

219	3-Digit Place-Value Mat

Ones

Tens

Hundreds

Game Master 220 (p. 479)

220	Target 50 Record Sheet

For each of your turns, record the number you made, whether you added or subtracted, and the final value of the base-10 blocks on your Place-Value Mat.

Number You Made	Add or Subtract?	Value on Place-Value Mat

Example

Alex was able to reach the target value of 50 in three turns:

Turn	Cards	Number Made	Addition or Subtraction on Place-Value Mat	Value on Mat
1	6, 5	56	**Add** 5 longs and 6 cubes.	56
2	8, 9	8	Exchange 1 long for 10 cubes. **Subtract** 8 cubes.	48
3	5, 2	2	**Add** 2 cubes. Exchange 10 cubes for 1 long.	50

Differentiation Options

READINESS Students may need to practice using base-10 blocks to add and subtract 1- and 2-digit numbers. Focusing on one operation may be helpful:

▶ Players add two flats to the materials. They choose either addition or subtraction before playing. For addition, the first player to exchange 10 longs for a flat wins. For subtraction, each player begins with a flat on his or her mat and the first player who does not have enough blocks left to subtract his or her number wins.

ENRICHMENT

▶ If players draw two cards with the same digit on a turn, they have a *Multiples Wild Card.* They draw two more cards. They make one of the cards into a multiple of ten that they add or subtract. They use the other card as is and must add it if they subtracted the multiple of ten or subtract it if they added the multiple of ten.

ELL SUPPORT Explain to students that in this game, they want to reach, or get to, a *target* of 50, or 5 longs. With a student, model how to play. Demonstrate the meanings of *equivalent* and *exchange* using the base-10 blocks. Show students how to complete the Record Sheet.

PK–K Teen Frame

Strand Number and Numeration

Skill Counting, representing, and comparing numbers to 20

Materials (per group)

◆ *Teen Frame* Gameboard (or Game Master 221, 1 per pair, and Game Master 222)

◆ 20 counters per player

◆ 10 scoring counters

◆ transparent spinner (or pencil and paper clip)

Players 2–4

Object of the game To collect the most scoring counters.

Games Across the Grades

Grades	PK	K	1	2	3	4	5	6
Advanced Learning								
Core Program	◆	◆						
Reteaching and Practice			◆					

Directions

Advance Preparation: Students can hold or tape the transparent spinner in place over the spinner face, or they can use a paper clip and pencil to create a spinner. (See the picture on Game Master 2.)

1. Players take turns. For each turn, the player spins a number and puts that number of counters on his or her Teen Frame.

2. After each round, players compare the number of counters on their Teen Frames.

3. The player who has the most counters wins the round and takes a scoring counter.

4. Players clear their Teen Frames and begin another round.

5. The player who has the most scoring counters after 5 rounds wins.

Another Way To Play

The player with the *fewest* counters takes the scoring counter.

Advanced Version

Players use a cube labeled 10 on each side, a dot die, and ten strips (1 per player) from Game Master 223. Each player rolls both dice, says the total, and represents the number with a ten strip and counters on the Teen Frame.

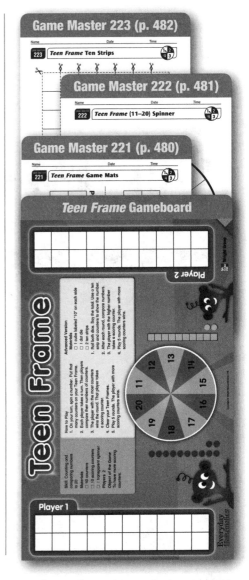

Differentiation Options

READINESS Students may need to review reading numerals 11–20, counting through 20, and comparing numbers. Beginning with smaller numbers may also be helpful:

▶ Create a spinner with the numbers 1–10. Each player uses a ten strip from Game Master 223 as the game mat.

▶ In Step 2, players may remove their counters from the Teen Frames and line them up with one-to-one correspondence in order to compare them. Each player states all of the totals and says whether his or her total is the largest, the smallest, or neither.

ENRICHMENT

▶ Players take turns telling how much larger (or smaller) the winning number is than their own total.

▶ Create a spinner with the numbers 21–30. Players color 2 ten strips that they will use to represent tens, and use a blank ten strip as a game mat for ones.

ELL SUPPORT Use counters to discuss the meaning of the word *compare.* Discuss the difference between the counters that are placed on the Teen Frame and the scoring counters. You may want students to use two different colors of counters to emphasize the different uses.

GRADES 2–3 Three Addends

Games Across the Grades									
Grades	PK	K	1	2	3	4	5	6
Advanced Learning			◆					
Core Program				◆	◆			
Reteaching and Practice						◆	◆	◆

Strand Operations and Computation

Skill Adding three 1- and 2-digit numbers

Materials (per pair)

◆ For Grade 2: Game Master 224 (Record Sheet, 2 copies)

◆ For Grade 3: *Three Addends* Gameboard (or Game Master 224)

◆ Everything Math Deck

Players 2

Object of the game To earn more points by finding easy ways to add.

Grade 3
SRB
314

Directions

1. Players shuffle and stack the cards whole-number side down.

2. One player turns over 3 cards from the top of the deck.

3. On their Record Sheets, both players use the 3 numbers as addends in an addition model. Players may add the numbers in any order, but they should try to arrange the numbers so that they are easy to add.

4. Players compare their answers. Each player gets a point for a correct answer.

5. Players continue until time runs out or until one player has a predetermined number of points.

Advanced Versions

- Players give the sum without writing a number model.
- Players draw 4 cards and solve problems with 4 addends.

Differentiation Options

READINESS Students may need to practice adding three numbers. Limiting the addends to 1-digit numbers or using a calculator may be helpful:

▶ Instead of drawing cards, players roll a die three times for their addends.

▶ Players use a calculator to add and then discuss the order in which they chose to add.

ENRICHMENT

▶ Players agree to make one, two, or three of their numbers into multiples of 10. For example, if the cards show 14, 15, and 6, players may choose to add 140 + 150 + 60.

ELL SUPPORT Write three 1-digit numbers on the board. Discuss with students how they would add the numbers and why some combinations are easier to add than others. Discuss the meanings of *addend, sum,* and *compare.* Introduce the game and model how to play.

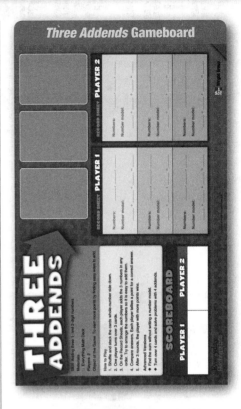

Three Addends Gameboard

Game Master 224 (p. 483)

3-D Shape Sort

GRADES 5–6

Games Across the Grades

Grades	PK	K	1	2	3	4	5	6
Advanced Learning						♦	♦	
Core Program							♦	♦
Reteaching and Practice								

Strand Geometry

Skill Identifying properties of 3-D shapes

Materials (per pair)

◆ For Grade 6: *Shape Sort* Gameboard (optional)

◆ Shape Cards (or Game Master 225)

◆ Property Cards (or Game Master 226)

Players 2, or 2 teams of 2

Object of the game To collect more Shape Cards.

Grade 5 SRB 332   Grade 6 SRB 335

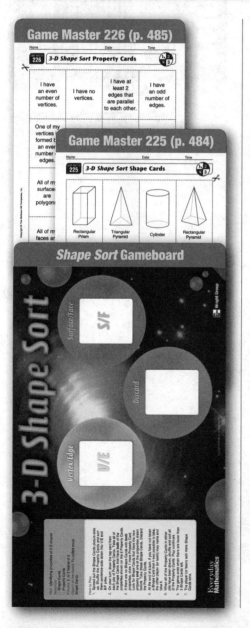

Game Master 226 (p. 485)

Game Master 225 (p. 484)

Shape Sort Gameboard

Directions

Advance Preparation: Have students write *V/E* on the back of each Property Card that mentions a vertex or edge. Have them write *S/F* on the back of each Property Card that mentions a surface or face.

1. One player spreads out the Shape Cards picture-side up. Another player shuffles the Property Cards and sorts them sentence-side down into V/E and S/F piles.

2. Players (or teams) take turns drawing the top card from each pile of Property Cards and then taking all of the Shape Cards that have **both** of the properties shown on the 2 Property Cards.

3. If there are no Shape Cards with both properties, the player (or team) draws 1 additional Property Card—either a V/E Card or an S/F Card. The player (or team) looks for Shape Cards that have the new property and one of the properties drawn before and takes those Shape Cards.

4. At the end of a turn, the player discards the Property Cards. If a player (or team) has not taken a Shape Card that it was possible to take, the other player (or team) may name and take it.

5. When all of the Property Cards in either pile have been drawn, one player shuffles *all* of the Property Cards and sorts them sentence-side down into V/E-card and S/F-card piles. Play continues.

6. The game ends when there are fewer than 3 Shape Cards left.

7. The player (or team) with more Shape Cards wins.

Differentiation Options

READINESS Students may need to practice identifying properties of 3-D shapes. Using 3-D objects or considering one property at a time may be helpful:

▶ Players use 3-D objects instead of the Shape Cards. They collect shapes in the classroom or use a set of 3-D solids.

▶ Players first draw one card and take all of the shapes having this property. Players then draw a second card and put back all of the shapes that do not have the second property.

ENRICHMENT

▶ Players mix 2 sets of Property Cards together (both V/E and S/F cards). Players draw 2 Property Cards and use 1 or 2 to make a match. They collect only 1 shape per turn. Players "win" the Property Card(s) they use and the Shape Card they collect. Any remaining Property Cards can be kept and used in the next round. The player with the most cards wins.

ELL SUPPORT Ensure that students understand the meaning of *property* in this context. Discuss the meanings of some of the expressions used on the Property Cards, such as *at least one* and *fewer than 6*. Discuss the meanings of *even, odd, vertices, edges, parallel, perpendicular, faces, surface,* and *regular.* Model a few turns with a small group of students. Emphasize that students should take *all* of the shapes that match the selected properties.

GRADES 1–2

3, 2, 1 Game

Strand Operations and Computation

Skill Mental subtraction skills

Materials (per pair)

◆ For Grade 1: *3, 2, 1 Game* Gameboard (or 1 piece of paper)

◇ For Grade 2: 1 piece of paper

◇ 2 different-colored markers (or pencils)

Players 2

Object of the game To reach exactly 0.

Grades 1–2

MRB
150

Games Across the Grades									
Grades	PK	K	1	2	3	4	5	6
Advanced Learning								
Core Program			◆	◆				
Reteaching and Practice					◆			

Directions

1. One player writes *21* at the top of the paper or gameboard.

2. Players take turns subtracting 1, 2, or 3 mentally from 21 and recording the subtraction.

NOTE: You can vary the game by allowing players to use a calculator or by choosing different starting numbers.

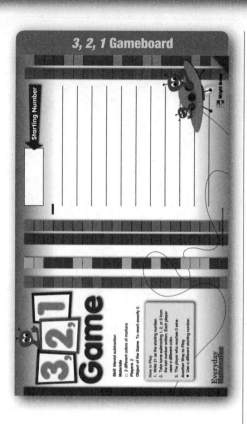

3, 2, 1 Gameboard

3. Players continue taking turns subtracting 1, 2, or 3 from the last number written until a player gets 0 as the answer. The first player to reach 0 as an answer wins.

Differentiation Options

READINESS Students may need to review counting back, regrouping, or other strategies for subtracting 1, 2, and 3 from a two-digit number. Using a smaller starting number and counters may be helpful:

▶ Each player begins with 15 counters and subtracts from 15 instead of 21. They remove counters each time they subtract.

ENRICHMENT

▶ Players record a strategy or pattern they found that might help someone win the game. Once they have identified a strategy that will always work, change the numbers that can be subtracted to 1, 3, and 5, and the starting total to 25.

ELL SUPPORT Write *21* on the board. Explain that in this game, students will start with 21 and then take turns subtracting numbers to try to reach 0. Tell students they will choose to subtract either 1, 2, or 3 for each turn. Explain that although 1 is easier to subtract, subtracting 2 or 3 would get them closer to 0. However, students should be aware that every move closer to 0 also brings the opponent closer to 0. Have two students model how to play. After each subtraction, ask: *Why did you choose that number to subtract?*

GRADES K–2 Time Match

Games Across the Grades									
Grades	PK	K	1	2	3	4	5	6	
Advanced Learning	◆								
Core Program		◆	◆	◆					
Reteaching and Practice				◆					

Strand Measurement and Reference Frames

Skill Telling time

Materials (per group)

◆ For Grade K: Game Masters 227 and 228 (clock cards)

◆ For Grades 1 and 2: Time Card Deck

Grades 1–2

Players 2 or 3

Object of the game To match the most cards.

Directions

Advance Preparation: Choose 8 or 12 analog time cards and the matching digital time cards for your students. You may want to begin with times to the hour from Game Masters 227 and 228, and then use the Time Card Deck, which includes half-hour and quarter-hour cards, as players become proficient. Then you can begin to incorporate the cards showing the time in words.

1. One player shuffles 8 (or 12) matching pairs of cards and places all the cards facedown in a 4-by-4 (or 4-by-6) array.

2. Players take turns turning over 2 cards:

   • If the cards match, the player takes them and his or her turn is over.

   • If the cards don't match, the player returns them facedown. His or her turn is over.

3. When all of the cards have been collected, the player with the most matches wins.

Differentiation Options

READINESS Students may need to review identifying and using the hour hand and the minute hand on analog clocks. Playing a few practice rounds may also be helpful:

▶ Players play with all of the cards faceup.

ENRICHMENT

▶ Players receive a bonus point if they can tell what time it would be one-half hour later than the time shown on one of the cards they win. Bonus points count as cards.

▶ Instead of matching clocks, players shuffle all of the cards, draw two, and tell how much time elapses between the two times shown.

ELL SUPPORT Discuss the meanings of *same* and *match* as you model how to play the game. Explain that students have to pay close attention and try to remember where specific clocks are located when they do not make a match, as this will help them in later turns.

Game Master 227 (p. 486)

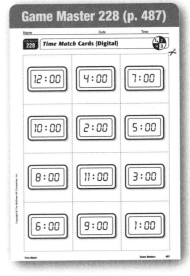

Game Master 228 (p. 487)

GRADES K–2 Top-It

Games Across the Grades									
Grades	PK	K	1	2	3	4	5	6
Advanced Learning		◆						
Core Program			◆	◆	◆			
Reteaching and Practice						◆	◆	

Strand Number and Numeration

Skill Reading and comparing numbers 1–20

Materials (per pair)

◆ For Kindergarten: 2 Number Card Decks (number cards 1–20, 2 of each)

◆ For Grades 1 and 2: 2 Everything Math Decks (number cards 1–20, 2 of each)

Grades 1–2

MRB 154

Players 2

Object of the game To collect more cards.

NOTE: To simplify the game, you may want to remove number cards 11–20 (or 16–20) from each deck.

Directions

1. One player shuffles and stacks the cards whole-number side down.

2. Each player turns over 1 card and reads the number aloud.

3. The player with the larger number takes both cards. If both cards show the same number, each player turns over another card. The player with the larger number then takes all 4 cards for that round.

4. The game ends when all of the cards have been turned over.

5. The player with more cards wins. (Alternatively, players can decide that the last player to win a hand will win the game.)

Other Ways to Play

- *Opposite Top-It (or Bottom-It):* In this game, the player with the smaller number takes both cards.

- *Top-It with a Spinner:* Players use a spinner with sections labeled "Larger" and "Smaller" or flip a penny before each round to decide whether the player with the larger or smaller number takes both cards.

- *Domino Top-It:* Players use dominoes instead of cards.

- *Wild-Card Top-It:* Include the unnumbered cards from both decks. A player who draws one of these "wild cards" may write down any number to play.

- *Top-It with Relation Symbols:* Players spread out the Number Deck cards with relation symbols (< or =), or index cards marked with these symbols. Players take turns placing the correct symbol between the cards played and reading the number sentence as they determine who takes the cards.

Differentiation Options

READINESS Students may need to practice reading numerals or comparing numbers. Using smaller numbers or dot patterns for support may be helpful:

▶ Replace the number cards with a dot die, or make a set of number cards that also show dot patterns.

ENRICHMENT

▶ For each round, players record their number and their partner's number with tally marks and circle the winning number.

▶ Create card decks with numbers greater than 20.

▶ Each player draws 2 cards to form a 2-digit number.

▶ See *Addition Top-It*.

ELL SUPPORT Explain that *Top-It* is an expression that means "beat that." For example, a card showing 14 "tops" a card showing 13. Ask if anyone has heard the question: *Can you top that?* Discuss what it means. Introduce the game and model how to play. Explain what to do in case of a tie.

GRADES 5–6

Top-It Games with Positive and Negative Numbers

Strand Operations and Computation

Skill Adding and subtracting positive and negative numbers

Materials (per group)

◆ Everything Math Deck

◇ 1 calculator (optional)

Players 2 to 4

Object of the game To collect the most cards.

Grade 5 335

Grade 6 337

Games Across the Grades									
Grades	PK	K	1	2	3	4	5	6
Advanced Learning							◆		
Core Program								◆	◆
Reteaching and Practice									

Addition Top-It with Positive and Negative Numbers

Directions

1. One player shuffles and stacks the cards whole-number side down.

2. Each player turns over 2 cards and calls out their sum.

NOTE: In the Everything Math Deck, black numbers are positive and blue numbers are negative.

NOTE: Players can use Game Master 4 to record and compare sums and differences.

Game Master 4 (p. 263)

3. The player with the largest sum takes all of the cards. In case of a tie, each tied player turns over 2 more cards and calls out the sum. The player with the largest sum takes all of the cards from both plays. If necessary, players can check sums with a calculator.

4. Play continues until there are too few cards left for each player to have another turn.

5. The player with the most cards wins.

Example

Jaime turns over a blue 5 and a black 7. $-5 + 7 = 2$

Kevin turns over a blue 3 and a blue 4. $-3 + (-4) = -7$

Jaime takes all 4 cards because 2 is greater than -7.

Advanced Version

Each player turns over 3 cards and finds the sum.

Subtraction Top-It with Positive and Negative Numbers

Directions

1. One player shuffles and stacks the cards whole-number side down.

2. Each player turns over 2 cards, one at a time, and subtracts the second number from the first number.

3. The player who calls out the largest difference takes all of the cards. In case of a tie, each tied player turns over 2 more cards and calls out the difference of the numbers. The player with the largest difference takes all of the cards from both plays. If necessary, players can check differences with a calculator.

4. Play continues until there are too few cards left for each player to have another turn.

5. The player with the most cards wins.

Example

Priya turns over a black 2 and then a blue 3. $+2 - (-3) = +5$

Jay turns over a blue 5 and then a black 8. $-5 - (+8) = -13$

Priya takes all 4 cards because 5 is greater than -13.

Differentiation Options

READINESS Students may need to review models for adding and subtracting positive and negative numbers. It may be helpful to model the problems:

▶ Players use counters of two colors: one color for positive numbers and one color for negative numbers. They model the numbers they draw, pair the positive and negative counters to make "zeros," and count the unpaired counters to find their negative or positive answer.

ENRICHMENT

▶ For each turn, players choose whether to add or subtract the numbers on their cards and write an addition or subtraction sentence.

ELL SUPPORT Explain that *Top-It* is an expression that means "beat that." For example, a card showing 14 "tops" a card showing 13. Explain that in this version of the game, the *color* of the card will determine whether the number is positive or negative—black cards are positive numbers and blue cards are negative numbers. Model a few turns using a number line to model adding (or subtracting) positive and negative numbers.

GRADES PK–K

Train Games

Strands Number and Numeration; Operations and Computation; Patterns, Functions, and Algebra

Skill Counting with one-to-one correspondence; modeling addition and subtraction

Materials (per group)
◆ *Train Games* gameboard (optional)
◆ 10–25 counters (or connecting cubes) per player
◆ 3 blank dice: 1 red, 1 green, 1 white

Players 2–4

Games Across the Grades

Grades	PK	K	1	2	3	4	5	6
Advanced Learning								
Core Program	◆	◆						
Reteaching and Practice			◆					

Growing Train Game

Object of the game To build a "train" of counters.

Directions

Advance Preparation: Mark the **green** die 1, 2, 3, 1, 2, 3. (Later, you may want to add a "+" symbol to each side.)

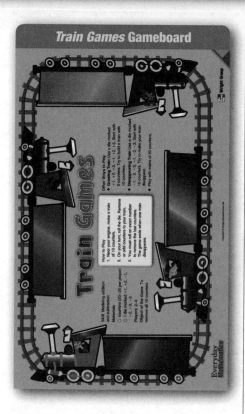

Choose a number of counters, such as 10 or 20, as the maximum train length. The gameboard accommodates approximately 12 counters per player in a 4-player game, but 2 players could build longer trains.

1. Players place the counters in a pile between them.

2. Players take turns rolling the green die, taking that number of counters, and adding them to their trains.

3. The game ends when one player reaches the predetermined number of counters with an exact roll.

Disappearing Train Game

Object of the game To remove all of the counters from a "train."

Directions

Advance Preparation: Mark the **red** die 1, 2, 3, 1, 2, 3. (Later, you may want to add a "−" symbol to each side.)

Choose a number of counters, such as 10 or 20, for each player to begin with. The gameboard accommodates approximately 12 counters per player in a 4-player game, but 2 players could build longer trains.

1. Players start with trains of equal length.

2. Players take turns rolling the red die and taking that number of counters away from the train.

3. The game ends when one train disappears on an exact roll.

Growing and Disappearing Train Game

Object of the game To remove all of the counters from a "train."

Directions

Advance Preparation: Color the **white** die red on four sides and green on two sides (or use red and green stickers to mark the sides). Mark the red sides 1, 2, 3, 3. Mark the green sides 1, 2. (Later, you may want to add a "+" or "−" symbol to each side of the die.)

1. Players start with trains of 10 counters.

2. Players take turns rolling the red-and-green die. Students add cubes according to the numbers on the green sides and take away cubes according to the numbers on the red sides. For example, a red 2 means to remove 2 counters; a green 2 means to add 2 counters to the train.

3. The game ends when one train disappears on an exact roll.

4. Players must roll an exact number to remove the last cubes. The game ends when one player's train disappears.

Differentiation Options

READINESS Students may need to practice counting with one-to-one correspondence. Using smaller numbers or dot patterns for support may be helpful:

▶ Players use dot-dice.

ENRICHMENT

▶ To practice recognizing operation symbols, players use a white die marked −1, −2, +1, +2, +3, and +4. Players begin with 0 counters and must roll a "+" number to begin play. The game ends when one player has 12 counters.

ELL SUPPORT Explain the meaning of *train* in this context. Explain that a train is formed by linking one or more things together. Demonstrate how to make a counter train and then introduce the game. Ensure that students understand that the green cube (or side) tells how many counters to add and the red cube (or side) tells how many counters to take away.

GRADES 1–2 Tric-Trac

Strands Number and Numeration; Operations and Computation

Skill Addition facts 0–10

Materials (per pair)
- ◆ For Grade 1: *Tric-Trac* Gameboard (or Game Master 229)
- ◆ For Grade 2: Game Master 229 (game mats)
- ◆ 2 dice
- ◆ 20 pennies

Players 2

Object of the game To have the lower sum of the uncovered numbers.

Grades 1–2

MRB
156

Games Across the Grades								
Grades	PK	K	1	2	3	4	5	6
Advanced Learning		◆						
Core Program			◆	◆				
Reteaching and Practice					◆			

Directions

1. Each player covers the 10 empty circles on his or her game mat with pennies.

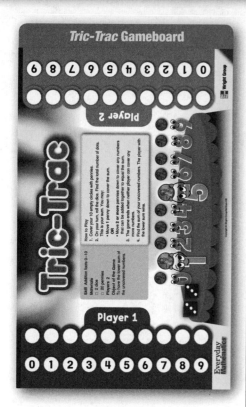

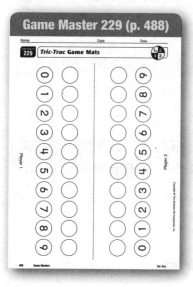

2. Players take turns rolling the dice and finding the sum of the dots. The player chooses to:

- move 1 penny to the lower row on the game mat to cover the sum, or

- move 2 or more pennies to cover any numbers that can be added together to equal the sum.

3. The game ends when neither player can cover any more numbers on his or her game mat.

4. Each player finds the sum of his or her uncovered numbers. The player with the lower sum wins.

Example

David rolled a 2 and a 2.
David's sum is 4.

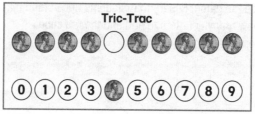

This is one way David can cover his sum.

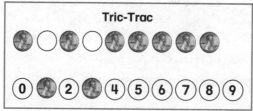

This is another way David can cover his sum.

Differentiation Options

READINESS Students may need to review addition facts and using addition to make equivalent names for numbers. Using sums no greater than 5 may be helpful:

► Change the *Tric-Trac* game mat to include two 1s, 2s, 3s, 4s, and 5s. Players roll only 1 die and move pennies to cover numbers that could be added to get the rolled number as a sum.

ENRICHMENT

► Players record a number sentence for each turn.

ELL SUPPORT Display the gameboard or game mat and introduce the game. Roll two dice and ask students for possible moves. As you identify possibilities, discuss the meanings of ***sum, cover,*** and ***uncovered numbers.***

GRADE
6

Venn Diagram Challenge

Strand Data and Chance

Skill Creating and using Venn diagrams

Materials (per group)

◆ Game Master 230 (game mat, 1–3 copies per player)

◆ Game Master 231 (Record Sheet)

◇ attribute blocks

Players 2 or 3

Object of the game To score the most points.

Games Across the Grades

Grades	PK	K	1	2	3	4	5	6
Advanced Learning					◆	◆	◆	
Core Program								◆
Reteaching and Practice								

Directions

1. For each round, players take turns randomly drawing 10 attribute blocks without looking.

2. Based on the selected blocks, each player decides which 3 of the 4 possible attributes he or she will use to label the rings of his or her game mat.

   Attributes include:

   • **color:** blue, red, or yellow

   • **shape:** circle, hexagon, rectangle, square, or triangle

   • **size:** large or small

   • **thickness:** thick or thin

3. Each player places each of his or her attribute blocks inside a ring, inside an area of overlapping rings, or outside the rings of his or her game mat. Players trade mats and check each other's placement of the blocks.

4. Each player finds his or her total points for the round. Points are awarded according to the correct placement of each block on the game mat:

   • **1 point:** block within 1 ring only

   • **5 points:** block within the overlapping area of 2 rings

   • **10 points:** block within the overlapping area of 3 rings

   • **20 bonus points:** all 10 blocks within rings of the game mat

5. For the second and third rounds, different players go first in choosing their 10 blocks.

6. The player with the highest score after 3 rounds wins.

NOTE: Each player needs only 1 copy of Game Master 230 if players write lightly and erase their labels between turns.

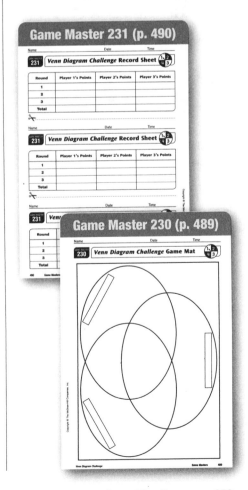

Differentiation Options

READINESS Students may need to review making Venn diagrams. Playing the game with a simpler Venn diagram may be helpful:

▶ Players use a Venn diagram that is made up of just two overlapping rings. Players select 2 attributes of the blocks and score 1 point for placing a block within 1 ring only, 2 points for placing a block within the overlapping area of 2 rings, and 3 bonus points if all 10 blocks are within rings.

ENRICHMENT Challenge students to develop new strategies:

▶ One player looks at the attribute blocks and chooses 10 blocks for the group. A second player is the Rule Maker who labels the rings and places the first block to score points. Players take turns placing the rest of the blocks and recording the points for each block that is placed.

ELL SUPPORT Draw a Venn Diagram on the board similar to the one on the game mat. Label the rings and ask students to provide some examples of blocks that can be placed in each section. Discuss why certain blocks can be placed in some sections and not others. Introduce the game and model how to play.

GRADE **K**

Walk Around the Clock

Games Across the Grades

Grades	PK	K	1	2	3	4	5	6
Advanced Learning	◆							
Core Program		◆						
Reteaching and Practice			◆					

Strands Number and Numeration; Measurement and Reference Frames

Skill Telling time to the hour on an analog clock; counting

Materials (per group)

◆ Game Master 232 (analog clock)

◆ 1 counter per player

◆ 1 die with sides marked 1, 2, 3, 1, 2, 3

Players 2–5

Object of the game To land on 12 on the clock.

NOTE: Although hands are provided on Game Master 232, they are not used for the basic version of this game.

Directions

1. Players put their counters on 12 on the clock.

2. Players take turns rolling the die and moving their counters that number of hours ahead. After players move their counters, they say the time to the hour that their counters landed on.

3. Players continue taking turns until one player lands on 12 with an exact roll.

Game Master 232 (p. 491)

Differentiation Options

READINESS Students may need to review clockwise movement and stating the time. Using clock hands may be helpful:

▶ Remind students of the positions of the clock hands for times to the hour. Tape the minute hand to the clock pointing at the 12. Attach the hour hand to the clock with a paper fastener. After rolling the die, a player moves the hour hand that many hours ahead and says the time aloud.

ENRICHMENT

▶ Players name an activity that they might be doing at each time that they say aloud.

▶ Players use 1 each of the number cards 1–12 and an unlabeled analog clock. On each turn, they draw a card, label the clock with that hour, move the hour hand or a counter to that position, and say the time.

ELL SUPPORT Introduce the game and model how to play. Explain that the roll of the die will represent how many *hours* to move the counter. Discuss the meaning of landing on 12 with an *exact roll.*

GRADE 2 — What's My Attribute Rule?

Strand Geometry

Skill Sorting shapes according to their attributes

Materials (per group)

◆ Game Master 233 (attribute cards)

◆ 1 die

◇ 1 set of attribute blocks

◇ 2 sheets of paper

Players 2–5

Object of the game To identify the rule.

Games Across the Grades

Grades	PK	K	1	2	3	4	5	6
Advanced Learning			◆					
Core Program				◆				
Reteaching and Practice					◆	◆	◆	◆

W

Game Master 233 (p. 492)

|---|---|---|---|
| 233 | **Attribute Rule Cards** | | |

small, blue shapes	large, red shapes	large shapes, but not triangles	circles, but not red
blue and yellow shapes, but not circles	red and yellow small shapes	not triangles or squares	large triangles, but not yellow
large circles, but not red	large circles or squares		

Directions

1. One player labels a sheet of paper *These fit the rule.* Another player labels a second sheet of paper *These do NOT fit the rule.*

2. Players take turns rolling the die once. The player with the lowest number is the first "Rule Maker."

3. The Rule Maker shuffles and places the Attribute Rule Cards facedown.

4. The Rule Maker turns over the top Attribute Rule Card but does not show it to the other players or tell them what the rule is.

5. The Rule Maker chooses 3 or 4 attribute blocks that fit the rule on the card and puts them on the sheet labeled *These fit the rule.*

6. The Rule Maker chooses 3 or 4 blocks that do *not* fit the rule and puts them on the sheet labeled *These do NOT fit the rule.*

7. The other players take turns choosing a block that they think might fit the rule and placing it on the "fit" sheet.

8. If the Rule Maker says "No," the player moves the block to the "do NOT fit" sheet. If the Rule Maker says "Yes," the player gets to suggest what the rule might be. The Rule Maker then tells the player whether his or her rule is correct.

9. The round continues until someone figures out the rule. That person becomes the Rule Maker for the next round.

Differentiation Options

READINESS Students may need practice describing the attribute blocks. Looking for one attribute at a time may be helpful:

▶ The Rule Maker separates the rule into two rule statements. For example, if the card said, "small blue shapes," the Rule Maker says: *The shape must be blue* and *The shape must be small.* The other players try to guess one part of the rule at a time.

▶ Players choose one card at a time and match as many blocks as possible to that card.

ENRICHMENT

▶ Players fill in the blank Attribute Rule Cards on Game Master 233 with rules of their own. Each card should include at least two attributes (size, shape, or color).

▶ Players mark up each Attribute Rule Card with a third attribute: *thick* or *thin.*

▶ The Rule Maker chooses 3 blocks for *one* category—either "fit" or "do NOT fit"—and no blocks for the other category.

ELL SUPPORT Explain the meaning of *Rule Maker* in this context. Discuss the meanings of *fit the rule* and *do not fit the rule* using examples. Introduce the game and model how to play.

6 X and O—Tic-Tac-Toe

Strand Measurement and Reference Frames

Skill Plotting ordered pairs on a coordinate grid

Materials (per pair)

◆ Everything Math Deck (number cards 0–10, 4 of each)

◆ Game Master 174 (coordinate grid)

Players 2

Object of the game To get 4 Xs or Os in a row, column, or diagonal.

Games Across the Grades								
Grades	**PK**	**K**	**1**	**2**	**3**	**4**	**5**	**6**
Advanced Learning							◆	◆
Core Program								◆
Reteaching and Practice								

Directions

1. One player shuffles the cards and places the deck whole-number side down.

2. For each round, Player 1 draws 2 cards and uses the numbers in any order to form an ordered pair. Player 1 marks this ordered pair on the grid with an *X* and discards both cards.

3. Player 2 draws 2 cards and follows the same procedure, except that he or she uses an *O* to mark the ordered pair.

4. If the 2 possible ordered pairs that the player can form have already been marked, the player may not mark the grid.

5. The first player to get 4 *X*s or *O*s in a row, column, or diagonal wins. (It is not necessary for the points to be exactly next to each other as long as they are in a straight line.)

Game Master 174 (p. 433)

| Name | Date | Time |

174 Coordinate Grid

Differentiation Options

READINESS Students may need to practice finding ordered pairs. Removing the element of strategy may simplify the game:

▶ On each turn, a player marks and labels both possible points.

ENRICHMENT

▶ Players use all 4 quadrants. Players can use each card number as either a positive or negative number. For example, if a player draws a 5 and a 6, he or she could plot and label (5,6), (6,5), (−5,6), (−6,5), (5,−6), (6,−6), (−5,−6), or (−6,−5).

ELL SUPPORT Discuss the meaning of *ordered pair* and show how they are generated in this game. For example, if 2 and 3 are drawn, (2,3) and (3,2) are the possible ordered pairs. Model how to play the game, showing examples of winning grids with a *row, column,* and *diagonal.*

PART 3 Game Masters

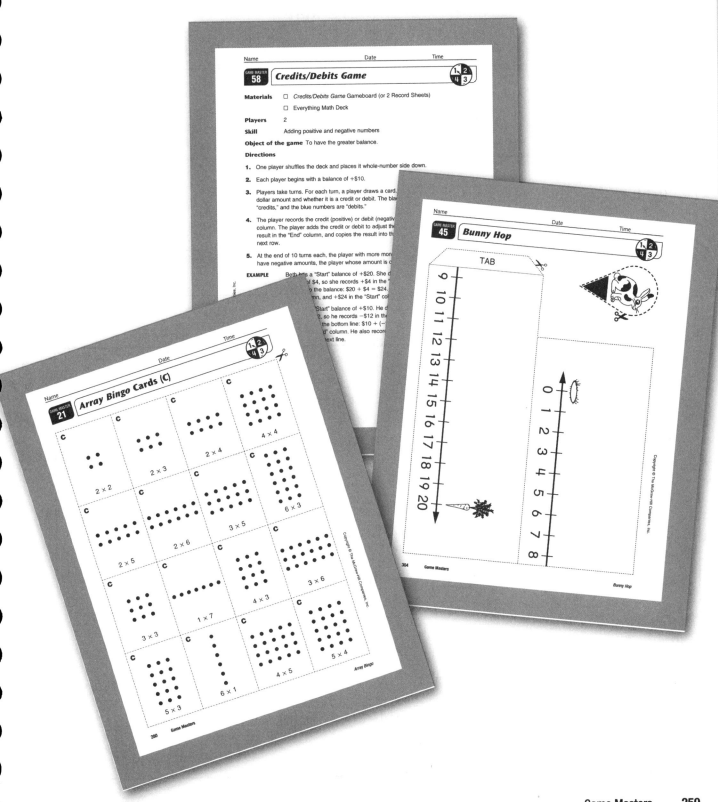

Credits/Debits Game

GAME MASTER 58

Name _____ Date _____ Time _____

Materials
☐ *Credits/Debits Game* Gameboard (or 2 Record Sheets)
☐ Everything Math Deck

Players 2

Skill Adding positive and negative numbers

Object of the game To have the greater balance.

Directions

1. One player shuffles the deck and places it whole-number side down.

2. Each player begins with a balance of +$10.

3. Players take turns. For each turn, a player draws a card, dollar amount and whether it is a credit or debit. The bla "credits," and the blue numbers are "debits."

4. The player records the credit (positive) or debit (negativ column. The player adds the credit or debit to adjust the result in the "End" column, and copies the result into th next row.

5. At the end of 10 turns each, the player with more mon have negative amounts, the player whose amount is c

EXAMPLE Beth has a "Start" balance of +$20. She d of $4, so she records +$4 in the the balance: $20 + $4 = $24. mn, and +$24 in the "Start" col

"Start" balance of +$10. He d so he records −$12 in the the bottom line: $10 + (− d column. He also record next line.

Array Bingo Cards (C)

GAME MASTER 21

Name _____ Date _____ Time _____

C — 2 × 2

C — 2 × 3

C — 2 × 4

C — 4 × 4

C — 2 × 5

C — 2 × 6

C — 3 × 5

C — 6 × 3

C — 3 × 3

C — 1 × 7

C — 4 × 3

C — 3 × 6

C — 5 × 3

C — 6 × 1

C — 4 × 5

C — 5 × 4

280 *Game Masters*

Array Bingo

Bunny Hop

GAME MASTER 45

Name _____ Date _____ Time _____

TAB

9 10 11 12 13 14 15 16 17 18 19 20

0 1 2 3 4 5 6 7 8

304 *Game Masters*

Bunny Hop

Addition Card Draw Score Sheet

Game 1

1st turn:

____ + ____ + ____ = ____

2nd turn:

____ + ____ + ____ = ____

3rd turn:

____ + ____ + ____ = ____

Total: _____

Game 3

1st turn:

____ + ____ + ____ = ____

2nd turn:

____ + ____ + ____ = ____

3rd turn:

____ + ____ + ____ = ____

Total: _____

Game 2

1st turn:

____ + ____ + ____ = ____

2nd turn:

____ + ____ + ____ = ____

3rd turn:

____ + ____ + ____ = ____

Total: _____

Game 4

1st turn:

____ + ____ + ____ = ____

2nd turn:

____ + ____ + ____ = ____

3rd turn:

____ + ____ + ____ = ____

Total: _____

GAME MASTER 2

Addition Spin **Spinner Faces**

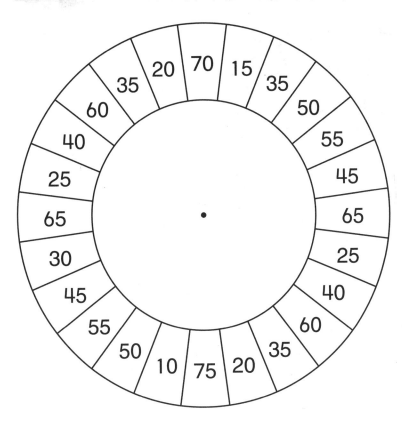

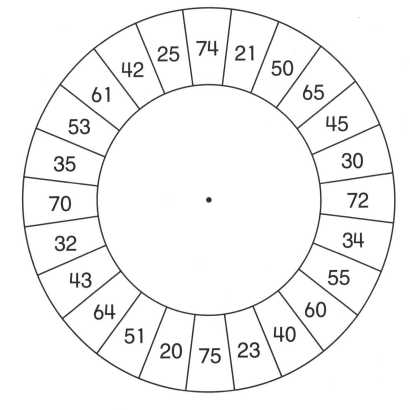

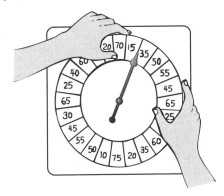

Use either way to make a spinner:

Place the clear spinner over the spinner face.

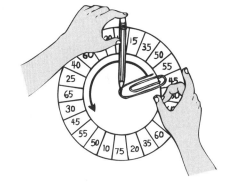

Use a pencil and paper clip.

GAME MASTER 3

Blank *Addition Spin* Spinner Faces

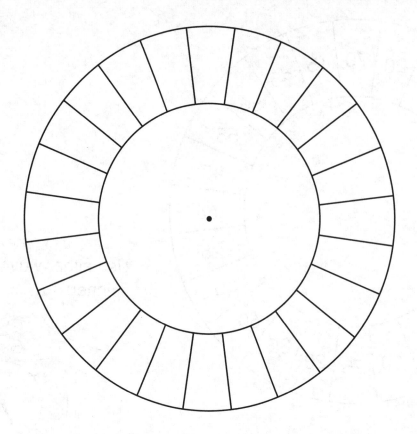

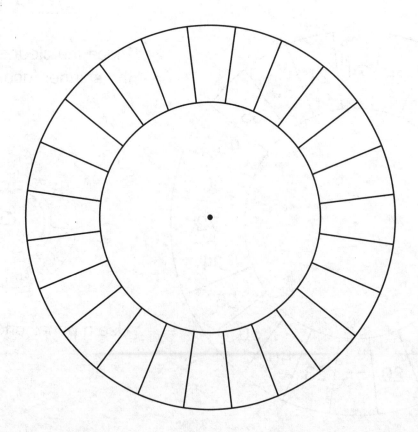

Addition Spin

Top-It Record Sheets

Play a round of *Top-It.* Write your number sentence and the other player's number sentence. Write <, >, or = to compare the number sentences.

Round	Player 1	>, <, =	Player 2
1			
2			
3			
4			
5			
6			

✂ -

Play a round of *Top-It.* Write your number sentence and the other player's number sentence. Write <, >, or = to compare the number sentences.

Round	Player 1	>, <, =	Player 2
1			
2			
3			
4			
5			
6			

GAME MASTER 5

Addition Top-It: Decimals

Materials	☐ Everything Math Deck (number cards 0–10, 4 of each)
	☐ 4 pennies or counters
	☐ 1 calculator (optional)
Players	2–4
Skill	Adding and comparing two decimals; place-value concepts

Object of the game To collect the most cards.

Directions

1. Shuffle and stack the cards whole-number side down.

2. Each player draws 4 cards and forms 2 numbers, each with a whole-number portion and a decimal portion. Use the pennies or counters as decimal points.

3. Each player finds the sum of his or her 2 decimals.

4. Players check each other's sums, using a calculator if needed.

5. The player with the greatest sum wins the round and takes all of the cards.

6. The game ends when not enough cards are left for each player to have another turn.

7. The player with the most cards wins.

Round	**Player 1**	**>, <, =**	**Player 2**
1			
2			
3			
4			
5			
6			

GAME MASTER 6

Electoral Vote Map

1 2
4 3

NOTE: Alaska and Hawaii are not drawn to scale.

GAME MASTER 7

Electoral Vote Map *continued*

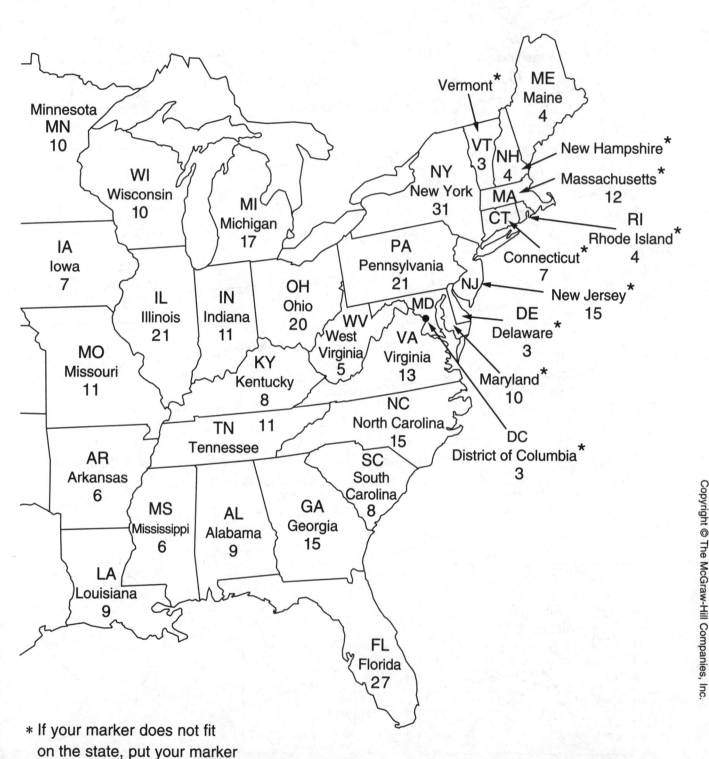

Minnesota
MN
10

WI
Wisconsin
10

IA
Iowa
7

MI
Michigan
17

IL
Illinois
21

IN
Indiana
11

OH
Ohio
20

MO
Missouri
11

KY
Kentucky
8

WV
West
Virginia
5

TN 11
Tennessee

AR
Arkansas
6

MS
Mississippi
6

AL
Alabama
9

GA
Georgia
15

Vermont *

ME
Maine
4

VT
3

NH
4

New Hampshire *

NY
New York
31

MA

Massachusetts *
12

CT

RI
Rhode Island *
4

Connecticut *
7

PA
Pennsylvania
21

NJ

New Jersey *
15

MD

DE
Delaware *
3

VA
Virginia
13

Maryland *
10

NC
North Carolina
15

DC
District of Columbia *
3

SC
South
Carolina
8

LA
Louisiana
9

FL
Florida
27

* If your marker does not fit
on the state, put your marker
on the state's name.

First to 100 Problem Cards

How many inches are there in *x* feet? How many centimeters are there in *x* meters? 1	How many quarts are there in *x* gallons? 2	What is the smallest number of *x*'s you can add to get a sum greater than 100? 3	Is $50 * x$ greater than 1,000? Is $\frac{x}{10}$ less than 1? 4
$\frac{1}{2}$ of *x* = ? $\frac{1}{10}$ of *x* = ? 5	$1 - x = ?$ $x + 998 = ?$ 6	If *x* people share 1,000 stamps equally, how many stamps will each person get? 7	What time will it be *x* minutes from now? What time was it *x* minutes ago? 8
It is 102 miles to your destination. You have gone *x* miles. How many miles are left? 9	What whole or mixed number equals *x* divided by 2? 10	Is *x* a prime or a composite number? Is *x* divisible by 2? 11	The time is 11:05 A.M. The train left *x* minutes ago. What time did the train leave? 12
Bill was born in 1939. Freddy was born the same day, but *x* years later. In what year was Freddy born? 13	Which is larger: $2 * x$ or $x + 50$? 14	There are *x* rows of seats. There are 9 seats in each row. How many seats are there in all? 15	Sargon spent *x* cents on apples. If he paid with a $5 bill, how much change should he get? 16

First to 100 Problem Cards *continued*

The temperature was 25°F. It dropped *x* degrees. What was the new temperature? **17**	Each story in a building is 10 ft high. If the building has *x* stories, how tall is it? **18**	Which is larger: $2 * x$ or $\dfrac{100}{x}$? **19**	$20 * x = ?$ **20**
Name all the whole-number factors of *x*. **21**	Is *x* an even or an odd number? Is *x* divisible by 9? **22**	Shalanda was born on a Tuesday. Linda was born *x* days later. On what day of the week was Linda born? **23**	Will had a quarter plus *x* cents. How much money did he have in all? **24**
Find the perimeter and area of this square. *x* cm, *x* cm **25**	What is the median of these weights? 5 pounds 21 pounds *x* pounds What is the range? **26**	$x°$?° **27**	$x^2 = ?$ 50% of $x^2 = ?$ **28**
$(3x + 4) - 8 = ?$ **29**	*x* out of 100 students voted for Ruby. Is this more than 25%, less than 25%, or exactly 25% of the students? **30**	There are 200 students at Wilson School. *x*% speak Spanish. How many students speak Spanish? **31**	People answered a survey question either Yes or No. *x*% answered Yes. What percent answered No? **32**

Algebra Election

GAME MASTER 10

Algebra Election Cards, Set 1

Find:

x squared

x to the fourth power

$\frac{1}{x}$

Find n. (*Hint: n* could be a negative number.)

$1,000 + n = x$

$1,000 + n = -x$

Complete.

$x * 10^6 = $ ___ million

$x * 10^9 = $ ___ billion

$x * 10^{12} = $ ___ ___

What is the value of n?

$-20 + x = n$

$-100 + (-x) = n$

Insert parentheses in

$10 * x - 10$

so that its value is greater than 0 and less than 100.

Find n. (*Hint: n* could be a negative number.)

$n + 10 = x$

$n - 10 = x$

What is the value of n?

$n = ((5 * x) - 4) / 2$

What is the value of n?

$20 + (-x) = n$

$-20 - (-x) = n$

If $B = 80$ and $H = 100x$, what does T equal?

$T = B - (2 * \frac{H}{1,000})$

Find n.

$n = (2 * x) / 10$

$n + 1 = (2 * x)$

Suppose you earn x dollars per hour.

Complete the table.

Time	Earnings
1 hr	$
2 hr	$
4 hr	$
10 hr	$

Which is greater:

x^2 or 10^3?

x^3 or 10^4?

Tell whether each is true or false.

$10 * x > 100$

$\frac{1}{2} * x * 100 < 10^3$

$x^3 * 1,000 > 4 * 10^4$

Which number is this?

$x * 10^2$

$x * 10^5$

A boulder dropped off a cliff falls approximately $16 * x^2$ feet in x seconds.

How many feet is that?

Which is less:

$\frac{x^3}{10}$ or $(x + 10)^2$?

$10 * x^2$ or $(x + 10)^3$?

Name _____ Date _____ Time _____

GAME MASTER 11

Algebra Election Cards, Set 2

What is n?

$$5 + 2 * x = n + x$$

$x + \triangle$ 200 oz

1 $\triangle$ weighs ——— ounces.

Insert parentheses so that the equation is true.

$$10 * x + 4 = 10 * x + 40$$

Is point (x, x) above, below, or on the line through points A and B?

$A(0,30)$ $B(60,30)$

0 10 20 30 40 50 60

Tell which is correct for each: $<$, $=$, or $>$.

$x \quad < = > \quad 30 - x$

$x \quad < = > \quad 20 - x$

$x \quad < = > \quad 10 - x$

Name a number n such that $x - n$ is a negative number greater than -10.

Suppose you have 10 ⊞ markers and $2 * x$ ⊟ markers.

What is your balance?

Suppose you have x ⊞ markers and 40 ⊟ markers.

What is your balance?

Is point (x, x) to the left of, to the right of, or on the line through points A and B?

$B(30,60)$ $A(30,0)$

0 10 20 30 40 50 60

What is the value of n?

$$10 + (-x) = n$$

$$-10 - (-x) = n$$

What is the median of 4, 8, 12, 13, and x?

If $(2 * x) + n = 100$, what is the value of n?

Is $\frac{1}{x}$ greater than, less than, or equal to $\frac{1}{10}$?

Subtract.

$x - 100 = ?$

$x - (-100) = ?$

Add.

$-25 + x = ?$

$x + 3 - 10 = ?$

Suppose you travel x miles per hour. Complete the table.

Time	Distance
1 hr	
2 hr	
4 hr	
10 hr	

GAME MASTER 12

Circular Geoboard Paper

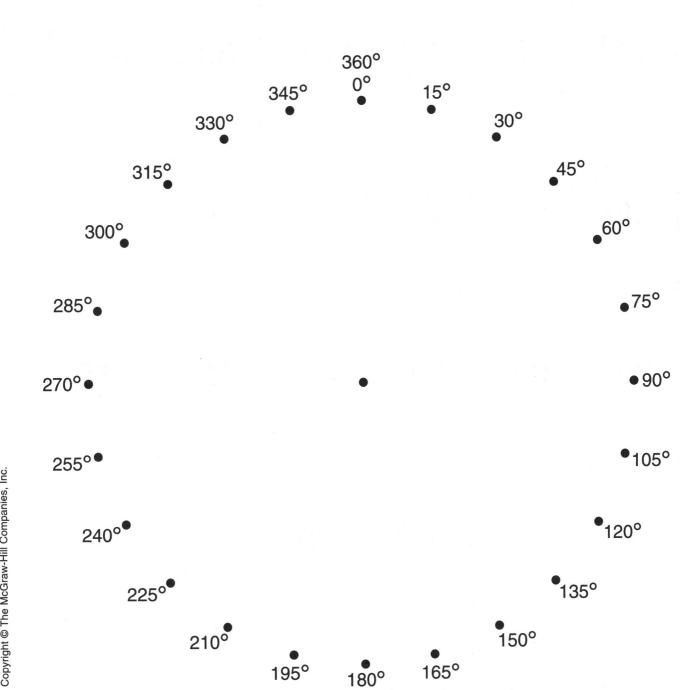

GAME MASTER 13   *Angle Race* **Degree-Measure Cards**

15°	15°	15°	15°	30°	30°
30°	30°	45°	45°	45°	45°
60°	60°	60°	75°	75°	75°
90°	90°	90°	120°	120°	150°
180°	210°	240°			

Name _____   Date _____   Time _____

Angle Tangle **Record Sheet**

Round	Angle	Estimated measure	Actual measure	Score
1		____°	____°	
2		____°	____°	
3		____°	____°	
4		____°	____°	
5		____°	____°	
			Total Score	

GAME MASTER 15   **Animal Cards (Weight)**

First-grade girl
41 lb

7-year-old boy
50 lb

Cheetah
120 lb

Porpoise
98 lb

Penguin
75 lb

Beaver
56 lb

Animal Cards (Length)

7-year-old boy
50 in.

First-grade girl
43 in.

Porpoise
72 in.

Cheetah
48 in.

Beaver
30 in.

Penguin
36 in.

GAME MASTER 17 | **Animal Cards (Weight)** *continued*

Cat
7 lb

Fox
14 lb

Koala
19 lb

Raccoon
23 lb

Rabbit
6 lb

Eagle
15 lb

GAME MASTER 18 | Animal Cards (Length) *continued*

Fox
20 in.

Cat
12 in.

Raccoon
23 in.

Koala
24 in.

Eagle
35 in.

Rabbit
11 in.

GAME MASTER 19

Animal Weight Top-It

Materials   ☐   1 set of Animal Cards

Players   2

Skill   Adding, subtracting, and comparing 2-digit numbers

Object of the game To earn more points than the other player.

Directions

1. Shuffle the cards. Stack them weight-side down.

2. Player 1 turns over the two top cards. Player 2 turns over the next card.

3. Player 1 finds the total weight of the animals on his or her cards. He or she tells whether the total is more or less than the weight of Player 2's animal.

4. If the total is more, Player 1 scores the difference between his or her total and Player 2's cards. If it is less, Player 2 scores the difference between his or her card and Player 1's total. In case of a tie, neither player scores.

5. Players trade roles and keep playing.

6. The game ends when all cards from the stack have been played. The player with more points wins.

Another Way to Play

◆ Use the Length cards to play a game that compares the lengths of animals.

GAME MASTER 20 | *Array Bingo* **Cards (A and B)**

A	A	A	B
2 by 2	2 by 3	2 by 4	4 by 4

A	A	B	B
2 by 5	2 by 6	3 by 5	6 by 3

A	A	A	B
3 by 3	1 by 7	4 by 3	3 by 6

B	A	B	B
5 by 3	6 by 1	4 by 5	5 by 4

GAME MASTER 21 — *Array Bingo* **Cards (C)**

C	**C**	**C**	**C**
2 × 2	2 × 3	2 × 4	4 × 4
C	**C**	**C**	**C**
2 × 5	2 × 6	3 × 5	6 × 3
C	**C**	**C**	**C**
3 × 3	1 × 7	4 × 3	3 × 6
C	**C**	**C**	**C**
5 × 3	6 × 1	4 × 5	5 × 4

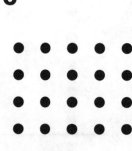
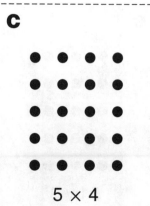

Array Bingo Cards (D, Front)

D 7×7	**D** 7×6	**D** 7×5	**D** 7×4
D 7×3	**D** 6×2	**D** 5×7	**D** 4×7
D 5×2	**D** 6×6	**D** 5×5	**D** 5×6
D 6×5	**D** 4×6	**D** 6×4	**D** 2×7

Array Bingo Cards (D, Back)

D

7 × 4

D

7 × 5

D

7 × 6

D

7 × 7

D

4 × 7

D

5 × 7

D

6 × 2

D

7 × 3

D

5 × 6

D

5 × 5

D

6 × 6

D

5 × 2

D

2 × 7

D

6 × 4

D

4 × 6

D

6 × 5

Array Bingo

GAME MASTER 24

Array Bingo **Number Cards**

49	42	35	28
21	12	35	28
10	36	25	30
30	24	24	14

Attribute Spinner Game Spinners

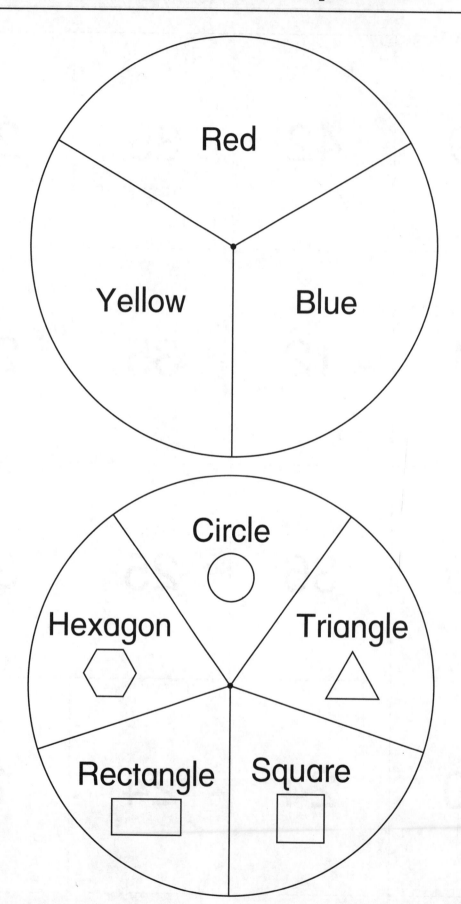

Attribute Spinner Game Spinners *cont.*

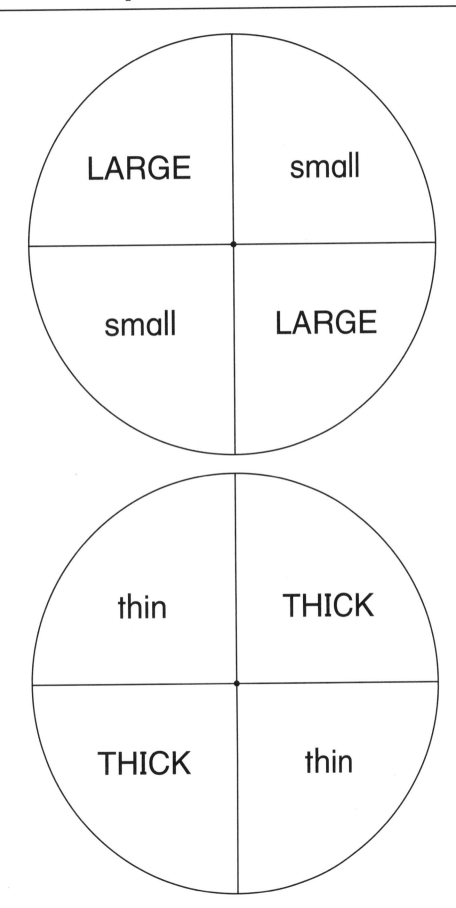

GAME MASTER 27 | *Attribute Train Game*

Materials   ☐ 1 set of attribute blocks

Players   3 to 5

Skill   Finding blocks that differ by just one attribute (shape, size, or color)

Object of the game To put the last block in the train, or to have the fewest blocks left.

Directions

1. Players put the blocks between them.

2. The first player takes a block and puts it down to start a train.

3. The second player chooses a block that is different in only one way—shape, size, or color—from the first block. The second player adds that block to the train.

4. Players take turns until no more blocks can be played.

5. The last player to put a block in the train wins.

EXAMPLE

small red circle	small red **triangle**	small **yellow** triangle	**large** yellow triangle	large **blue** triangle

Another Way to Play

1. Players share the blocks equally among all of the players.

2. The first player begins the train by laying down a block.

3. The next player adds a block that is different in only one way.

4. Players take turns. Any player who does not have a block that is different in only one way loses that turn.

5. Play continues until no more blocks can be played.

6. The player with the fewest blocks left wins.

Place-Value Mat

Cubes		
1s		
Pennies		
$0.01 1¢		

Longs		
10s		
Dimes		
$0.10 10¢		

Flats		
100s		
Dollars		
$1.00 100¢		

Base-10 Exchange and Base-10 Trading

Materials	☐ 2 Place-Value Mats
	☐ 2 dice
	☐ base-10 blocks
Players	2
Skill	Place-value concepts; counting and exchanging blocks

Base-10 Exchange

Directions

1. Players put 1 flat, 30 longs, and 30 cubes in a "bank".

2. Players take turns. For each turn, a player rolls the dice and announces the total number of dots.

3. The player who rolled takes that number of cubes from the bank and places them in the Cubes column of the mat.

4. Whenever possible, a player exchanges 10 cubes for 1 long and places it in the Longs column. When there are 10 longs, a player exchanges them for 1 flat.

5. The player not rolling the dice checks the exchanges.

6. The first player to make an exchange for a flat wins.

Base-10 Trading

Directions

1. Players put 20 longs and 40 cubes in a "bank". Each player puts 1 flat on his or her Place-Value Mat.

2. Players take turns. For each turn, a player rolls the dice and announces the total number of dots.

3. The player who rolled returns that number of cubes to the bank. A player makes exchanges with the bank as needed.

4. The player not rolling the dice checks the exchanges.

5. The first player to clear his or her mat wins.

GAME MASTER
30

Place-Value Mat

Cubes

$0.01
0.01

Hundredths

Pennies

Longs

$0.10
0.1

Tenths

Dimes

Flats

$1.00
1

Ones

Dollars

GAME MASTER 31

Base-10 Decimal Exchange

Materials   ☐   2 Place-Value Mats

              ☐   2 dice

              ☐   base-10 blocks: 1 flat, 30 longs, and 30 cubes

Players   2

Skill   Decimal place value; counting and exchanging blocks

Object of the game   To make an exchange for a flat (one).

Directions

1. Players put the base-10 blocks in a "bank" between them. The cubes are hundredths, the longs are tenths, and the flats are ones.

2. Players take turns. For each turn, a player rolls the dice and announces the total number of dots.

3. The player who rolled takes that number of cubes from the bank and places them in the Cubes column of the mat.

4. Whenever possible, a player exchanges 10 cubes for 1 long and places it in the Longs column. When there are 10 longs, a player exchanges them for 1 flat.

5. The player not rolling the dice checks the exchanges.

6. The first player to make an exchange for a flat (one) wins.

Advanced Version

♦ Players use the Place-Value Mat with thousandths, and 1 big cube, 30 flats, 30 longs, and 30 cubes. The cubes are thousandths, the longs are hundredths, the flats are tenths, and the big cube is one. The first player to exchange 10 flats for a big cube wins.

Place-Value Mat (Thousandths)

one-thousandth
$\dfrac{1}{1,000}$
0.001

one-hundredth
$\dfrac{1}{100}$
0.01

one-tenth
$\dfrac{1}{10}$
0.1

ONE
$\dfrac{1}{1}$
1

Baseball Multiplication Game Mat

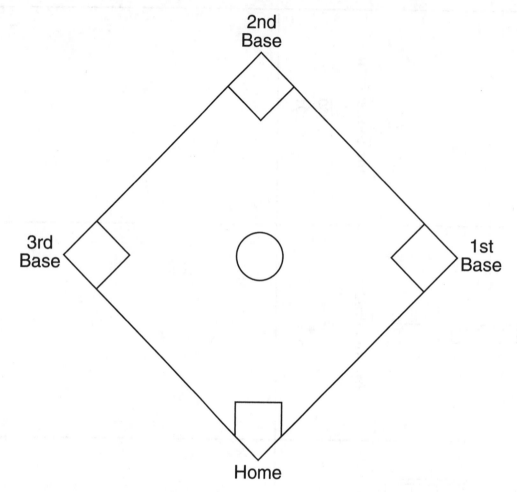

2nd
Base

3rd
Base

1st
Base

Home

Scoreboard				
Inning	1	2	3	Final
Team 1				
Team 2				

Runs-and-Outs Tally			
Team 1		Team 2	
Runs	Outs	Runs	Outs

Hitting Table (for 2 six-sided dice)	
36 = Home run (score a run)	6 to 15 = Single (1 base)
25 to 35 = Triple (3 bases)	5 or less = Out (record an out)
16 to 24 = Double (2 bases)	

GAME MASTER 34 — Hitting Tables (Advanced Versions)

1 to 10 Facts	
90 to 100 = Home run (score a run)	25 to 45 = Single (1 base)
72 to 81 = Triple (3 bases)	1 to 21 = Out (record an out)
48 to 70 = Double (2 bases)	

10s * 10s Game with 2 Dice	
3,600 = Home run (score a run)	600 to 1,500 = Single (1 base)
2,600 to 3,500 = Triple (3 bases)	500 or less = Out (record an out)
1,600 to 2,500 = Double (2 bases)	

1 to 12 Facts	
80 to 144 = Home run (score a run)	25 to 49 = Single (1 base)
66 to 77 = Triple (3 bases)	1 to 24 = Out (record an out)
50 to 64 = Double (2 bases)	

2 to 12 Facts	
80 to 144 = Home run (score a run)	25 to 49 = Single (1 base)
66 to 77 = Triple (3 bases)	4 to 24 = Out (record an out)
50 to 64 = Double (2 bases)	

Three-Factors Game	
180 to 216 = Home run (score a run)	60 to 90 = Single (1 base)
125 to 150 = Triple (3 bases)	1 to 54 = Out (record an out)
96 to 120 = Double (2 bases)	

10s * 10s Game with 4 Dice	
7,200 to 8,100 = Home run (score a run)	2,100 to 4,000 = Single (1 base)
5,600 to 6,400 = Triple (3 bases)	100 to 2,000 = Out (record an out)
4,200 to 5,400 = Double (2 bases)	

Basketball Addition

	Points Scored			
	Team 1		Team 2	
	1st Half	2nd Half	1st Half	2nd Half
Player 1				
Player 2				
Player 3				
Player 4				
Player 5				
Team Score				

Scoreboard

Point Totals	1st Half	2nd Half	Final
Team 1	_____	_____	_____
Team 2	_____	_____	_____

1. Which team won the first half? _____

By how much? _____ points

2. Which team won the second half? _____

By how much? _____ points

3. Which team won the game? _____

By how much? _____ points

Basketball Addition

GAME MASTER 36 | **Fact Power Table**

0 + 0	0 + 1	0 + 2	0 + 3	0 + 4	0 + 5	0 + 6	0 + 7	0 + 8	0 + 9
1 + 0	1 + 1	1 + 2	1 + 3	1 + 4	1 + 5	1 + 6	1 + 7	1 + 8	1 + 9
2 + 0	2 + 1	2 + 2	2 + 3	2 + 4	2 + 5	2 + 6	2 + 7	2 + 8	2 + 9
3 + 0	3 + 1	3 + 2	3 + 3	3 + 4	3 + 5	3 + 6	3 + 7	3 + 8	3 + 9
4 + 0	4 + 1	4 + 2	4 + 3	4 + 4	4 + 5	4 + 6	4 + 7	4 + 8	4 + 9
5 + 0	5 + 1	5 + 2	5 + 3	5 + 4	5 + 5	5 + 6	5 + 7	5 + 8	5 + 9
6 + 0	6 + 1	6 + 2	6 + 3	6 + 4	6 + 5	6 + 6	6 + 7	6 + 8	6 + 9
7 + 0	7 + 1	7 + 2	7 + 3	7 + 4	7 + 5	7 + 6	7 + 7	7 + 8	7 + 9
8 + 0	8 + 1	8 + 2	8 + 3	8 + 4	8 + 5	8 + 6	8 + 7	8 + 8	8 + 9
9 + 0	9 + 1	9 + 2	9 + 3	9 + 4	9 + 5	9 + 6	9 + 7	9 + 8	9 + 9

Beat the Calculator Triangle

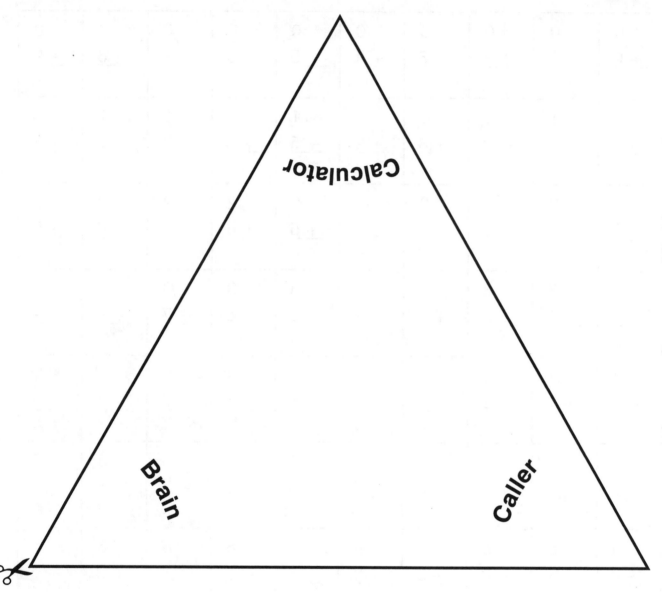

Using the Triangle

1. Players sit around a table. Place the triangle in the middle of the table.

2. Look at how the triangle is pointing at the players. Use the triangle to decide who will be the Calculator, the Caller, and the Brain.

3. After every 10 games, rotate the triangle to give each player a new role.

         Beat the Calculator (Addition)

GAME MASTER 38

Beat the Calculator: Multiplication (Advanced)

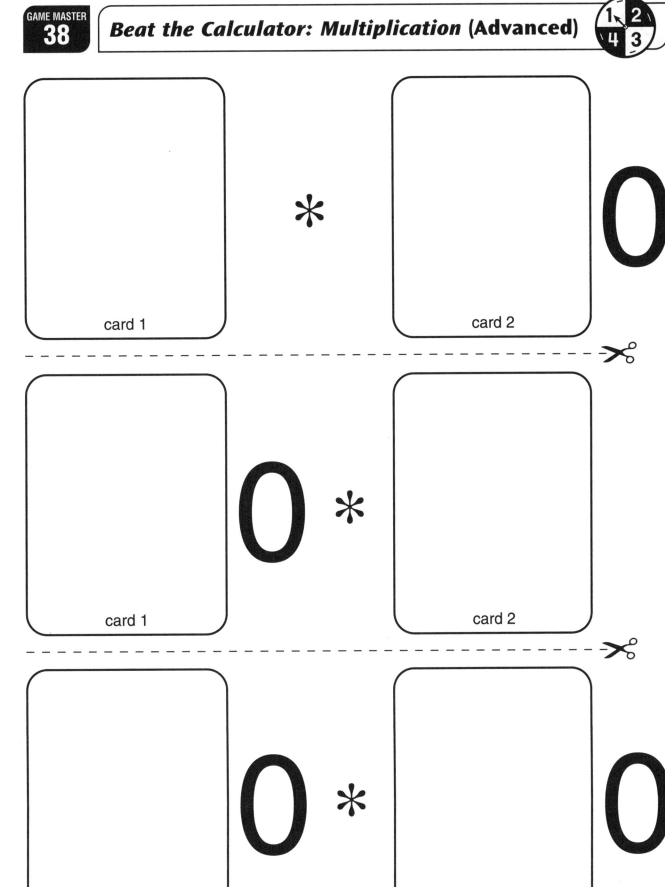

card 1   *   card 2   0

0   *   card 2

card 1

0   *   card 2   0

card 1

Broken Calculator

Materials   ☐ 1 Record Sheet

☐ 1 calculator

Players   2

Skill   Finding equivalent names for numbers

Object of the game To have the lower final score.

Directions

1. Players pretend that one of the number keys is broken.

2. One player says a number.

3. The other player tries to display that number on the calculator without using the "broken" key.

4. A player's score is the number of keys pressed to display the number.

5. After 5 rounds, each player finds his or her total score. The player with the lower score wins.

Advanced Versions

Broken Operation Key

Players pretend that one of the operation keys is broken. One player says an open sentence, such as $452 + x = 735$. The other player tries to solve the sentence on the calculator without using the broken key. A player's score in each round is the number of guesses it took to get a true number sentence. The player with the lower score wins.

Negative Numbers

Players choose a starting number, ending number, and broken key and record them. They change the display in their calculators from the starting number to the ending number without using the broken key by **only adding or subtracting negative numbers.** Scoring is the same as for the basic game.

GAME MASTER 40 | *Broken Calculator* **(Operations)**

Broken Key:	
To Solve:	

Broken Key:	
To Solve:	

Broken Key:	
To Solve:	

Broken Key:	
To Solve:	

Broken Key:	
To Solve:	

Broken Key:	
To Solve:	

GAME MASTER 41   *Broken Calculator* **(Negative Numbers)**

Change the display in the calculator without using the "broken" key. *You may only add and subtract negative numbers to reach the ending number.* Choose different starting numbers, ending numbers, and broken keys, and follow the example given in the first row.

Starting Number	Ending Number	Broken Key	Keystrokes
38	48	0	38 [−] [(−)] 5 [−] [(−)] 5 [Enter =]

Make up five problems of your own. When you have finished, trade papers with your partner, and solve each other's problems. *You may only add and subtract negative numbers to reach the ending number.*

Starting Number	Ending Number	Broken Key	Keystrokes

GAME MASTER 42

Build-It Game Mat

Closest to 0

Closest to 1

Closest to 0

Closest to 1

Build-It Card Deck

$\dfrac{5}{9}$	$\dfrac{1}{3}$	$\dfrac{11}{12}$	$\dfrac{1}{12}$
$\dfrac{7}{12}$	$\dfrac{3}{8}$	$\dfrac{1}{4}$	$\dfrac{1}{5}$
$\dfrac{2}{3}$	$\dfrac{3}{7}$	$\dfrac{4}{7}$	$\dfrac{3}{4}$
$\dfrac{3}{5}$	$\dfrac{4}{5}$	$\dfrac{7}{9}$	$\dfrac{5}{6}$

GAME MASTER 44

6-Part and Blank Spinners

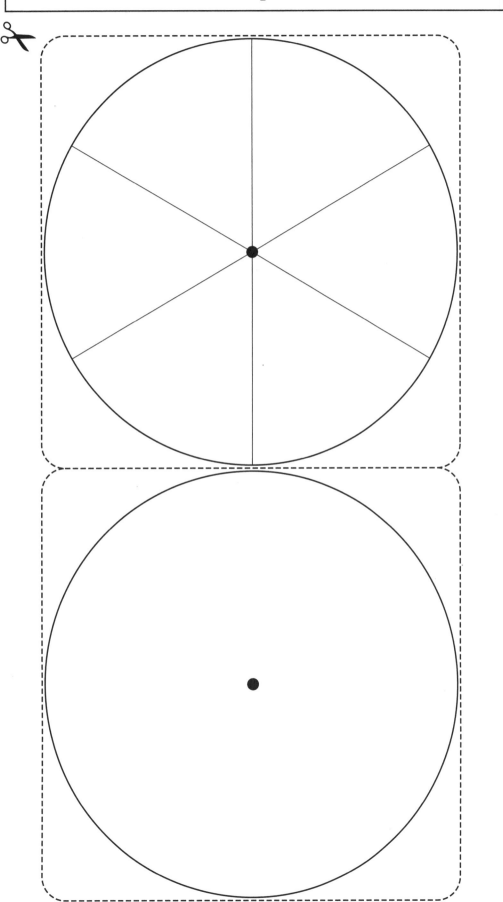

GAME MASTER 45

Bunny Hop

TAB

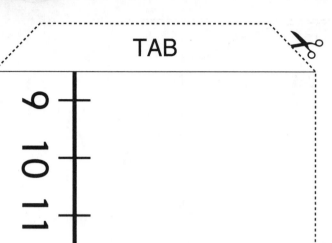

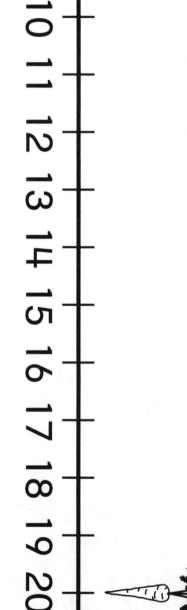

9 10 11 12 13 14 15 16 17 18 19 20

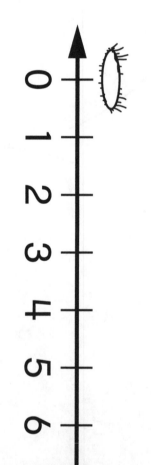

0 1 2 3 4 5 6 7 8

GAME MASTER 46

Chances Are Game Mat

EVENT CARDS

PROBABILITY CARDS

GAME MASTER 47 *Chances Are* **Event Cards**

It is _____
that Katie's spinner will land
on an odd number.

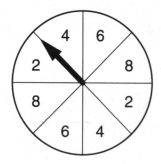

It is _____
that Jimal's spinner will land
on a number greater than 2.

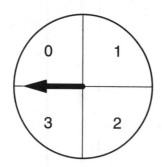

It is _____
that Omar's spinner will
land on an even number.

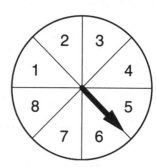

It is _____
that Emily's spinner will land
on a number less than 5.

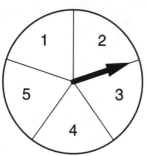

It is _____
that Benji's spinner will land
on a 2-digit number.

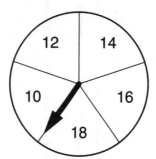

It is _____
that LaShawn will roll a 7.

regular 6-sided die

It is _____
that Ryan will roll a 6.

regular 6-sided die

It is _____
that Mei will roll an even
number.

regular 6-sided die

It is _____
that Shana will roll a
number greater than 1.

regular 6-sided die

Chances Are

Chances Are **Event Cards** *continued*

It is _____ that Charlene will roll a number less than 7.

regular 6-sided die

If Carlos takes a ball without looking, it is _____ that he will choose a blue ball.

If Tamika takes a ball without looking, it is _____ that she will choose a red ball.

If Emil takes a ball without looking, it is _____ that he will choose a green ball.

If Priya takes a ball without looking, it is _____ that she will choose a red ball.

If Marta takes a ball without looking, it is _____ that she will choose a yellow ball.

If Chelsea chooses a block without looking, it is _____ that she will choose a green block.

If Ling chooses a block without looking, it is _____ that he will choose a red block.

If Dimitri chooses a block without looking, it is _____ that he will choose a green block.

GAME MASTER 49

Chances Are Probability Cards

Impossible	Impossible	Impossible
No chance	No chance	No chance
Can't happen	Can't happen	Can't happen
No way	No way	No way
Unlikely	Unlikely	Unlikely
Less than half	Less than half	Less than half
Slight chance	Slight chance	Slight chance
Not much	Not much	Not much
Unlikely	50-50	50-50
Less than half	About half	About half
Slight chance	Even chance	Even chance
Not much		

GAME MASTER 50

Chances Are Probability Cards *continued*

50-50 About half Even chance	50-50 About half Even chance	Likely More than half Good chance Probably
Likely More than half Good chance Probably	Likely More than half Good chance Probably	Likely More than half Good chance Probably
Certain Sure thing Positive Absolutely	Certain Sure thing Positive Absolutely	Certain Sure thing Positive Absolutely

GAME MASTER 51

Checkerboard

GAME MASTER 52

Coin Top-It

(D) (D) (N)		(D) (N) (P) (P) (P)	
(Q) (P) (P) (P)		(D) (D) (D) (D)	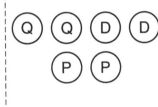
		(Q) (D) (D) (N) (N) (N) (N) (P)	(Q) (Q) (D) (D) (P) (P)
(D) (D) (Q) (N) (Q) (Q)	(Q) (Q) (N) (P) (D) (Q) (N)	(D) (D) (D) (D) (D) (D) (D) (Q)	(D) (Q) (D) (N) (D) (Q) (D) (N)

GAME MASTER 53 Coin Cards

(N)(N)(P)
(P)(P)(P)

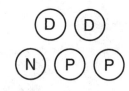

(Q)(D)(P)
(P)(P)(P)

(Q)(D)(N)
(P)(P)(P)

(Q)(D)(D)
(P)(P)(P)

(Q)(Q)(D)
(N)(P)(P)

(Q)(Q)(D)
(D)(P)

(Q)(Q)(D)
(P)(P)(P)

(Q)(Q)(Q)
(N)(P)
(P)(P)

(Q)(Q)(Q)
(D)(N)(P)

(Q)(Q)(Q)
(D)(D)(P)

(Q)(Q)(Q)
(D)(D)(N)

(Q)(Q)(Q)(Q)
(D)(P)(P)

Cover All Game Mats

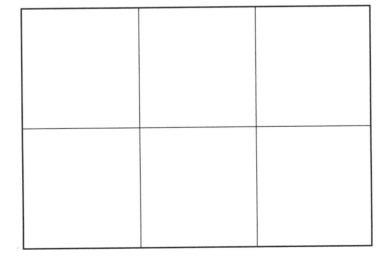

Cover All **Game Mats** *continued*

Cover All

Cover Half

Materials   ☐ 1 game mat

☐ 1 die marked 1, 2, 3, 1, 2, 3

☐ counters

Players   2

Skill   Counting, recognizing half of a group

Object of the game To cover half of the game mat.

Directions

1. Players take turns rolling the die.

2. For each roll, the player puts that many counters on the mat.

3. The game ends when half of the game mat is covered.

<table>
<tr><td></td><td></td><td></td><td></td></tr>
<tr><td></td><td></td><td></td><td></td></tr>
<tr><td></td><td></td><td></td><td></td></tr>
<tr><td></td><td></td><td></td><td></td></tr>
</table>

GAME MASTER 57

Credits/Debits Games Record Sheets

Record Sheet: Credits/Debits Game

	Start	Change	End, and next Start
1	+ $10		
2			
3			
4			
5			
6			
7			
8			
9			
10			

Record Sheet: Credits/Debits Game (Advanced Version)

	Start	Change		End, and next Start
		Add or Subtract	Credit or Debit	
1				
2				
3				
4				
5				
6				
7				
8				
9				
10				

Number line (vertical): −22 −21 −20 −19 −18 −17 −16 −15 −14 −13 −12 −11 −10 −9 −8 −7 −6 −5 −4 −3 −2 −1 0 1 2 3 4 5 6 7 8 9 10 11 12 13 14 15 16 17 18 19 20 21 22

GAME MASTER 58 — *Credits/Debits Game*

Materials
- ☐ *Credits/Debits Game* Gameboard (or 2 Record Sheets)
- ☐ Everything Math Deck

Players   2

Skill   Adding positive and negative numbers

Object of the game   To have the greater balance.

Directions

1. One player shuffles the deck and places it whole-number side down.

2. Each player begins with a balance of +$10.

3. Players take turns. For each turn, a player draws a card. The card tells the dollar amount and whether it is a credit or debit. The black numbers are "credits," and the blue numbers are "debits."

4. The player records the credit (positive) or debit (negative) in the "Change" column. The player adds the credit or debit to adjust the balance, records the result in the "End" column, and copies the result into the "Start" column in the next row.

5. At the end of 10 turns each, the player with more money wins. If both players have negative amounts, the player whose amount is closer to 0 wins.

EXAMPLE   Beth has a "Start" balance of +$20. She draws a black 4. This is a credit of $4, so she records +$4 in the "Change" column. She adds $4 to the balance: $20 + $4 = $24. She records +$24 in the "End" column, and +$24 in the "Start" column on the next line.

Alex has a "Start" balance of +$10. He draws a blue 12. This is a debit of $12, so he records −$12 in the "Change" column. He adds −$12 to the bottom line: $10 + (−$12) = −$2. Alex records −$2 in the "End" column. He also records −$2 in the "Start" column on the next line.

GAME MASTER 59 *Dart Game*

Materials   ☐ Transparent mirror

Players   2

Skill   Finding lines of reflection

Object of the game To have the higher score.

Directions

1. Players practice before playing the game. One player uses Dart A and the other player uses Dart B. Players try to hit the target with their own darts, using the transparent mirror. **Players should not practice with each other's darts.**

2. After practicing, players switch darts. Each player uses the dart that he or she did not use for practice.

3. Players take turns. For each turn, a player tries to hit the target by placing the transparent mirror on the page **without looking through the mirror.**

4. After a player has placed the mirror on the page, he or she looks through the mirror to see where the dart hit the target.

5. Players record their scores. The player with the higher total score after 3 rounds wins.

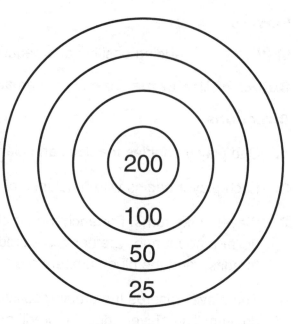

GAME MASTER 60 | **Movement Cards**

JUMP

CLAP

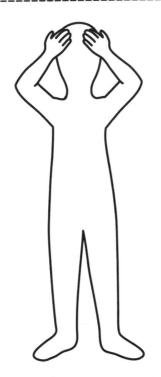

TOUCH HEAD

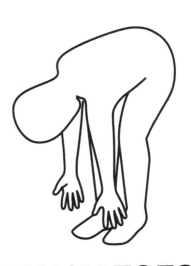

TOUCH TOES

GAME MASTER 61 | **Movement Cards** *continued*

HOP

PAT TUMMY

TAP SHOULDERS

NOD HEAD

Dice Movement

GAME MASTER 62 | **_Dice Race_ Grid (1–6)**

1	2	3	4	5	6
1	2	3	4	5	6
1	2	3	4	5	6
1	2	3	4	5	6
1	2	3	4	5	6
1	2	3	4	5	6
1	**2**	**3**	**4**	**5**	**6**

GAME MASTER 63

Dice Race Grid (2–12)

2	2	2	2	2	2	2	2	2	2
3	3	3	3	3	3	3	3	3	3
4	4	4	4	4	4	4	4	4	4
5	5	5	5	5	5	5	5	5	5
6	6	6	6	6	6	6	6	6	6
7	7	7	7	7	7	7	7	7	7
8	8	8	8	8	8	8	8	8	8
9	9	9	9	9	9	9	9	9	9
10	10	10	10	10	10	10	10	10	10
11	11	11	11	11	11	11	11	11	11
12	12	12	12	12	12	12	12	12	12

GAME MASTER 64

Dime-Nickel-Penny Grab Record Sheet

	Dimes ⓓ	Nickels ⓝ	Pennies ⓟ	My Total	My Partner's Total
Round 1					
Round 2					
Round 3					
Round 4					

GAME MASTER 65 **Divisibility Dash Record Sheets**

Record Sheet

Player 1

Round	Cards in your hand	Divisor	2-digit or 3-digit multiples
1			
2			
3			
4			
5			
6			
7			
8			
9			
10			

Record Sheet

Player 2

Round	Cards in your hand	Divisor	2-digit or 3-digit multiples
1			
2			
3			
4			
5			
6			
7			
8			
9			
10			

GAME MASTER 66

Division Arrays Record Sheet

Your score is the number of counters per row. If there are 0 leftover counters, your score is double the number of counters per row.

Round	Counters in All	Number of Rows	Counters per Row	Leftover Counters	Score
Sample	14	3	4	2	4
1					
2					
3					
4					
5					
				Total Score	

 ✂ -

 GAME MASTER 66

Division Arrays Record Sheet

Your score is the number of counters per row. If there are 0 leftover counters, your score is double the number of counters per row.

Round	Counters in All	Number of Rows	Counters per Row	Leftover Counters	Score
Sample	14	3	4	2	4
1					
2					
3					
4					
5					
				Total Score	

GAME MASTER 67

Division Dash **Record Sheet**

	Division Problem	Quotient	Score
Sample	49 ÷ 4	12 R1	12
1			
2			
3			
4			
5			
6			

GAME MASTER 67

Division Dash **Record Sheet**

	Division Problem	Quotient	Score
Sample	49 ÷ 4	12 R1	12
1			
2			
3			
4			
5			
6			

Name _____ Date _____ Time _____

 Doggone Decimal Record Sheet

For each round, circle the Target Number. Then write a number sentence by recording the numbers you form and the product of those numbers.

Player 1

Target Number	0.1 1 10 100
Number Sentence	_____ * _____ = _____
Target Number	0.1 1 10 100
Number Sentence	_____ * _____ = _____
Target Number	0.1 1 10 100
Number Sentence	_____ * _____ = _____
Target Number	0.1 1 10 100
Number Sentence	_____ * _____ = _____

 ✂ --

 Doggone Decimal Record Sheet

For each round, circle the Target Number. Then write a number sentence by recording the numbers you form and the product of those numbers.

Player 2

Target Number	0.1 1 10 100
Number Sentence	_____ * _____ = _____
Target Number	0.1 1 10 100
Number Sentence	_____ * _____ = _____
Target Number	0.1 1 10 100
Number Sentence	_____ * _____ = _____
Target Number	0.1 1 10 100
Number Sentence	_____ * _____ = _____

GAME MASTER 69

Dollar Rummy Cards

10¢	20¢	30¢	40¢
Dollar Rummy	Dollar Rummy	Dollar Rummy	Dollar Rummy
10¢	20¢	30¢	40¢

50¢	50¢	50¢	50¢
Dollar Rummy	Dollar Rummy	Dollar Rummy	Dollar Rummy
50¢	50¢	50¢	50¢

60¢	70¢	80¢	90¢
Dollar Rummy	Dollar Rummy	Dollar Rummy	Dollar Rummy
60¢	70¢	80¢	90¢

Dollar Rummy

GAME MASTER 70

Dollar Rummy Cards (Advanced)

5¢ Dollar Rummy 5¢	**15¢** Dollar Rummy 15¢	**25¢** Dollar Rummy 25¢	**25¢** Dollar Rummy 25¢
35¢ Dollar Rummy 35¢	**45¢** Dollar Rummy 45¢	**55¢** Dollar Rummy 55¢	**65¢** Dollar Rummy 65¢
75¢ Dollar Rummy 75¢	**75¢** Dollar Rummy 75¢	**85¢** Dollar Rummy 85¢	**95¢** Dollar Rummy 95¢

GAME MASTER 71 **Doubles or Nothing Record Sheet**

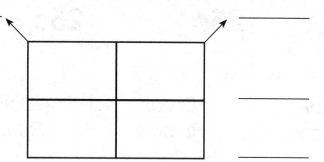

Total 1 _____

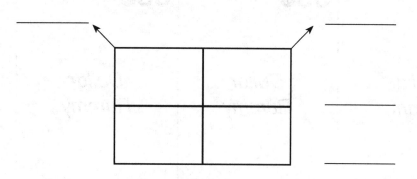

Total 2 _____

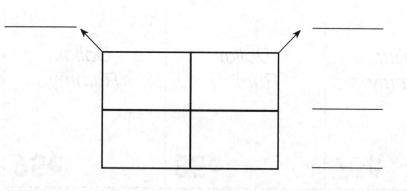

Total 3 _____

Grand Total _____

Doubles or Nothing

Materials
- ☐ 2 Record Sheets
- ☐ Everything Math Deck (number cards 0–9, 3 of each)
- ☐ 1 coin
- ☐ 1 calculator

Players   2

Skill   Addition facts

Object of the Game To get the higher (or lower) Grand Total.

Directions

1. One player shuffles and stacks the cards whole-number side down.

2. Players take turns. On your turn, take the top card. Write the number in any small rectangle on your Record Sheet.

3. When all 3 large rectangles are filled in, add the numbers across each row, down each column, and along the diagonals of each large rectangle.

4. Circle any pairs of identical sums for each large rectangle. Add the circled numbers to find the Total for that large rectangle.

5. If there are no pairs, the Total for that large rectangle is zero.

6. Use a calculator to add the 3 Totals. This is the Grand Total for all 3 large rectangles.

7. At the end of the game, one player flips a coin. If it lands on heads, the player with the higher Grand Total wins. If it lands on tails, the player with the lower Grand Total wins.

Fraction Cards 1

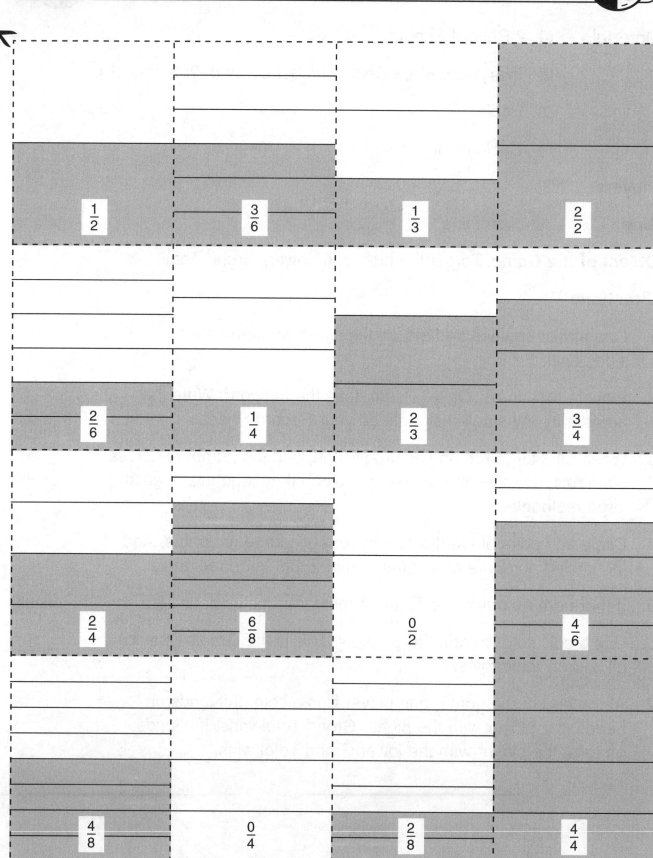

Equivalent Fractions Game

Name Date Time

GAME MASTER 74

Fraction Cards 2

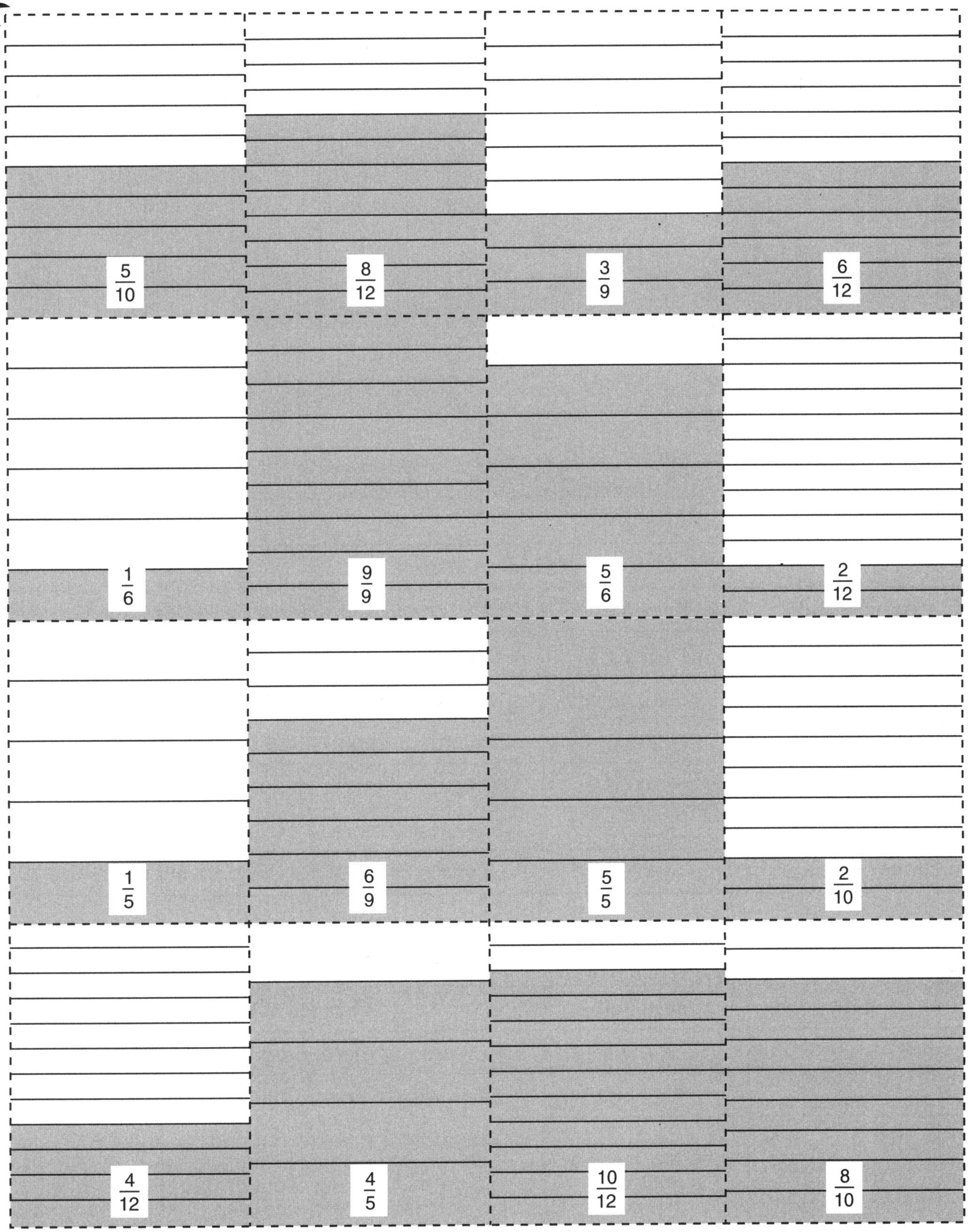

5/10
8/12
3/9
6/12
1/6
9/9
5/6
2/12
1/5
6/9
5/5
2/10
4/12
4/5
10/12
8/10

GAME MASTER 75

Exponent Ball Game Mat

Goal Line — 10 20 30 40 50 40 30 20 10 — Goal Line

10   20   30   40   50   40   30   20   10

Table 1: Runs

Value of Roll	Move Ball	Chances of Gaining on the Ground
1	−15 yd	−15 yards: 1 out of 6, or about 17%
2 to 6	+10 yd	10 yards or more: 5 out of 6, or about 83%
8 to 81	+20 yd	20 yards or more: 4 out of 6, or about 67%
in the 100s	+30 yd	30 yards or more: 13 out of 36, or about 36%
in the 1,000s	+40 yd	40 yards or more: 7 out of 36, or about 19%
in the 10,000s	+50 yd	50 yards: 1 out of 18, or about 6%

Table 2: Kicks

Roll	Move Ball	Chances of Kicking
1	+10 yd	10 yards or more: 6 out of 6, or 100%
2	+20 yd	20 yards or more: 5 out of 6, or about 83%
3	+30 yd	30 yards or more: 4 out of 6, or about 67%
4	+40 yd	40 yards or more: 3 out of 6, or 50%
5	+50 yd	50 yards or more: 2 out of 6, or about 33%
6	+60 yd	60 yards: 1 out of 6, or about 17%

GAME MASTER 76

Fact Power Game Mat

0 +0	0 +1	0 +2	0 +3	0 +4	0 +5	0 +6	0 +7	0 +8	0 +9
1 +0	1 +1	1 +2	1 +3	1 +4	1 +5	1 +6	1 +7	1 +8	1 +9
2 +0	2 +1	2 +2	2 +3	2 +4	2 +5	2 +6	2 +7	2 +8	2 +9
3 +0	3 +1	3 +2	3 +3	3 +4	3 +5	3 +6	3 +7	3 +8	3 +9
4 +0	4 +1	4 +2	4 +3	4 +4	4 +5	4 +6	4 +7	4 +8	4 +9
5 +0	5 +1	5 +2	5 +3	5 +4	5 +5	5 +6	5 +7	5 +8	5 +9
6 +0	6 +1	6 +2	6 +3	6 +4	6 +5	6 +6	6 +7	6 +8	6 +9
7 +0	7 +1	7 +2	7 +3	7 +4	7 +5	7 +6	7 +7	7 +8	7 +9
8 +0	8 +1	8 +2	8 +3	8 +4	8 +5	8 +6	8 +7	8 +8	8 +9
9 +0	9 +1	9 +2	9 +3	9 +4	9 +5	9 +6	9 +7	9 +8	9 +9

START → (top row)

END ← (bottom row)

GAME MASTER 77 *Factor Bingo* **Game Mat**

Write any of the numbers 2–90 in the grid above.

You may use a number only once.

To help you keep track of the numbers you use, circle them in the list.

	2	3	4	5	6	7	8	9	10
11	12	13	14	15	16	17	18	19	20
21	22	23	24	25	26	27	28	29	30
31	32	33	34	35	36	37	38	39	40
41	42	43	44	45	46	47	48	49	50
51	52	53	54	55	56	57	58	59	60
61	62	63	64	65	66	67	68	69	70
71	72	73	74	75	76	77	78	79	80
81	82	83	84	85	86	87	88	89	90

Factor Bingo

Factor Bingo

Materials   ☐ *Factor Bingo* Game Mat

                 ☐ Everything Math Deck (number cards 2–9, 4 of each)

                 ☐ 12 counters per player

Players   2–4

Skill   Finding factors of a number

Object of the Game   To cover 5 numbers in a row, a column, or a diagonal; or to cover 12 numbers anywhere on the Bingo grid.

Directions

1. Each player chooses 25 different numbers from 2 through 90 to fill in a Bingo grid. Players should mix the numbers up.

2. One player shuffles the cards, stacks them whole-number side down, and turns over the top card. This card is the "factor."

3. Players check their grids for a number that has the card number as a factor. Players who find such a number cover that number with a counter. A player may place only 1 counter on the grid for each card that is turned over.

4. Another player turns over the next card, and play continues.

5. The first player who covers 5 numbers in a row, column, or diagonal; or 12 numbers anywhere on the Bingo grid, calls out "Bingo!" and wins the game.

6. If all of the cards are used before someone wins, one player shuffles the cards and play continues.

GAME MASTER 79

Factor Captor Grid 1 (Beginning)

1	2	2	2	2	2
2	3	3	3	3	3
3	4	4	4	4	5
5	5	5	6	6	7
7	8	8	9	9	10
10	11	12	13	14	15
16	18	20	21	22	24
25	26	27	28	30	32

GAME MASTER 80

Factor Captor Grid 2 (Advanced)

1	2	2	2	2	2	3
3	3	3	3	4	4	4
4	5	5	5	5	6	6
6	7	7	8	8	9	9
10	10	11	12	13	14	15
16	17	18	19	20	21	22
23	24	25	26	27	28	30
32	33	34	35	36	38	39
40	42	44	45	46	48	49
50	51	52	54	55	56	60

GAME MASTER 81

Finding Factors Game Mat/Factor Strip

Game 1

1	2	3	4	5	6
7	8	9	10	12	14
15	16	18	20	21	24
25	27	28	30	32	35
36	40	42	45	48	49
54	56	63	64	72	81

Game 2

1	2	3	4	5	6
7	8	9	10	12	14
15	16	18	20	21	24
25	27	28	30	32	35
36	40	42	45	48	49
54	56	63	64	72	81

Factor Strip

9
8
7
6
5
4
3
2
1

GAME MASTER 82 *First to 100* **Record Sheet**

Example:

x =	Card Number	Number Model/ Response	Score
30	20	20 * 30 = 600	30

x =	Card Number	Number Model/ Response	Score

GAME MASTER 83

Fishing for Digits **Record Sheet**

	Beginning Number						
Round 1	New Number (first guess)						
	New Number (second guess)						
Round 2	New Number (first guess)						
	New Number (second guess)						
Round 3	New Number (first guess)						
	New Number (second guess)						
Round 4	New Number (first guess)						
	New Number (second guess)						
Round 5	New Number (first guess)						
	New Number (second guess)						

✂ -

GAME MASTER 83

Fishing for Digits **Record Sheet**

	Beginning Number						
Round 1	New Number (first guess)						
	New Number (second guess)						
Round 2	New Number (first guess)						
	New Number (second guess)						
Round 3	New Number (first guess)						
	New Number (second guess)						
Round 4	New Number (first guess)						
	New Number (second guess)						
Round 5	New Number (first guess)						
	New Number (second guess)						

500 Spinner/Score Sheet

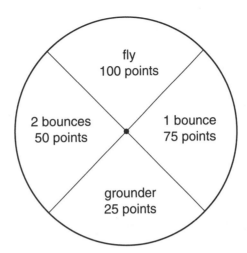

Score Sheet

Spin: Roll	Points Scored	Total Score
Grounder: catch	+25	25

Frac-Tac-Toe **Number-Card Board**

NUMERATOR PILE

PLACE CARDS FACEDOWN.

**WHEN ALL CARDS ARE USED,
SHUFFLE AND REPLACE.**

NUMERATOR PILE

PLAY EACH CARD FACEUP.

DENOMINATOR PILE

PLACE CARDS FACEDOWN.

**WHEN ALL CARDS ARE USED,
JUST REPLACE.
DO NOT SHUFFLE!**

DENOMINATOR PILE

PLAY EACH CARD FACEUP.

2-4-5-10 Frac-Tac-Toe (Decimal Version)

Before you begin playing, remove cards greater than 10 from the Everything Math Deck.

Use different-colored counters or coins as markers. If you use coins, one player is "heads" and the other player is "tails."

If you use a pencil to initial the squares, print lightly so you can erase and use the board again.

Remember that you need to cover 3 squares in a row in any direction (horizontal, vertical, or diagonal) to win.

Numerator Pile

All remaining cards

Denominator Pile

Two each of 2, 4, 5, and 10 cards

>1.0	0 or 1	>2.0	0 or 1	>1.0
0.1	0.2	0.25	0.3	0.4
>1.5	0.5	>1.5	0.5	>1.5
0.6	0.7	0.75	0.8	0.9
>1.0	0 or 1	>2.0	0 or 1	>1.0

GAME MASTER 87

2-4-5-10 Frac-Tac-Toe (Decimal Bingo Version)

Before you begin playing, remove cards greater than 10 from the Everything Math Deck.

Fill in the grid by entering these numbers in the empty spaces:

0	0	0.1	0.2	0.25	0.3	0.4	0.5
0.5	0.6	0.7	0.75	0.8	0.9	1	1

Use different-colored counters or coins as markers. If you use coins, one player is "heads" and the other player is "tails."

If you use a pencil to initial the squares, print lightly so you can erase and use the board again.

Remember that you need to cover 5 squares in a row in any direction (horizontal, vertical, or diagonal) to win.

Numerator Pile

All remaining cards

Denominator Pile

Two each of 2, 4, 5, and 10 cards

> 1.0		> 2.0		> 1.0
> 1.5		> 1.5		> 1.5
> 1.0		> 2.0		> 1.0

GAME MASTER 88

2-4-5-10 Frac-Tac-Toe (Percent Version)

Before you begin playing, remove cards greater than 10 from the Everything Math Deck.

Use different-colored counters or coins as markers. If you use coins, one player is "heads" and the other player is "tails."

If you use a pencil to initial the squares, print lightly so you can erase and use the board again.

Remember that you need to cover 3 squares in a row in any direction (horizontal, vertical, or diagonal) to win.

> **Numerator Pile**
>
> All remaining cards

> **Denominator Pile**
>
> Two each of 2, 4, 5, and 10 cards

>100%	0% or 100%	>200%	0% or 100%	>100%
10%	20%	25%	30%	40%
>100%	50%	>200%	50%	>100%
60%	70%	75%	80%	90%
>100%	0% or 100%	>200%	0% or 100%	>100%

GAME MASTER 89

2-4-5-10 Frac-Tac-Toe (Percent Bingo Version)

Before you begin playing, remove cards greater than 10 from the Everything Math Deck.

Fill in the grid by entering these numbers in the empty spaces:

0%	0%	10%	20%	25%	30%	40%	50%

50%	60%	70%	75%	80%	90%	100%	100%

Use different-colored counters or coins as markers. If you use coins, one player is "heads" and the other player is "tails."

If you use a pencil to initial the squares, print lightly so you can erase and use the board again.

Remember that you need to cover 5 squares in a row in any direction (horizontal, vertical, or diagonal) to win.

Numerator
Pile

All remaining
cards

Denominator
Pile

Two each
of 2, 4, 5,
and 10 cards

>100%		>200%		>100%
>100%		>200%		>100%
>100%		>300%		>100%

GAME MASTER 90 | **2-4-8 Frac-Tac-Toe (Decimal Version)**

Before you begin playing, remove cards greater than 10 from the Everything Math Deck.

Use different-colored counters or coins as markers. If you use coins, one player is "heads" and the other player is "tails."

If you use a pencil to initial the squares, print lightly so you can erase and use the board again.

Remember that you need to cover 3 squares in a row in any direction (horizontal, vertical, or diagonal) to win.

Numerator Pile

All remaining cards

Denominator Pile

Two each of 2, 4, and 8 cards

>2.0	0 or 1	>1.5	0 or 1	>2.0
1.5	0.125	0.25	0.375	1.5
>1.0	0.5	0.25 or 0.75	0.5	>1.0
2.0	0.625	0.75	0.875	2.0
>2.0	0 or 1	1.125	0 or 1	>2.0

GAME MASTER 91

2-4-8 Frac-Tac-Toe (Decimal Bingo Version)

Before you begin playing, remove cards greater than 10 from the Everything Math Deck.

Fill in the grid by entering these numbers in the empty spaces:

0	0	0.125	0.25	0.375	0.5	0.5	0.625

0.75	0.875	1	1	1.5	1.5	2	2

Use different-colored counters or coins as markers. If you use coins, one player is "heads" and the other player is "tails."

If you use a pencil to initial the squares, print lightly so you can erase and use the board again.

Remember that you need to cover 5 squares in a row in any direction (horizontal, vertical, or diagonal) to win.

Numerator Pile

All remaining cards

Denominator Pile

Two each of 2, 4, and 8 cards

> 2.0		> 1.5		> 2.0
> 1.0		0.25 or 0.75		> 1.0
> 2.0		1.125		> 2.0

GAME MASTER 92 | **2-4-8 Frac-Tac-Toe (Percent Version)**

Before you begin playing, remove cards greater than 10 from the Everything Math Deck.

Use different-colored counters or coins as markers. If you use coins, one player is "heads" and the other player is "tails."

If you use a pencil to initial the squares, print lightly so you can erase and use the board again.

Remember that you need to cover 3 squares in a row in any direction (horizontal, vertical, or diagonal) to win.

Numerator Pile

All remaining cards

Denominator Pile

Two each of 2, 4, and 8 cards

>200%	0% or 100%	>150%	0% or 100%	>200%
150%	$12\frac{1}{2}\%$	25%	$37\frac{1}{2}\%$	150%
>100%	50%	25% or 75%	50%	>100%
200%	$62\frac{1}{2}\%$	75%	$87\frac{1}{2}\%$	200%
>200%	0% or 100%	$112\frac{1}{2}\%$	0% or 100%	>200%

GAME MASTER 93

2-4-8 Frac-Tac-Toe (Percent Bingo Version)

Before you begin playing, remove cards greater than 10 from the Everything Math Deck.

Fill in the grid by entering these numbers in the empty spaces:

0%   0% $12\frac{1}{2}$%   25% $37\frac{1}{2}$%   50%   50% $62\frac{1}{2}$%

75% $87\frac{1}{2}$%   100%   100%   150%   150%   200%   200%

Use different-colored counters or coins as markers. If you use coins, one player is "heads" and the other player is "tails."

If you use a pencil to initial the squares, print lightly so you can erase and use the board again.

Remember that you need to cover 5 squares in a row in any direction (horizontal, vertical, or diagonal) to win.

Numerator Pile
All remaining cards

Denominator Pile
Two each of 2, 4, and 8 cards

>200%		>150%		>200%
>100%		25% or 75%		>100%
>200%		$112\frac{1}{2}$%		>200%

3-6-9 Frac-Tac-Toe (Decimal Version)

Before you begin playing, remove cards greater than 10 from the Everything Math Deck.

Use different-colored counters or coins as markers. If you use coins, one player is "heads" and the other player is "tails."

If you use a pencil to initial the squares, print lightly so you can erase and use the board again.

Remember that you need to cover 3 squares in a row in any direction (horizontal, vertical, or diagonal) to win.

Numerator Pile

All remaining cards

Denominator Pile

Two each of 3, 6, and 9 cards

>1.0	0 or 1	$0.\overline{1}$	0 or 1	>1.0
$0.1\overline{6}$	$0.\overline{2}$	$0.\overline{3}$	$0.\overline{3}$	$0.\overline{4}$
>2.0	$0.\overline{5}$	>1.0	$0.\overline{6}$	>2.0
$0.\overline{6}$	$0.\overline{7}$	$0.8\overline{3}$	$0.\overline{8}$	$1.\overline{3}$
>1.0	0 or 1	$1.\overline{6}$	0 or 1	>1.0

GAME MASTER 95

3-6-9 Frac-Tac-Toe (Decimal Bingo Version)

Before you begin playing, remove cards greater than 10 from the Everything Math Deck.

Fill in the grid by entering these numbers in the empty spaces:

0	0	$0.1\overline{6}$	$0.\overline{3}$	$0.\overline{3}$	$0.\overline{6}$
$0.\overline{6}$	$0.8\overline{3}$	1	1	$1.\overline{3}$	$1.\overline{6}$

Use different-colored counters or coins as markers. If you use coins, one player is "heads" and the other player is "tails."

If you use a pencil to initial the squares, print lightly so you can erase and use the board again.

Remember that you need to cover 5 squares in a row in any direction (horizontal, vertical, or diagonal) to win.

> **Numerator Pile**
>
> All remaining cards

> **Denominator Pile**
>
> Two each of 3, 6, and 9 cards

> 1.0		$0.\overline{1}$		> 1.0
	$0.\overline{2}$			$0.\overline{4}$
> 2.0	$0.\overline{5}$	> 1.0		> 2.0
	$0.\overline{7}$		$0.\overline{8}$	
> 1.0				> 1.0

GAME MASTER 96

3-6-9 Frac-Tac-Toe (Percent Version)

Before you begin playing, remove cards greater than 10 from the Everything Math Deck.

Use different-colored counters or coins as markers. If you use coins, one player is "heads" and the other player is "tails."

If you use a pencil to initial the squares, print lightly so you can erase and use the board again.

Remember that you need to cover 3 squares in a row in any direction (horizontal, vertical, or diagonal) to win.

Numerator Pile

All remaining cards

Denominator Pile

· Two each of 3, 6, and 9 cards

>100%	0% or 100%	11.1%	0% or 100%	>100%
$16\frac{2}{3}\%$	22.2%	$33\frac{1}{3}\%$	33.3%	44.4%
>200%	55.5%	>100%	66.6%	>200%
$66\frac{2}{3}\%$	77.7%	$83\frac{1}{3}\%$	88.8%	$133\frac{1}{3}\%$
>100%	0% or 100%	$166\frac{2}{3}\%$	0% or 100%	>100%

GAME MASTER 97

3-6-9 Frac-Tac-Toe (Percent Bingo Version)

Before you begin playing, remove cards greater than 10 from the Everything Math Deck.

Fill in the grid by entering these numbers in the empty spaces:

0%	0%	100%	$16\frac{2}{3}\%$	$33\frac{1}{3}\%$	33.3%
66.6%	$83\frac{1}{3}\%$	100%	$133\frac{1}{3}\%$	$166\frac{2}{3}\%$	$66\frac{2}{3}\%$

Use different-colored counters or coins as markers. If you use coins, one player is "heads" and the other player is "tails."

If you use a pencil to initial the squares, print lightly so you can erase and use the board again.

Remember that you need to cover 5 squares in a row in any direction (horizontal, vertical, or diagonal) to win.

> **Numerator Pile**
>
> All remaining cards

> **Denominator Pile**
>
> Two each of 3, 6, and 9 cards

>100%		11.1%		>100%
	22.2%			44.4%
>200%	55.5%	>100%		>200%
	77.7%		88.8%	
>100%				>100%

GAME MASTER 98

Fraction Action/Fraction Friction Cards

$\dfrac{1}{2}$	$\dfrac{1}{3}$	$\dfrac{2}{3}$	$\dfrac{1}{4}$
$\dfrac{3}{4}$	$\dfrac{1}{6}$	$\dfrac{1}{6}$	$\dfrac{5}{6}$
$\dfrac{1}{12}$	$\dfrac{1}{12}$	$\dfrac{5}{12}$	$\dfrac{5}{12}$
$\dfrac{7}{12}$	$\dfrac{7}{12}$	$\dfrac{11}{12}$	$\dfrac{11}{12}$

GAME MASTER 99

Fraction Capture Game Mat

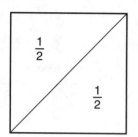

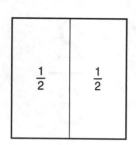

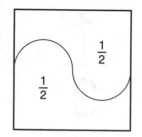

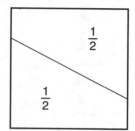

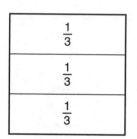

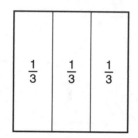

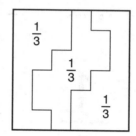

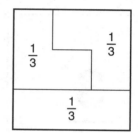

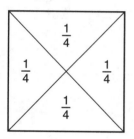

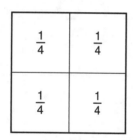

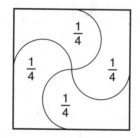

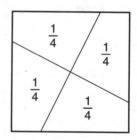

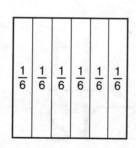

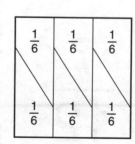

Fraction Capture **Record Sheet**

Player 1

Round	Dice Roll	Fraction	Fraction Addition Expression
1			
2			
3			
4			
5			
6			

Fraction Capture **Record Sheet**

Player 2

Round	Dice Roll	Fraction	Fraction Addition Expression
1			
2			
3			
4			
5			
6			

GAME MASTER 101

Fraction Match Cards

$\frac{0}{2}$ ⟶ $\frac{0}{2}$	$\frac{1}{2}$ ⟶ $\frac{1}{2}$	$\frac{2}{2}$ ⟶ $\frac{2}{2}$	$\frac{0}{3}$ ⟶ $\frac{0}{3}$
$\mathbf{\frac{0}{2}}$	$\mathbf{\frac{1}{2}}$	$\mathbf{\frac{2}{2}}$	$\mathbf{\frac{0}{3}}$
$\frac{1}{3}$ ⟶ $\frac{1}{3}$	$\frac{2}{3}$ ⟶ $\frac{2}{3}$	$\frac{3}{3}$ ⟶ $\frac{3}{3}$	$\frac{0}{4}$ ⟶ $\frac{0}{4}$
$\mathbf{\frac{1}{3}}$	$\mathbf{\frac{2}{3}}$	$\mathbf{\frac{3}{3}}$	$\mathbf{\frac{0}{4}}$
$\frac{1}{4}$ ⟶ $\frac{1}{4}$	$\frac{2}{4}$ ⟶ $\frac{2}{4}$	$\frac{3}{4}$ ⟶ $\frac{3}{4}$	$\frac{4}{4}$ ⟶ $\frac{4}{4}$
$\mathbf{\frac{1}{4}}$	$\mathbf{\frac{2}{4}}$	$\mathbf{\frac{3}{4}}$	$\mathbf{\frac{4}{4}}$
$\frac{0}{5}$ ⟶ $\frac{0}{5}$	$\frac{1}{5}$ ⟶ $\frac{1}{5}$	$\frac{2}{5}$ ⟶ $\frac{2}{5}$	$\frac{3}{5}$ ⟶ $\frac{3}{5}$
$\mathbf{\frac{0}{5}}$	$\mathbf{\frac{1}{5}}$	$\mathbf{\frac{2}{5}}$	$\mathbf{\frac{3}{5}}$

Fraction Match Cards *continued*

$\frac{4}{5}$ $\quad$ $\frac{4}{5}$	$\frac{5}{5}$ $\quad$ $\frac{5}{5}$	$\frac{0}{6}$ $\quad$ $\frac{0}{6}$	$\frac{1}{6}$ $\quad$ $\frac{1}{6}$
$\frac{\mathbf{4}}{\mathbf{5}}$	$\frac{\mathbf{5}}{\mathbf{5}}$	$\frac{\mathbf{0}}{\mathbf{6}}$	$\frac{\mathbf{1}}{\mathbf{6}}$
$\frac{2}{6}$ $\quad$ $\frac{2}{6}$	$\frac{3}{6}$ $\quad$ $\frac{3}{6}$	$\frac{4}{6}$ $\quad$ $\frac{4}{6}$	$\frac{5}{6}$ $\quad$ $\frac{5}{6}$
$\frac{\mathbf{2}}{\mathbf{6}}$	$\frac{\mathbf{3}}{\mathbf{6}}$	$\frac{\mathbf{4}}{\mathbf{6}}$	$\frac{\mathbf{5}}{\mathbf{6}}$
$\frac{6}{6}$ $\quad$ $\frac{6}{6}$	$\frac{0}{8}$ $\quad$ $\frac{0}{8}$	$\frac{2}{8}$ $\quad$ $\frac{2}{8}$	$\frac{4}{8}$ $\quad$ $\frac{4}{8}$
$\frac{\mathbf{6}}{\mathbf{6}}$	$\frac{\mathbf{0}}{\mathbf{8}}$	$\frac{\mathbf{2}}{\mathbf{8}}$	$\frac{\mathbf{4}}{\mathbf{8}}$
$\frac{6}{8}$ $\quad$ $\frac{6}{8}$	$\frac{8}{8}$ $\quad$ $\frac{8}{8}$	$\frac{0}{9}$ $\quad$ $\frac{0}{9}$	$\frac{3}{9}$ $\quad$ $\frac{3}{9}$
$\frac{\mathbf{6}}{\mathbf{8}}$	$\frac{\mathbf{8}}{\mathbf{8}}$	$\frac{\mathbf{0}}{\mathbf{9}}$	$\frac{\mathbf{3}}{\mathbf{9}}$

GAME MASTER 103 **Fraction Match Cards** *continued*

$\frac{6}{9}$ $\frac{6}{9}$ $$\frac{6}{9}$$	$\frac{9}{9}$ $\frac{9}{9}$ $$\frac{9}{9}$$	$\frac{0}{10}$ $\frac{0}{10}$ $$\frac{0}{10}$$	$\frac{2}{10}$ $\frac{2}{10}$ $$\frac{2}{10}$$
$\frac{4}{10}$ $\frac{4}{10}$ $$\frac{4}{10}$$	$\frac{5}{10}$ $\frac{5}{10}$ $$\frac{5}{10}$$	$\frac{6}{10}$ $\frac{6}{10}$ $$\frac{6}{10}$$	$\frac{8}{10}$ $\frac{8}{10}$ $$\frac{8}{10}$$
$\frac{10}{10}$ $\frac{10}{10}$ $$\frac{10}{10}$$	$\frac{0}{12}$ $\frac{0}{12}$ $$\frac{0}{12}$$	$\frac{2}{12}$ $\frac{2}{12}$ $$\frac{2}{12}$$	$\frac{3}{12}$ $\frac{3}{12}$ $$\frac{3}{12}$$
$\frac{4}{12}$ $\frac{4}{12}$ $$\frac{4}{12}$$	$\frac{6}{12}$ $\frac{6}{12}$ $$\frac{6}{12}$$	$\frac{8}{12}$ $\frac{8}{12}$ $$\frac{8}{12}$$	$\frac{9}{12}$ $\frac{9}{12}$ $$\frac{9}{12}$$

GAME MASTER 104   *Fraction Match* **Cards** *continued*

$\frac{10}{12}$ $\qquad$ $\frac{10}{12}$ $$\frac{10}{12}$$	$\frac{12}{12}$ $\qquad$ $\frac{12}{12}$ $$\frac{12}{12}$$	**WILD** $\qquad$ **WILD** **WILD** Name an equivalent fraction with a denominator of 2, 3, 4, 5, 6, 8, 9, 10, or 12.	**WILD** $\qquad$ **WILD** **WILD** Name an equivalent fraction with a denominator of 2, 3, 4, 5, 6, 8, 9, 10, or 12.
WILD $\qquad$ **WILD** **WILD** Name an equivalent fraction with a denominator of 2, 3, 4, 5, 6, 8, 9, 10, or 12.	**WILD** $\qquad$ **WILD** **WILD** Name an equivalent fraction with a denominator of 2, 3, 4, 5, 6, 8, 9, 10, or 12.	**WILD** $\qquad$ **WILD** **WILD** Name an equivalent fraction with a denominator of 2, 3, 4, 5, 6, 8, 9, 10, or 12.	**WILD** $\qquad$ **WILD** **WILD** Name an equivalent fraction with a denominator of 2, 3, 4, 5, 6, 8, 9, 10, or 12.
WILD $\qquad$ **WILD** **WILD** Name an equivalent fraction with a denominator of 2, 3, 4, 5, 6, 8, 9, 10, or 12.	**WILD** $\qquad$ **WILD** **WILD** Name an equivalent fraction with a denominator of 2, 3, 4, 5, 6, 8, 9, 10, or 12.	**WILD** $\qquad$ **WILD** **WILD** Name an equivalent fraction with a denominator of 2, 3, 4, 5, 6, 8, 9, 10, or 12.	**WILD** $\qquad$ **WILD** **WILD** Name an equivalent fraction with a denominator of 2, 3, 4, 5, 6, 8, 9, 10, or 12.
WILD $\qquad$ **WILD** **WILD** Name an equivalent fraction with a denominator of 2, 3, 4, 5, 6, 8, 9, 10, or 12.	**WILD** $\qquad$ **WILD** **WILD** Name an equivalent fraction with a denominator of 2, 3, 4, 5, 6, 8, 9, 10, or 12.	**WILD** $\qquad$ **WILD** **WILD** Name an equivalent fraction with a denominator of 2, 3, 4, 5, 6, 8, 9, 10, or 12.	**WILD** $\qquad$ **WILD** **WILD** Name an equivalent fraction with a denominator of 2, 3, 4, 5, 6, 8, 9, 10, or 12.

Fraction Of Game Mat/Record Sheet

Fraction card	**of**	WHOLE (Choose 1 of these sets.) Set card

Round	"Fraction of" Problem	Points
Sample	$\frac{1}{5}$ of 25	5
1		
2		
3		
4		
5		
6		
7		
8		
	Total Score	

Fraction Of

GAME MASTER 106

Fraction Of Fraction Cards 1

$\dfrac{0}{2}$	$\dfrac{1}{2}$	$\dfrac{1}{3}$	$\dfrac{1}{3}$
$\dfrac{1}{4}$	$\dfrac{1}{4}$	$\dfrac{2}{4}$	$\dfrac{1}{5}$
$\dfrac{1}{5}$	$\dfrac{1}{10}$	$\dfrac{5}{10}$	$\dfrac{10}{10}$
$\dfrac{2}{2}$	$\dfrac{0}{3}$	$\dfrac{2}{3}$	$\dfrac{3}{3}$

GAME MASTER 107

Fraction Of **Fraction Cards 2**

$\dfrac{0}{4}$	$\dfrac{3}{4}$	$\dfrac{4}{4}$	$\dfrac{0}{5}$
$\dfrac{2}{5}$	$\dfrac{3}{5}$	$\dfrac{4}{5}$	$\dfrac{5}{5}$
$\dfrac{1}{10}$	$\dfrac{2}{10}$	$\dfrac{3}{10}$	$\dfrac{4}{10}$
$\dfrac{6}{10}$	$\dfrac{7}{10}$	$\dfrac{8}{10}$	$\dfrac{9}{10}$

GAME MASTER 108

Fraction Of Set Cards

3 counters 20 counters 15 counters	4 counters 21 counters 30 counters	5 counters 12 counters 20 counters	6 counters 28 counters 40 counters
8 counters 27 counters 20 counters	10 counters 32 counters 24 counters	12 counters 30 counters 25 counters	15 counters 36 counters 20 counters
18 counters 36 counters 10 counters	20 counters 4 counters 3 counters	21 counters 30 counters 24 counters	25 counters 6 counters 40 counters
28 counters 35 counters 30 counters	30 counters 32 counters 15 counters	36 counters 20 counters 24 counters	40 counters 18 counters 25 counters

Name ______ Date ______ Time ______

GAME MASTER **109**

Fraction Spin Record Sheet

Name

_____ + _____ < 1

_____ + _____ > 1

_____ − _____ $< \frac{1}{2}$

_____ − _____ $> \frac{1}{2}$

_____ + _____ < 1

_____ + _____ $< \frac{1}{4}$

_____ + _____ $> \frac{1}{4}$

_____ + _____ $= 1$

_____ − _____ $< \frac{1}{4}$

_____ − _____ $> \frac{1}{4}$

_____ + _____ $< \frac{3}{4}$

_____ + _____ $> \frac{3}{4}$

Name

_____ + _____ < 1

_____ + _____ > 1

_____ − _____ $< \frac{1}{2}$

_____ − _____ $> \frac{1}{2}$

_____ + _____ < 1

_____ + _____ $< \frac{1}{4}$

_____ + _____ $> \frac{1}{4}$

_____ + _____ $= 1$

_____ − _____ $< \frac{1}{4}$

_____ − _____ $> \frac{1}{4}$

_____ + _____ $< \frac{3}{4}$

_____ + _____ $> \frac{3}{4}$

Fraction Spin Spinner

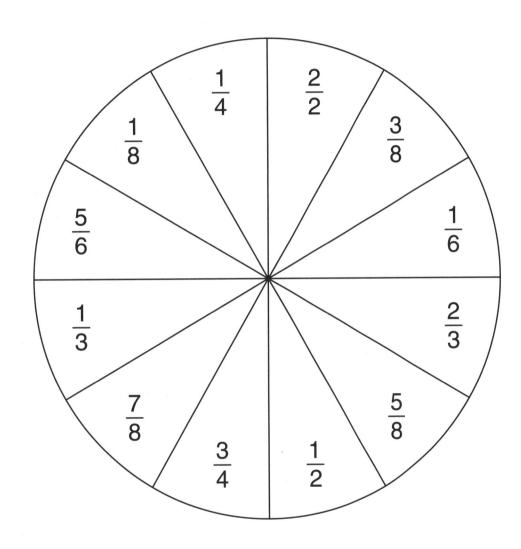

GAME MASTER 111

Fraction Top-It Cards 1

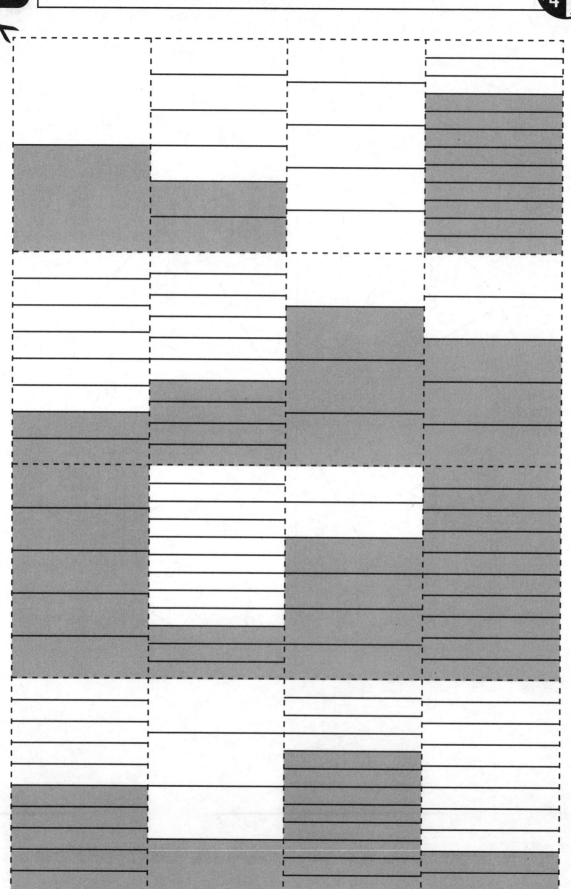

Fraction Top-It

Fraction Top-It Cards 2

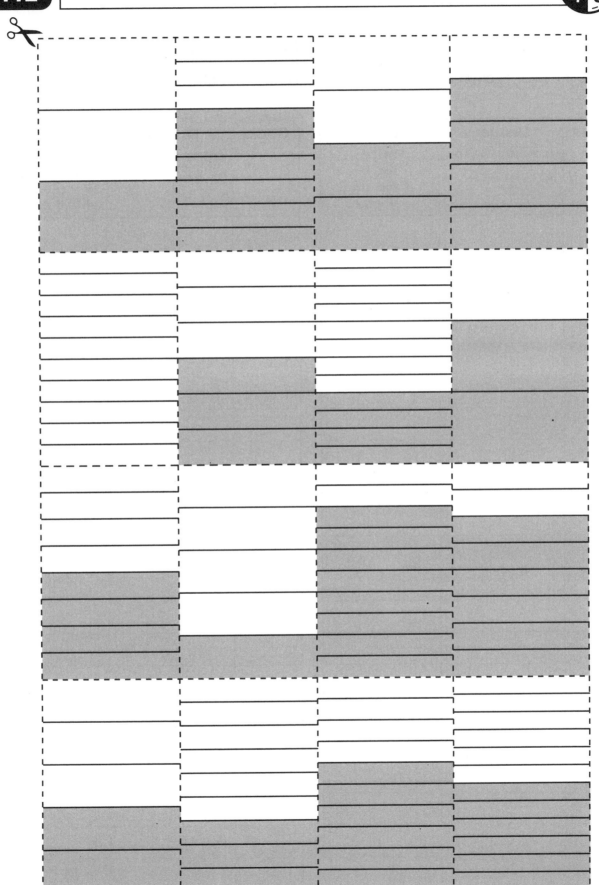

GAME MASTER 113 *Getting to One* **Record Sheets**

Player's Name _____

Draw a line after each round.

Guess	Display on calculator (to nearest 0.01)	Result Write: L if too large S if too small ✓ if exact

Player's Name _____

Draw a line after each round.

Guess	Display on calculator (to nearest 0.01)	Result Write: L if too large S if too small ✓ if exact

Go Forward, Back Up

Materials   ☐ cube marked 0–5

☐ cube with 4 green sides marked + and 2 red sides marked –

☐ 2 different-colored counters

Players   2

Skill   Counting; addition and subtraction concepts

Object of the Game To reach the end of the path.

Directions

Take turns. Roll both cubes. Move ahead (+) or back (–) the correct number of spaces.

Start →

End

115 | *Grab Bag*

Materials   ☐   2 Record Sheets

              ☐   *Grab Bag* Cards

              ☐   3 dice

Players   2, or 2 teams of 2

Skill   Variable substitution; calculating probabilities

Object of the Game   To score more points.

Directions

1. Shuffle the *Grab Bag* Cards and stack them facedown.

2. Players (or teams) take turns. For each turn, turn over a card. Two quantities are missing. They are shown with the variables *x* and *y*.

3. Roll the 3 dice and substitute the numbers rolled for *x* and *y*:

   • Replace *x* with the number shown on 1 die.

   • Replace *y* with the sum of the numbers on the other 2 dice.

4. Solve the problem. The opposing player (or team) checks the answer. The score for the round is:

   • 10 points if the event is unlikely (probability less than $\frac{1}{2}$).

   • 30 points if the event is likely (probability greater than $\frac{1}{2}$).

   • 50 points if the event has a 50–50 chance (probability exactly $\frac{1}{2}$).

5. The player (or team) with the higher score after 5 rounds wins.

GAME MASTER
116

Grab Bag Cards

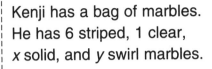

Lina has a bag of ribbons. She has 2 red, 2 blue, *x* pink, and *y* green ribbons.

What are the chances that she will pick a green ribbon without looking?

Mario has a bag of art pencils. He has 3 purple, 1 white, *x* violet, and *y* yellow pencils.

What are the chances that he will pick a yellow pencil without looking?

Kenji has a bag of marbles. He has 6 striped, 1 clear, *x* solid, and *y* swirl marbles.

What are the chances that he will pick a swirl marble without looking?

There are 2 red, 2 white, *x* black, and *y* brown beans in a bag.

Without looking, what are the chances of picking a brown bean?

There are 3 clear, 3 blue, *x* white, and *y* orange beads in a bag.

Without looking, what are the chances of picking an orange bead?

There are 5 lemon, 2 strawberry, *x* cherry, and *y* grape lollipops in a bag.

Without looking, what are the chances of picking a grape lollipop?

A bag of markers has 1 yellow, 2 green, *x* pink, and *y* blue markers.

Without looking, Kendra picks a blue marker and then returns it to the bag.

Without looking, what is the probability that Kendra will pick a blue marker again?

A bag of erasers has 3 pink, 3 white, *x* blue, and *y* red erasers.

Without looking, Cyrus picks a red eraser and returns it to the bag.

Without looking, what is the probability that Cyrus will pick a red eraser again?

ERASER

A bag of buttons has 2 green, 3 gray, *x* black, and *y* white buttons.

Without looking, Amir picks a white button and returns it to the bag.

Without looking, what is the probability that Amir will pick a white button again?

GAME MASTER 117

Grab Bag Cards *continued*

Rosa has a bag of 2 red, 6 green, *x* white, and *y* blue centimeter cubes.

If she picks one out of the bag without looking, what is the probability that it will be a blue centimeter cube?

Ingrid has a bag of 3 red, 5 green, *x* blue, and *y* yellow flag stickers.

If she picks one out of the bag without looking, what is the probability that it will be a yellow flag sticker?

Boris has a bag of 1 red, 5 black, *x* orange, and *y* green toy cars.

If he picks one out of the bag without looking, what is the probability that it will be a green car?

Jesse has a bag of painted blocks: 2 with flowers, 3 with leaves, *x* with animals, and *y* with dots.

Without looking, what is the probability that he will pull a block with dots from the bag?

Victor has a bag of family photos: 3 of his parents, 4 of his brothers, *x* of his cousins, and *y* of his grandma.

Without looking, what is the probability that he will pull a picture of his grandma from the bag?

Simone has a bag of playing cards: 1 diamond, 4 hearts, *x* spades, and *y* clubs.

Without looking, what is the probability that she will pull a club from the bag?

There are 1 green, 2 blue, *x* red, and *y* yellow paper clips in a bag.

Without looking, what are the chances of picking a yellow paper clip?

There are 3 orange, 2 blue, *x* green, and *y* pink dice in a bag.

Without looking, what are the chances of picking a pink die?

There are 2 green, 2 purple, *x* gold, and *y* silver crayons in a bag.

Without looking, what are the chances of picking a silver crayon?

Grab Bag

GAME MASTER 118

Grab Bag Record Sheet

Round	Number of Items Shown on Card		x	y	Total Number of Items in Bag	Probability of Event Occurring	Score
Sample	2	2	1	6 + 4 = 10	15	$\frac{10}{15}$	30
1							
2							
3							
4							
5							
						Total Score	

✂ -

GAME MASTER 118

Grab Bag Record Sheet

Round	Number of Items Shown on Card		x	y	Total Number of Items in Bag	Probability of Event Occurring	Score
Sample	2	2	1	6 + 4 = 10	15	$\frac{10}{15}$	30
1							
2							
3							
4							
5							
						Total Score	

GAME MASTER 119

Greedy Score Sheets

Name

Greedy Score Sheet	
Round	**Score**
1	
2	
3	
4	
5	
6	
Total Score	

Name

Greedy Score Sheet	
Round	**Score**
1	
2	
3	
4	
5	
6	
Total Score	

Name

Greedy Score Sheet	
Round	**Score**
1	
2	
3	
4	
5	
6	
Total Score	

Name

Greedy Score Sheet	
Round	**Score**
1	
2	
3	
4	
5	
6	
Total Score	

GAME MASTER 120

Grid Search Grids

Player A

Grid 1: Hide your queen here.

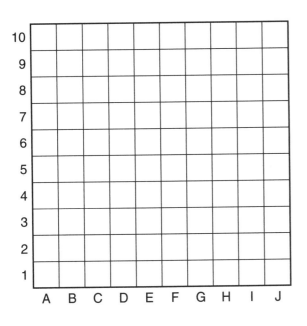

Grid 2: Make your guesses here.

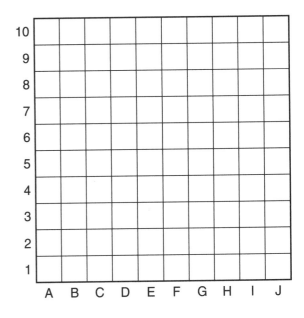

✂ -

Player B

Grid 1: Hide your queen here.

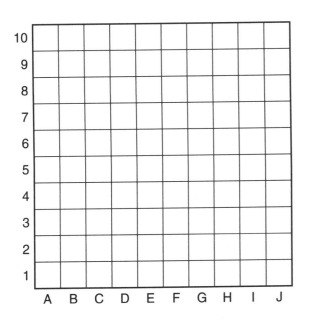

Grid 2: Make your guesses here.

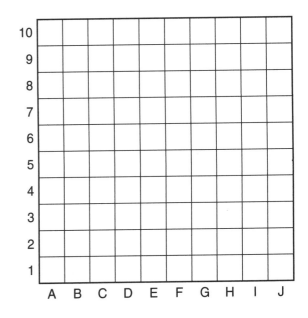

GAME MASTER 121 *Hidden Treasure* **Grids**

Player A

Grid 1: Hide your point here.

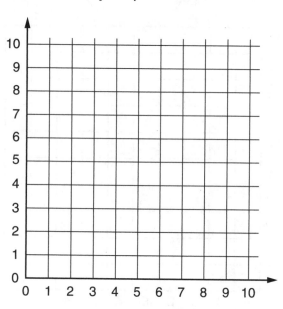

Grid 2: Guess other player's point here.

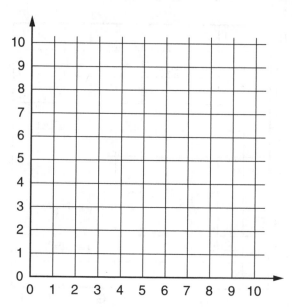

Player B

Grid 1: Hide your point here.

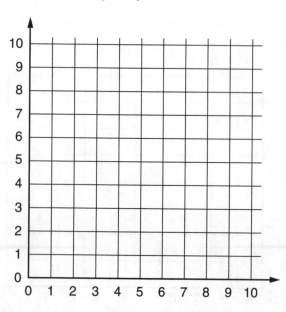

Grid 2: Guess other player's point here.

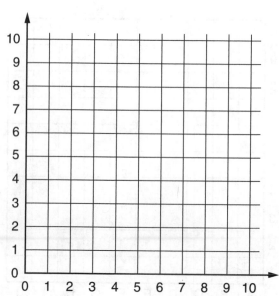

Hidden Treasure

GAME MASTER 122

Hidden Treasure **Grids (Advanced)**

Player A

Grid 1: Hide your point here.

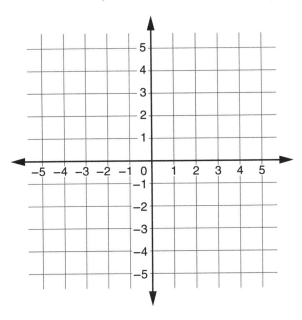

Grid 2: Guess other player's point here.

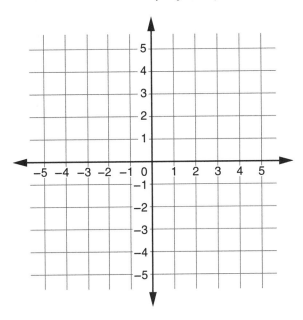

Player B

Grid 1: Hide your point here.

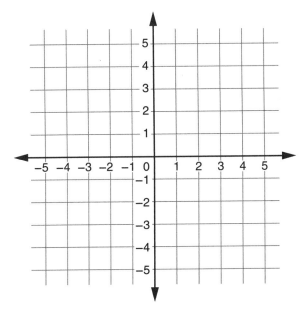

Grid 2: Guess other player's point here.

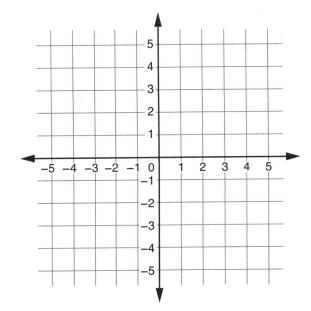

GAME MASTER 123

Number Cards (0–2)

0	0	0	0
1	1	1	1
2	2	2	2

High Low

GAME MASTER 124

Number Cards (3–5)

3	3	3	3
4	4	4	4
5	5	5	5

GAME MASTER 125

Number Cards (6–8)

6	6	6	6
7	7	7	7
8	8	8	8

GAME MASTER 126

Number Cards (9–10)

9

9

9

9

10

10

10

10

GAME MASTER 127

High-Number Toss Record Sheet

Hundred-Millions	Ten-Millions	Millions	,	Hundred-Thousands	Ten-Thousands	Thousands	,	Hundreds	Tens	Ones

_____ (Name)   _____ (Name)

Round	Player 1	>, <, =	Player 2
Sample	<u>1 3 2 | 6</u> <u>132,000,000</u>	>	<u>3 5 6 | 4</u> <u>3,560,000</u>
1	— — — |—		— — — — |—
2	— — — |—		— — — — |—
3	— — — |—		— — — — |—
4	— — — |—		— — — — |—
5	— — — |—		— — — |—

GAME MASTER 128 | *High-Number Toss: Decimal Version*

Circle the winning number for each round. Fill in the Score column each time you have the winning number.

_____ _____
(Name)   (Name)

Round	Player 1	Player 2	Score
Sample	0._6_ _5_ _4_	(0._7_ _5_ _3_)	0.753 − 0.654 0.099
1	0.___ ___ ___	0.___ ___ ___	
2	0.___ ___ ___	0.___ ___ ___	
3	0.___ ___ ___	0.___ ___ ___	
4	0.___ ___ ___	0.___ ___ ___	
5	0.___ ___ ___	0.___ ___ ___	
		Total Score	

High Roller

Materials   ☐ 1 Record Sheet per player

☐ 2 dice

☐ 10 counters per player

Players   2–4

Skill   Counting on; finding sums; comparing numbers

Object of the Game To collect 10 counters.

Directions

1. On your turn, roll both dice. Write the numbers in the first 2 squares.

2. Cross out the smaller number. Roll that die again. Write the number in the third square.

3. Find the sum of the 2 dice. Write it on the line.

4. The player with the highest sum takes a counter.

5. The first player to have 10 counters wins.

Another Way to Play

High Roller with Subtraction

Skill   Subtraction facts

Roll 2 dice. Subtract the lower number from the higher number. The player with the smaller difference takes a counter.

GAME MASTER 130 *High Roller* **Record Sheet**

Hit the Target **Record Sheet**

Round 1

Target Number: _____

Starting Number	Change	Result	Change	Result	Change	Result

Round 2

Target Number: _____

Starting Number	Change	Result	Change	Result	Change	Result

Round 3

Target Number: _____

Starting Number	Change	Result	Change	Result	Change	Result

Round 4

Target Number: _____

Starting Number	Change	Result	Change	Result	Change	Result

Hit the Target

GAME MASTER 132

3- and 4-Part Spinners

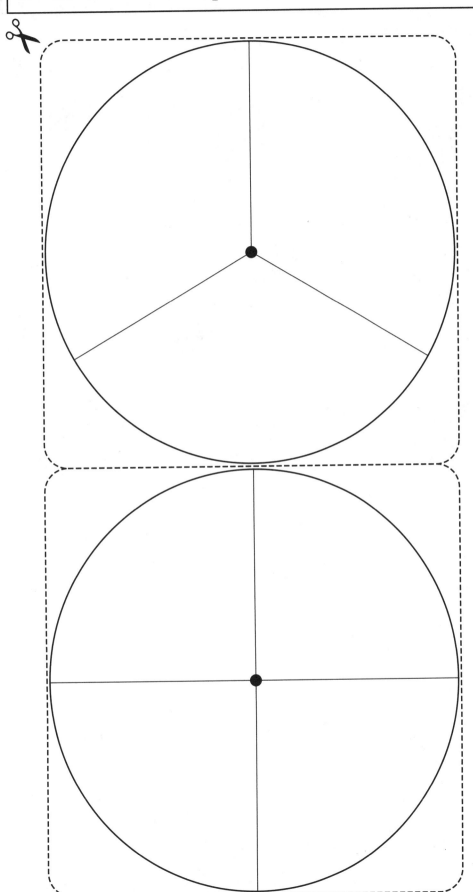

Landmark Shark Cards

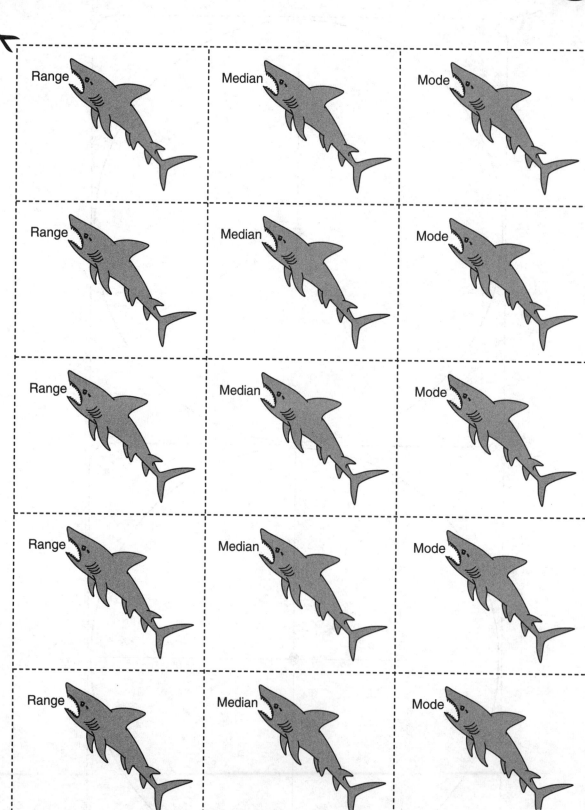

Name _____ Date _____ Time _____

Landmark Shark Score Sheet

		Player 1	**Player 2**	**Player 3**
Round 1:	Points Scored			
	Bonus Points			
	Round 1 Score			

		Player 1	Player 2	Player 3
Round 2:	Points Scored			
	Bonus Points			
	Round 2 Score			

		Player 1	Player 2	Player 3
Round 3:	Points Scored			
	Bonus Points			
	Round 3 Score			

		Player 1	Player 2	Player 3
Round 4:	Points Scored			
	Bonus Points			
	Round 4 Score			

		Player 1	Player 2	Player 3
Round 5:	Points Scored			
	Bonus Points			
	Round 5 Score			

Total Score for 5 Rounds			

GAME MASTER 135 | Dot Cards (1–12)

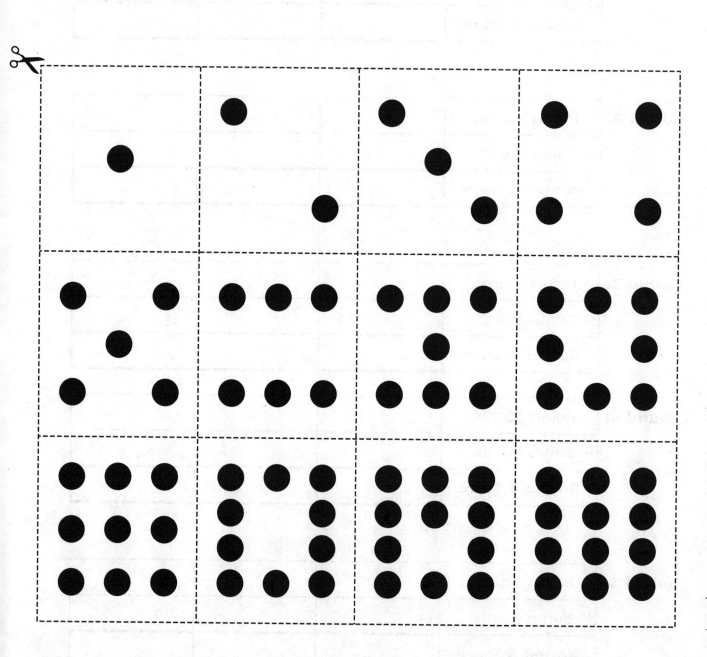

Name _____   Date _____   Time _____

Butterfly Picture Cards I

Horizontal Arrangements

GAME MASTER 137 | **Beetle Picture Cards I**

Horizontal Arrangements

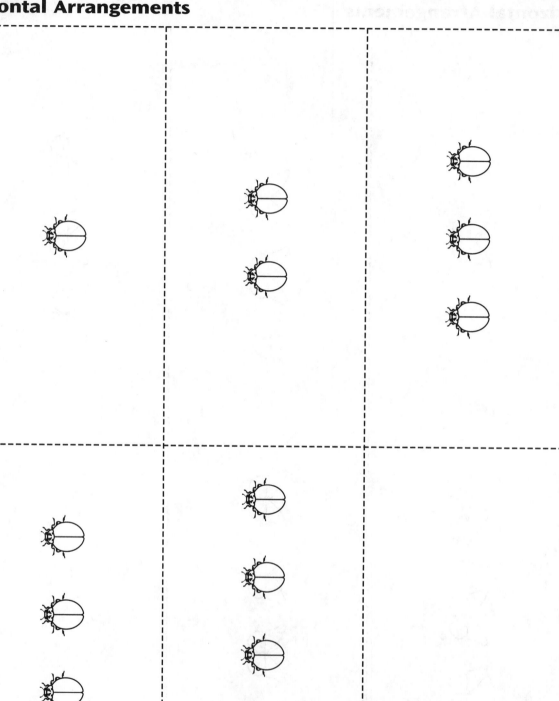

Butterfly Picture Cards II

Dice-dot Arrangements

Beetle Picture Cards II

Dice-dot Arrangements

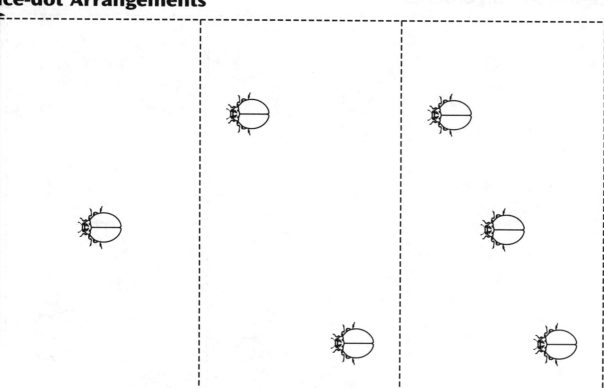

Matching Sets

Mixed-Number Spin **Record Sheet**

Name	**Name**

____ + ____ < 3	____ + ____ < 3
____ + ____ > 3	____ + ____ > 3
____ − ____ < 1	____ − ____ < 1
____ − ____ < $\frac{1}{2}$	____ − ____ < $\frac{1}{2}$
____ + ____ > 1	____ + ____ > 1
____ + ____ < 1	____ + ____ < 1
____ + ____ < 2	____ + ____ < 2
____ + ____ = 3	____ + ____ = 3
____ − ____ > 1	____ − ____ > 1
____ − ____ > $\frac{1}{2}$	____ − ____ > $\frac{1}{2}$
____ + ____ < 3	____ + ____ < 3
____ + ____ > 2	____ + ____ > 2

Mixed-Number Spin **Spinner**

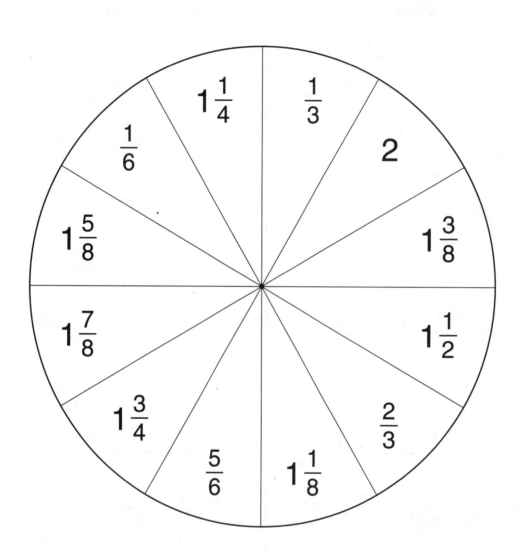

GAME MASTER 142 · **Place-Value Mat**

℗ pennies ▱ 1s	
Ⓓ dimes ▭ 10s	
$1 dollars ▦ 100s	
$10 ▦ 1,000s	

GAME MASTER 143

Money Grid Game Mat

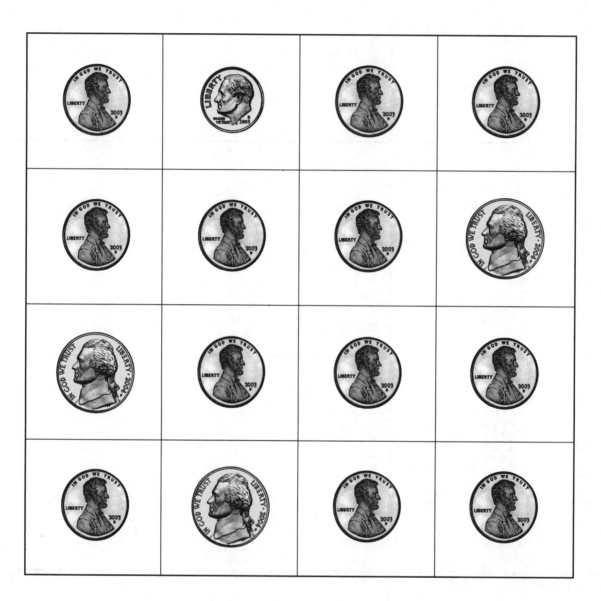

GAME MASTER 144 ## *Monster Squeeze* Mini Version

Fill in these boxes. Use numbers in order.

GAME MASTER 145

Monster Squeeze Monster (left side)

GAME MASTER 146

Monster Squeeze Monster (right side)

More or Less Spinners

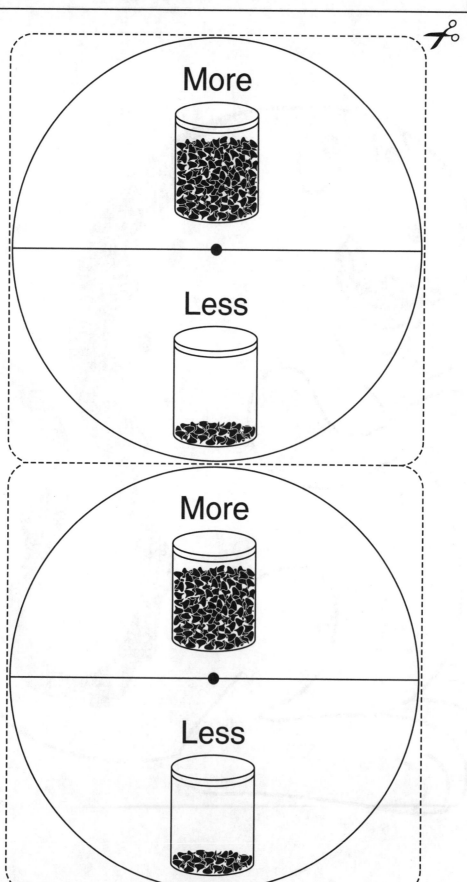

GAME MASTER 148

Paper Cookies (0–5)

GAME MASTER 149

Paper Cookies (6–11)

GAME MASTER 150 | *Multiplication Bingo* **Game Mat**

Each player uses a different grid in every game.

For a game with easy facts, use these numbers in your grid:
1, 4, 6, 8, 9, 12, 15, 16, 18, 20, 24, 25, 30, 36, 50, 100

For a game with all facts, use these numbers in your grid:
24, 27, 28, 32, 35, 36, 42, 45, 48, 49, 54, 56, 63, 64, 72, 81

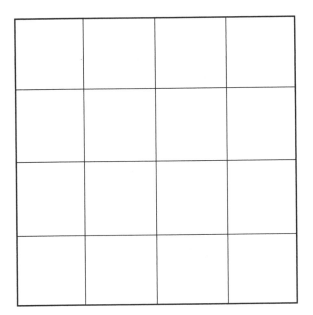

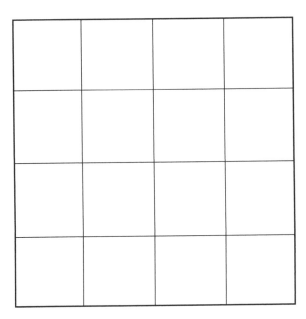

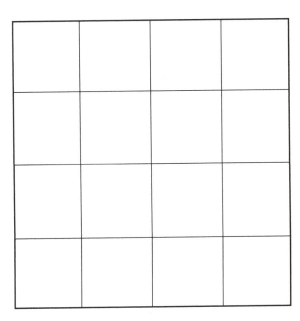

Record the facts you miss on the back of this page.
Be sure to practice them!

GAME MASTER 151

Multiplication Draw Record Sheets

Round 1	**Round 2**	**Round 3**
1st draw: ____ × ____ = ____	____ × ____ = ____	____ × ____ = ____
2nd draw: ____ × ____ = ____	____ × ____ = ____	____ × ____ = ____
3rd draw: ____ × ____ = ____	____ × ____ = ____	____ × ____ = ____
4th draw: ____ × ____ = ____	____ × ____ = ____	____ × ____ = ____
5th draw: ____ × ____ = ____	____ × ____ = ____	____ × ____ = ____
Sum of products: ____	____	____

✂ -

Round 1	**Round 2**	**Round 3**
1st draw: ____ × ____ = ____	____ × ____ = ____	____ × ____ = ____
2nd draw: ____ × ____ = ____	____ × ____ = ____	____ × ____ = ____
3rd draw: ____ × ____ = ____	____ × ____ = ____	____ × ____ = ____
4th draw: ____ × ____ = ____	____ × ____ = ____	____ × ____ = ____
5th draw: ____ × ____ = ____	____ × ____ = ____	____ × ____ = ____
Sum of products: ____	____	____

✂ -

Round 1	**Round 2**	**Round 3**
1st draw: ____ × ____ = ____	____ × ____ = ____	____ × ____ = ____
2nd draw: ____ × ____ = ____	____ × ____ = ____	____ × ____ = ____
3rd draw: ____ × ____ = ____	____ × ____ = ____	____ × ____ = ____
4th draw: ____ × ____ = ____	____ × ____ = ____	____ × ____ = ____
5th draw: ____ × ____ = ____	____ × ____ = ____	____ × ____ = ____
Sum of products: ____	____	____

Name _____ Date _____ Time _____

 Multiplication Wrestling Record Sheet

Round 1 Cards: _____ _____ _____ _____

Numbers formed: _____ * _____

Teams: (_____ + _____) * (_____ + _____)

Products: _____ * _____ = _____

_____ * _____ = _____

_____ * _____ = _____

_____ * _____ = _____

Total (add 4 products): _____

Round 2 Cards: _____ _____ _____ _____

Numbers formed: _____ * _____

Teams: (_____ + _____) * (_____ + _____)

Products: _____ * _____ = _____

_____ * _____ = _____

_____ * _____ = _____

_____ * _____ = _____

Total (add 4 products): _____

Round 3 Cards: _____ _____ _____ _____

Numbers formed: _____ * _____

Teams: (_____ + _____) * (_____ + _____)

Products: _____ * _____ = _____

_____ * _____ = _____

_____ * _____ = _____

_____ * _____ = _____

Total (add 4 products): _____

 **GAME MASTER 153**   *Name That Number* **Record Sheet**

Target

Number Sentence Solution: _____

_____

_____

_____

Reminder: Write each step separately! _____

✂ -

 GAME MASTER 153   *Name That Number* **Record Sheet**

Target

Number Sentence Solution: _____

_____

_____

_____

Reminder: Write each step separately! _____

Name That Number Record Sheet

Round 1

Target Number: _____ My Cards: _____ _____ _____ _____ _____

My Solution (number sentence): _____

Number of cards used: _____

Round 2

Target Number: _____ My Cards: _____ _____ _____ _____ _____

My Solution (number sentence): _____

Number of cards used: _____

Round 3

Target Number: _____ My Cards: _____ _____ _____ _____ _____

My Solution (number sentence): _____

Number of cards used: _____

Round 4

Target Number: _____ My Cards: _____ _____ _____ _____ _____

My Solution (number sentence): _____

Number of cards used: _____

Nickel-Penny Grab

Materials   ☐ 8 nickels, 20 pennies

Players   2

Skill   Counting and comparing collections of coins

Object of the Game To have more money in at least two rounds.

Directions

1. Mix the coins together in a pile.

2. One player grabs a handful of coins. The other player grabs the coins that are left.

3. Draw your coins in the table below. Find the total value.

4. Record your total and your partner's total in the table. Circle the greater total.

5. Switch roles and repeat Steps 1–4 two more times for a total of 3 rounds. The player who had more money in at least 2 rounds wins.

Record Sheet

	Nickels ⓝ	Pennies ⓟ	My Total	My Partner's Total
Round 1				
Round 2				
Round 3				

Name   Date   Time

 Number Board

       6

     5

4

     3

   2

   1

Number Board Games   **Game Masters**   415

Number Grid (–9 to 110)

–9	–8	–7	–6	–5	–4	–3	–2	–1	0
1	2	3	4	5	6	7	8	9	10
11	12	13	14	15	16	17	18	19	20
21	22	23	24	25	26	27	28	29	30
31	32	33	34	35	36	37	38	39	40
41	42	43	44	45	46	47	48	49	50
51	52	53	54	55	56	57	58	59	60
61	62	63	64	65	66	67	68	69	70
71	72	73	74	75	76	77	78	79	80
81	82	83	84	85	86	87	88	89	90
91	92	93	94	95	96	97	98	99	100
101	102	103	104	105	106	107	108	109	110

GAME MASTER 158

Number-Grid Difference Record Sheet

Round	My Number	My Partner's Number	Difference (Score)
1			
2			
3			
4			
5			
			Total _____

✂ -

GAME MASTER 158

Number-Grid Difference Record Sheet

Round	My Number	My Partner's Number	Difference (Score)
1			
2			
3			
4			
5			
			Total _____

GAME MASTER 159 | **Number Grid (0–110)**

									0
1	2	3	4	5	6	7	8	9	10
11	12	13	14	15	16	17	18	19	20
21	22	23	24	25	26	27	28	29	30
31	32	33	34	35	36	37	38	39	40
41	42	43	44	45	46	47	48	49	50
51	52	53	54	55	56	57	58	59	60
61	62	63	64	65	66	67	68	69	70
71	72	73	74	75	76	77	78	79	80
81	82	83	84	85	86	87	88	89	90
91	92	93	94	95	96	97	98	99	100
101	102	103	104	105	106	107	108	109	110

160 **Number-Line Squeeze**

Materials □ 2 counters

Players 2 or more

Skill Compare and order numbers

Object of the Game To guess a mystery number.

Directions

1. Place a counter on each end of the number line.

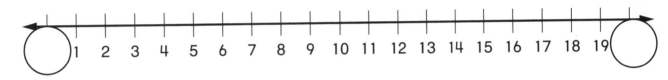

2. Player 1 thinks of a mystery number on the number line.

3. The other players guess the mystery number. If the guess is too high, Player 1 moves the right-hand counter over to cover the guess. If the guess is too low, Player 1 moves the left-hand counter over to cover the guess.

4. Players repeat Step 3 until the mystery number is guessed.

5. Players switch roles and play again.

Advanced Version

◆ Make a number line with more challenging numbers, such as numbers in the hundreds or negative numbers.

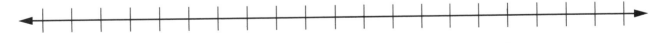

Number Top-It Game Mat

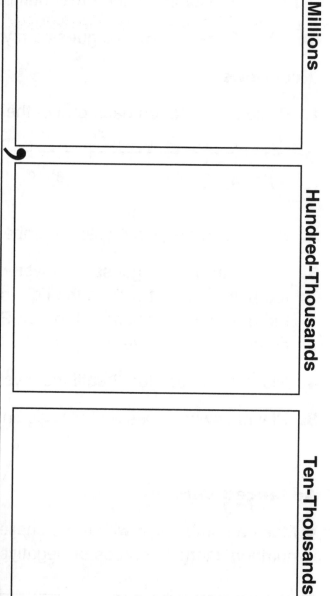

Millions

Hundred-Thousands

Ten-Thousands

Thous

GAME MASTER 162

Number Top-It **Game Mat** *continued*

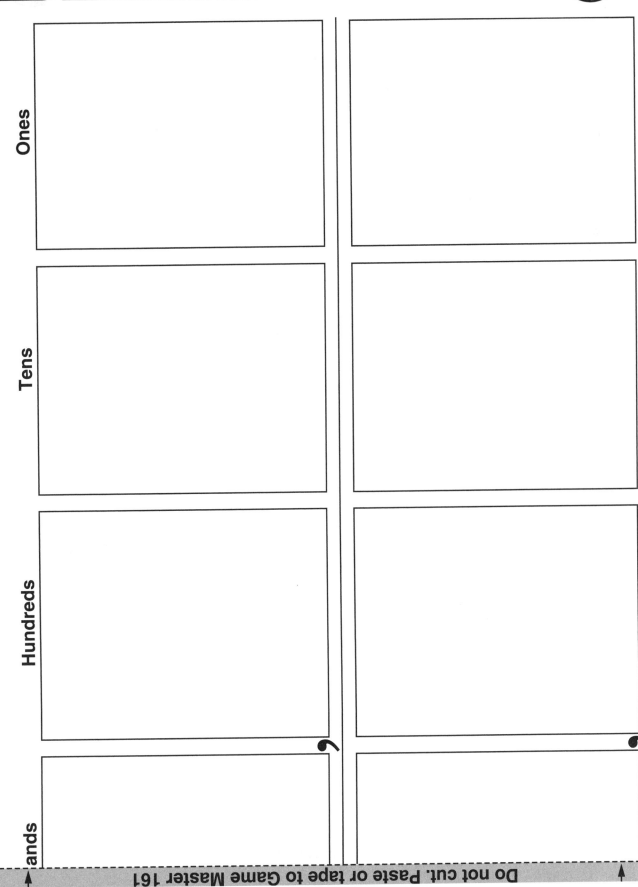

Ones

Tens

Hundreds

ands

Do not cut. Paste or tape to Game Master 161

Number Top-It Game Mat

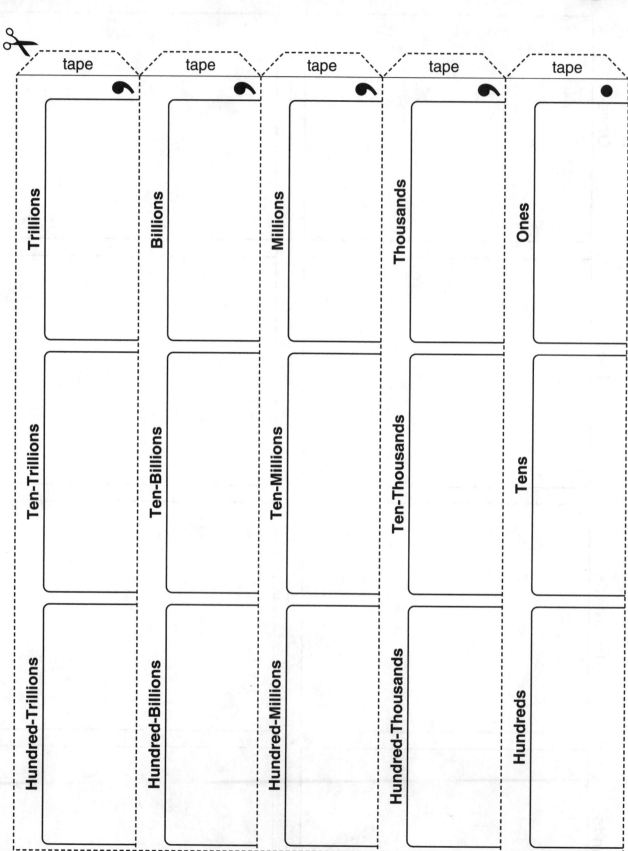

GAME MASTER 164 *Number Top-It* **Game Mat (3-Place Decimals)**

Ones

Tenths

Hundredths

Thousandths

Base-10 Grids

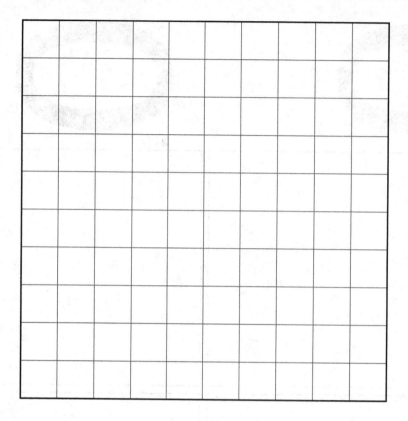

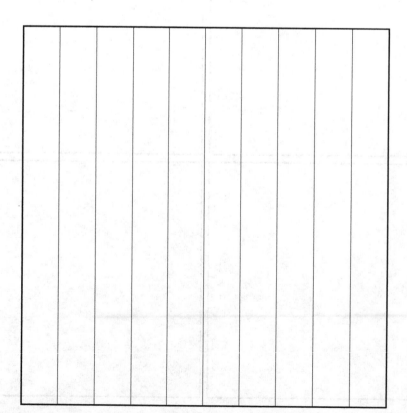

Name _____ Date _____ Time _____

Place-Value Mat

Cubes	1s	Pennies $0.01 1¢	Longs	10s	Dimes $0.10 10¢	Flats	100s	Dollars $1.00 100¢

Place-Value Mat

$0.01 0.01 **Hundredths** **Cubes** **Pennies**	$0.10 0.1 **Tenths Longs** **Dimes**	$1.00 1 **Ones Flats** **Dollars**

GAME MASTER 168 | ***One-Dollar Exchange Games***

Materials   ☐ 2 Place-Value Mats for pennies, dimes, and dollars

☐ $1 bill, dimes, pennies

☐ 2 dice

Players   2

Skill   Counting and exchanging money

One-Dollar Exchange (Penny-Dime-Dollar Exchange)

1. Players put one $1 bill, 30 dimes, and 30 pennies in a "bank."

2. On your turn, roll the dice. Say the total number of dots. Take that many pennies from the bank. Put them in the Pennies column of your mat.

3. Whenever possible, exchange 10 pennies for 1 dime and put it in the Dimes column. When there are 10 dimes, exchange them for one $1 bill.

4. The other player checks the exchanges.

5. The first player to make an exchange for a dollar wins.

Money Trading Game

1. Players put 20 dimes and 40 pennies in a "bank." Players put one $1 bill in the Dollars column of their Place-Value Mats.

2. On your turn, roll the dice. Say the total number of dots. Return that many pennies to the bank.

3. Exchange 1 dollar for 10 dimes, and 1 dime for 10 pennies from the bank as needed.

4. The other player checks the exchanges.

5. The first player to clear his or her mat wins.

GAME MASTER 169

Place-Value Mat for $1, $10, $100

One Dollar **$1** **100 pennies** **10 dimes**	
Ten Dollars **$10** **1,000 pennies** **100 dimes**	
One Hundred Dollars **$100** **10,000 pennies** **1,000 dimes**	

$1, $10, $100 Exchange Game

Materials ☐ 2 Place-Value Mats for $1, $10, and $100 bills

☐ thirty $1 bills, twenty $10 bills, one $100 bill

☐ 1 or 2 dice

Players 2

Skill Recognizing and exchanging $1, $10, and $100 bills

Object of the Game To exchange ten $10 bills for the $100 bill.

Directions

1. Put the money in a "bank."

2. Take turns rolling the dice (or die). Take that many $1 bills from the bank.

3. Whenever possible, trade ten $1 bills for one $10 bill, and ten $10 bills for one $100 bill. Put the bills in the correct columns on your mat.

4. The first player to make an exchange for a $100 bill wins.

GAME MASTER
171

Ones, Tens, Hundreds Game **Record Sheet**

Record how many single sticks, small bundles, and big bundles you have at the end of the *Ones, Tens, Hundreds Game.*

Big Bundles 100s	Bundles 10s	Single Sticks 1s

How many sticks did you collect all together?

_____

Over and Up Squares

Materials
- ☐ 1 coordinate grid
- ☐ 2 dice
- ☐ 2 different-colored pencils

Players 2

Skill Plotting ordered pairs on a coordinate grid; developing a winning strategy

Object of the Game To earn the higher score by connecting points on a coordinate grid.

Directions

1. Player 1 rolls 2 dice and uses the numbers to make an ordered pair. Either number can be used to name the *x*-coordinate (over) of the ordered pair. The other number is used to name the *y*-coordinate (up) of the ordered pair. After deciding which ordered pair to use, the player plots it on the grid with his or her colored pencil.

2. Player 1 records the ordered pair and the score on his or her Record Sheet. A player earns 10 points each time an ordered pair is plotted correctly.

3. Player 2 rolls the dice and decides how to make an ordered pair. If both possible ordered pairs are already marked on the grid, the player rolls the dice again. Or, the player can change one or both of the numbers to 0.

4. Player 2 uses the other colored pencil to plot the ordered pair and records the ordered pair and score in the second table.

5. Players take turns rolling the dice, plotting ordered pairs on the grid, and recording the results. In a player's turn, if 2 marked grid points are next to each other on the same side of one of the grid squares, the player connects them with a line segment. Sometimes more than 1 line segment may be drawn in a single turn. A player scores 10 points for each line segment.

6. If a player draws a line segment that completes a grid square (so that all 4 sides of the square are now drawn), that player colors in the square and earns 50 points.

7. The player with more points after 10 rounds wins.

GAME MASTER 173 **Over and Up Squares Grid and Record Sheet**

Player 1 _____

Round	Over (*x*-coordinate)	,	Up (*y*-coordinate)	Score
1				
2				
3				
4				
5				
6				
7				
8				
9				
10				
			Total Score	

Scoring	
Ordered pair	10 points
Line segment	10 points
Square	50 points

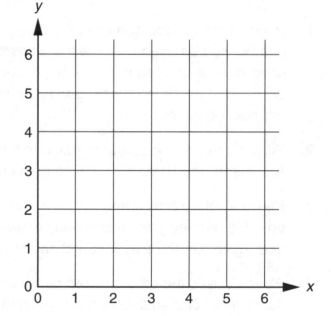

Player 2 _____

Round	Over (*x*-coordinate)	,	Up (*y*-coordinate)	Score
1				
2				
3				
4				
5				
6				
7				
8				
9				
10				
			Total Score	

GAME MASTER 174 — Coordinate Grid

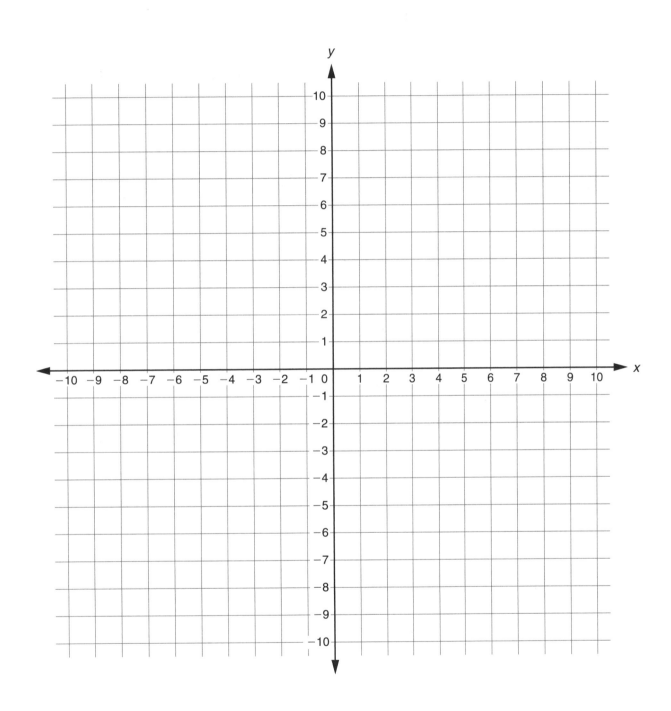

GAME MASTER 175

Paper Money Exchange Game

Materials ☐ 2 Place-Value Mats for $1, $10, and $100 bills

☐ 1 cube marked $1 on 2 sides, $5 on 2 sides, and $10 on 2 sides

☐ twenty-three $1 bills, nineteen $10 bills, one $100 bill

Players 2

Skill Recognizing and exchanging $1, $10, and $100 bills

Object of the Game To exchange ten $10 bills for the $100 bill.

Directions

1. Take turns rolling the cube and taking the correct amount of money from the bank.

2. Count your money after each turn.

3. When you have ten $1 bills, exchange them for one $10 bill. When you have ten $10 bills, exchange them for one $100 bill.

4. The first player to exchange ten $10 bills for one $100 bill wins.

Advanced Version

◆ Add a $1,000 bank draft and 18 more $100 bills to the bank. Use a cube marked $10 on 4 sides and $100 on 2 sides. You must exchange ten $100 bills for one $1,000 bank draft to win.

GAME MASTER 176 | *Penny-Dice Game*

Materials   ☐ 1 die

               ☐ 20 pennies

Players   2

Skill   Counting pennies; comparing quantities

Object of the Game To have more (or fewer) pennies.

Directions

1. Players take turns. On your turn, roll the die. Take that many pennies.

2. Keep taking turns until all of the pennies have been picked up. To pick up the last pennies, the number on the die must match the number of pennies left.

3. The player with more pennies wins, or players can flip a penny to determine who wins.

   • If the penny lands on **heads,** the player with **more** pennies wins.

   • If the penny lands on **tails,** the player with **fewer** pennies wins.

GAME MASTER 177 | **Penny Exchange Games**

Materials   ☐ 1 die

☐ pennies, nickels, and dimes

Players   2

Skill   Making exchanges with pennies, nickels, and dimes

Object of the Game To collect more nickels (or dimes).

> ### Penny-Nickel Exchange

1. Players put 20 pennies and 10 nickels in a "bank."

2. Take turns rolling the die and taking that many pennies.

3. As soon as you have 5 or more pennies, say "Exchange" and trade 5 pennies for a nickel from the bank.

4. The game ends when the bank is out of nickels. The player with more nickels wins. If players have the same number of nickels, the player with more pennies wins.

Advanced Version

◆ Add 1 quarter and 10 nickels to the bank. Use 2 dice. The first player to exchange for the quarter wins.

> ### Penny-Dime Exchange

Put 30 pennies and 5 dimes in the bank. Exchange 10 pennies for a dime whenever you can. When the bank is out of dimes, the player with more dimes wins. If players have the same number of dimes, the player with more pennies wins.

> ### Penny-Nickel-Dime Exchange

Put 20 pennies, 10 nickels, and 10 dimes in the bank. Exchange 2 nickels, or 5 pennies and 1 nickel, for a dime whenever you can. When the bank is out of dimes, the player with more dimes wins. If players have the same number of dimes, the player with more money wins.

GAME MASTER 178

Penny Grab

Materials   ☐ 40 pennies

Players   2

Skill   Counting and comparing groups of pennies

Object of the Game To have more money in at least two rounds.

Directions

1. Players place the pennies in a pile between them.

2. Each player grabs a handful of pennies. (Or Player 1 grabs a handful, and Player 2 grabs the rest.)

3. Draw your pennies in the table. Find the total value.

4. Record your total and your partner's total in the table. Circle the greater total.

5. Switch roles and repeat Steps 1–4 two more times for a total of 3 rounds. The player who had more money in at least 2 rounds wins.

Record Sheet

	Pennies Ⓟ	My Total	My Partner's Total
Round 1			
Round 2			
Round 3			

GAME MASTER 179 | **Penny Plate Record Sheet**

Example:

We started with __20__ pennies.

We could see __6__ pennies on top.

We figured there were __14__ pennies below.

We counted __14__ pennies below.

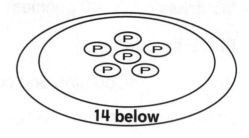

14 below

Round 1

We started with _____ pennies.

We could see _____ pennies on top.

We figured there were _____ pennies below.

We counted _____ pennies below.

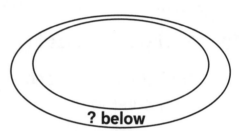

? below

Round 2

We started with _____ pennies.

We could see _____ pennies on top.

We figured there were _____ pennies below.

We counted _____ pennies below.

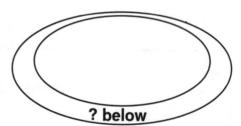

? below

Round 3

We started with _____ pennies.

We could see _____ pennies on top.

We figured there were _____ pennies below.

We counted _____ pennies below.

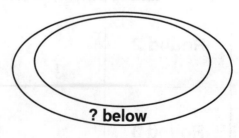

? below

Penny Plate

GAME MASTER 180 *Percent/Sector Match Up* Tiles

10%	**20%**	**25%**	$33\frac{1}{3}\%$
40%	**50%**	**60%**	$66\frac{2}{3}\%$
75%	**80%**	**90%**	**100%**

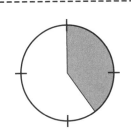 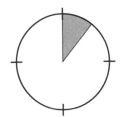 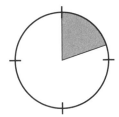 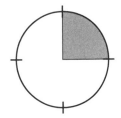 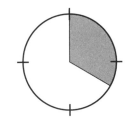 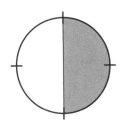 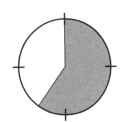 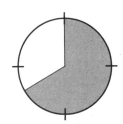 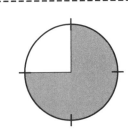 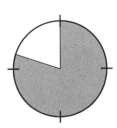 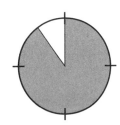 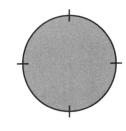

Pick-a-Coin Record Tables

	Ⓟ	Ⓝ	Ⓓ	Ⓠ	\$1	Total
1st turn						$_____._____
2nd turn						$_____._____
3rd turn						$_____._____
4th turn						$_____._____
					Grand Total	$_____._____

✂ -

	Ⓟ	Ⓝ	Ⓓ	Ⓠ	\$1	Total
1st turn						$_____._____
2nd turn						$_____._____
3rd turn						$_____._____
4th turn						$_____._____
					Grand Total	$_____._____

✂ -

	Ⓟ	Ⓝ	Ⓓ	Ⓠ	\$1	Total
1st turn						$_____._____
2nd turn						$_____._____
3rd turn						$_____._____
4th turn						$_____._____
					Grand Total	$_____._____

GAME MASTER 182

Plus or Minus Game Mats

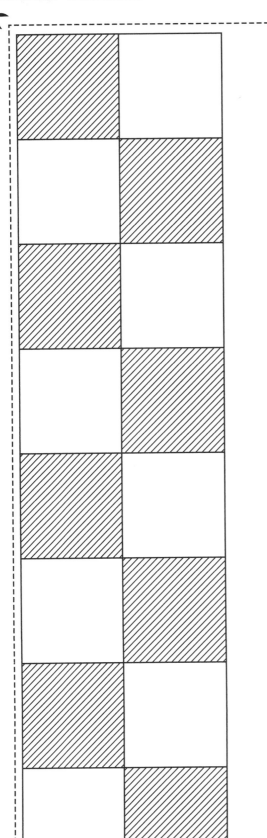

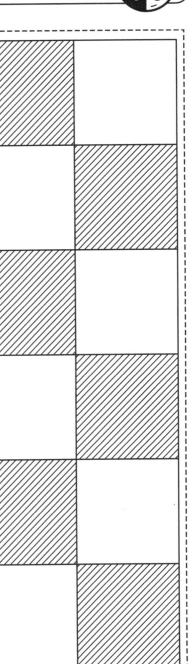

GAME MASTER
183

Pocket Billiards Game

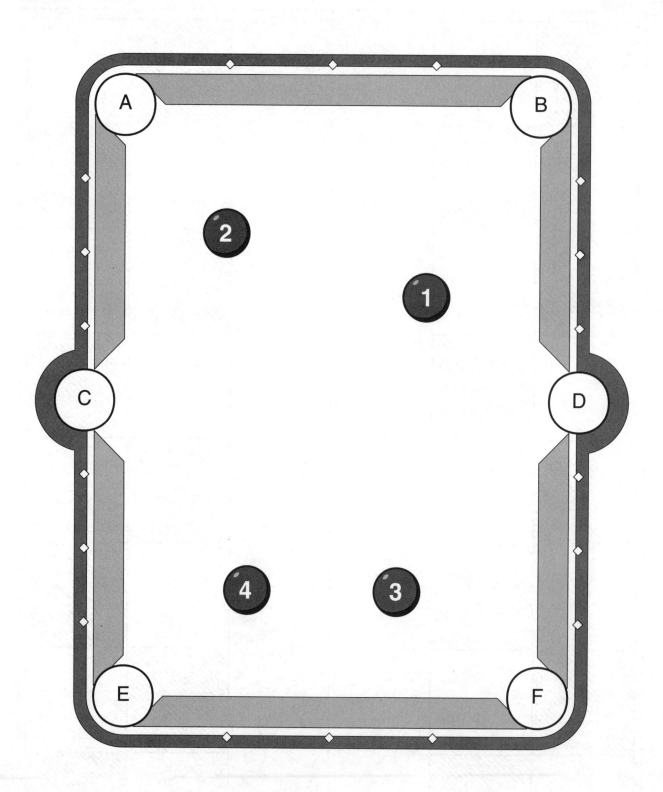

Polygon Capture Pieces

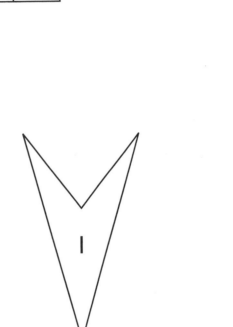

Polygon Capture Property Cards

There is only one right angle. **A**	There are one or more right angles. **A**	All angles are right angles. **A**	There are no right angles. **A**
There is at least one acute angle. **A**	At least one angle is more than 90°. **A**	All angles are right angles. **A**	There are no right angles. **A**
All opposite sides are parallel. **S**	Only one pair of sides is parallel. **S**	There are no parallel sides. **S**	All sides are the same length. **S**
All opposite sides are parallel. **S**	Some sides have the same length. **S**	All opposite sides have the same length. **S**	**Wild Card:** Pick your own side property. **S**

GAME MASTER 186

Polygon Pair-Up **Polygon Cards**

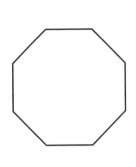
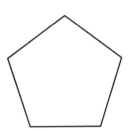
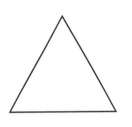
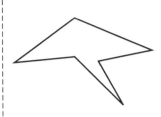

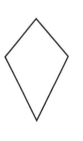

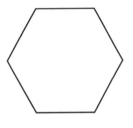

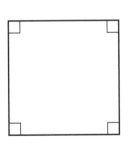
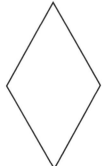
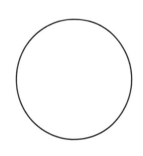
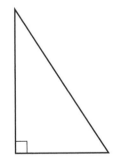

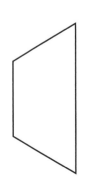
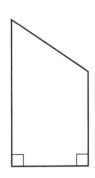

WILD
Polygon Card:
Pick a faceup
Property Card
and draw a
polygon to match
that card.

WILD
Polygon Card:
Pick a faceup
Property Card
and draw a
polygon to match
that card.

Polygon Pair-Up Property Cards

All sides are the same length.	All opposite sides are parallel.	All angles are right angles.	There are more than 4 sides.
There are 4 sides of equal length.	There is only 1 right angle.	There are 2 pairs of parallel sides.	This shape is NOT a polygon.
There are only 3 vertices.	There is only 1 pair of parallel sides.	There are only 4 sides.	This polygon is concave.
There are 4 equal sides and 4 equal angles.	Pairs of sides next to each other have the same length. There are no parallel sides.	**WILD Property Card:** Pick a faceup Polygon Card and name a property to match that card.	**WILD Property Card:** Pick a faceup Polygon Card and name a property to match that card.

GAME MASTER 188

Quarter-Dime-Nickel-Penny Grab

For each round:

- Draw your coins in the chart, using Ⓠ, Ⓓ, Ⓝ, and Ⓟ.
- Record your total.
- Record your partner's total.
- Circle the greater total.

	Quarters Ⓠ	Dimes Ⓓ	Nickels Ⓝ	Pennies Ⓟ	My Total	My Partner's Total
Round 1						
Round 2						
Round 3						

GAME MASTER 189

Start/Finish Track Sections

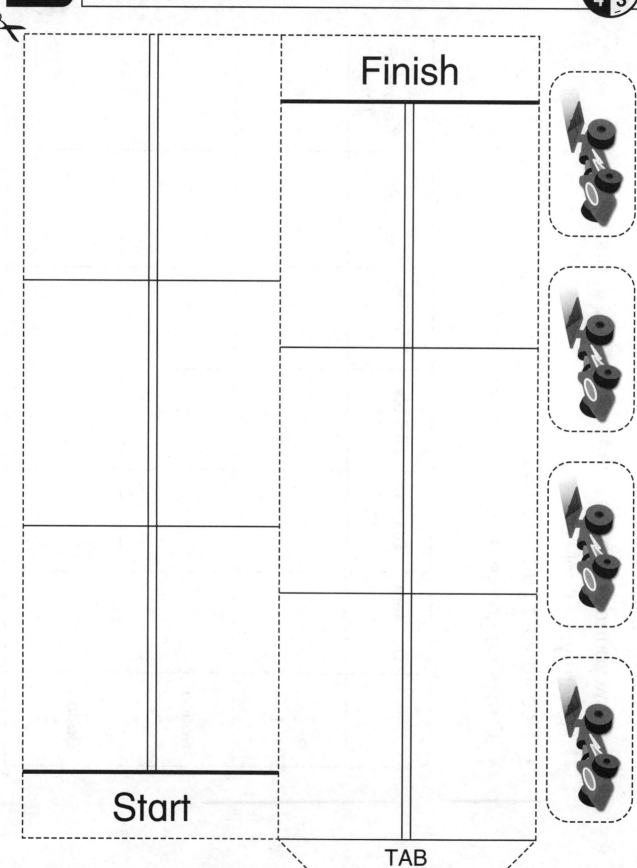

Finish

Start

TAB

GAME MASTER 190

Middle Track Sections

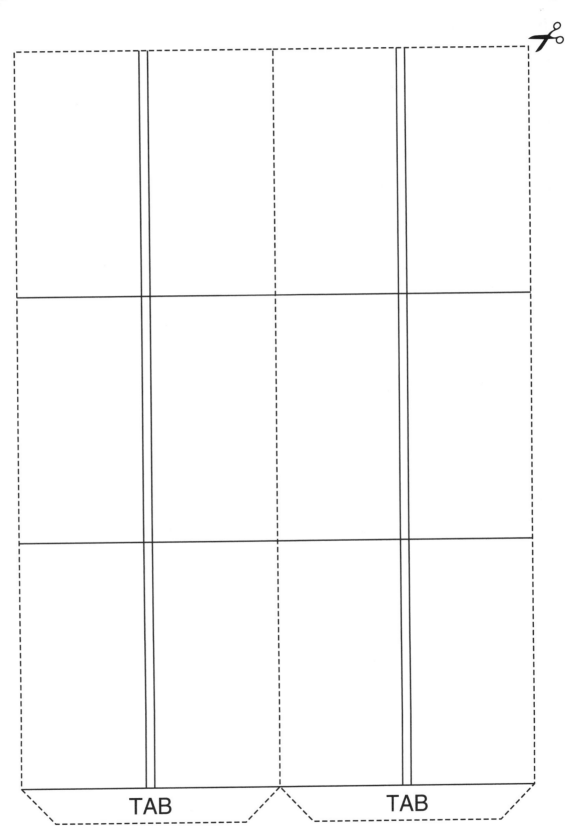

TAB

TAB

Robot Game

Materials	☐ sheet of paper with an arrow
Players	2
Skill	Exploring rotations and angles

Object of the Game   To reach the destination.

Directions

1. One player is the Controller and the other player is the Robot. The Robot stands on the piece of paper and faces the direction that the arrow is pointing.

2. The Controller picks a destination and gives the Robot "turn-and-move" directions, one at a time. The Controller gives the size of each turn and the number of steps. Each turn may be given as a fraction of a full turn or as a degree measure. The Controller gives directions until the Robot reaches the destination.

3. Players change roles and play the game again.

EXAMPLE:

The Controller says: *Make a half-turn. Go forward 5 steps.* The Robot follows the directions.

The Controller says: *Now turn clockwise a quarter-turn (90 degrees). Go back 3 steps.* The Robot follows the directions.

GAME MASTER 192

Rock, Paper, Scissors **Record Sheet**

Tallies

			Tied Game

✂ -

Name   Date   Time

GAME MASTER 192

Rock, Paper, Scissors **Record Sheet**

Tallies

			Tied Game

GAME MASTER 193

Roll to 100 Record Sheet

Write your score at the end of each turn.
The first player to reach or pass 100 wins.

Turn	Player 1 _____	Player 2 _____	Player 3 _____	Player 4 _____
1				
2				
3				
4				
5				
6				
7				
8				
9				
10				
11				
12				
13				
14				

Continue recording scores on the back of this page.

GAME MASTER 194

Rolling for 50 Directions and Game Mat

Roll	Spaces
1	3 forward
2	2 back
3	5 forward
4	6 back
5	8 forward
6	10 forward

Materials
- ☐ 1 die
- ☐ 2 counters

Players 2

Skill Counting forward and backward on a number grid

Object of the Game To reach 50.

Directions

1. Put your counters on 0.

2. Take turns rolling the die. Use the table to see how you should move.

3. The first player to reach 50 wins.

0

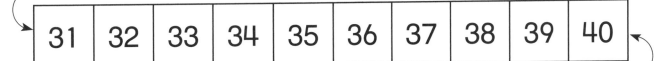

1	2	3	4	5	6	7	8	9	10

11	12	13	14	15	16	17	18	19	20

21	22	23	24	25	26	27	28	29	30

31	32	33	34	35	36	37	38	39	40

41	42	43	44	45	46	47	48	49	50

Name _____ Date _____ Time _____

Rugs and Fences Record Sheet

Round	Card number	Circle A (area) or P (perimeter)	Number model	Score
Sample	3	A or Ⓟ	10 + 10 + 2 + 2 = 24	24
1		A or P		
2		A or P		
3		A or P		
4		A or P		
5		A or P		
6		A or P		
7		A or P		
8		A or P		
			Total Score	

✂ -

GAME MASTER 195

Rugs and Fences Record Sheet

Round	Card number	Circle A (area) or P (perimeter)	Number model	Score
Sample	3	A or Ⓟ	10 + 10 + 2 + 2 = 24	24
1		A or P		
2		A or P		
3		A or P		
4		A or P		
5		A or P		
6		A or P		
7		A or P		
8		A or P		
			Total Score	

Rugs and Fences Polygon Deck A

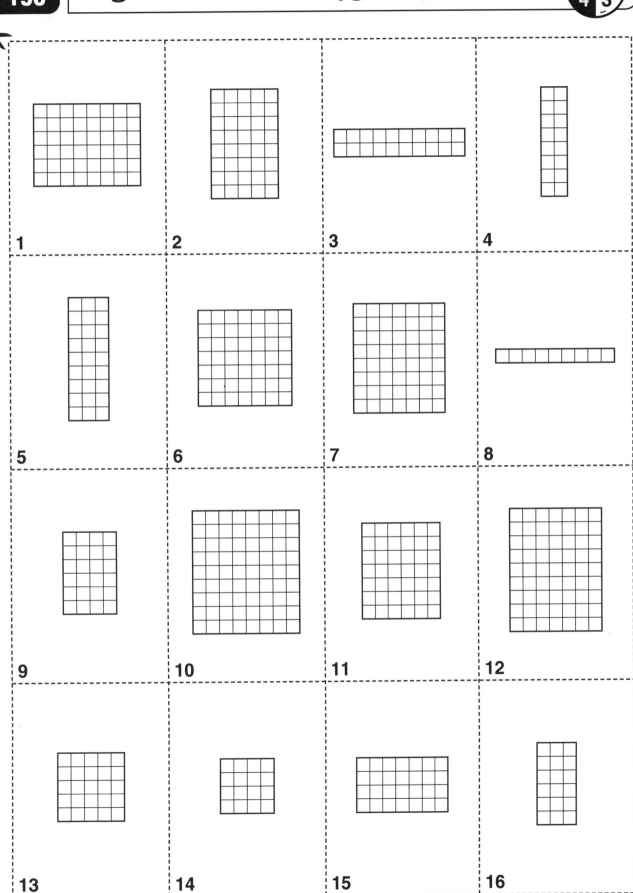

GAME MASTER 197 | *Rugs and Fences* Polygon Deck B

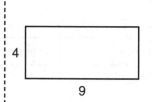

17

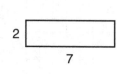

18

2

7

19

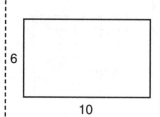

20

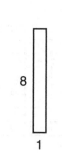

21

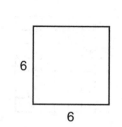

22

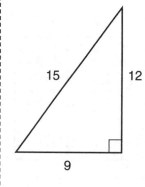

23

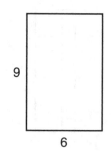

24

25

10   8   10

12

26

4   5

3

27

15   12

9

28

20   16   20

24

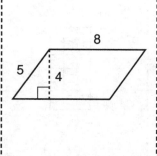

29

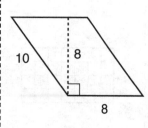

30

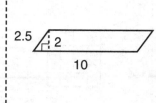

31

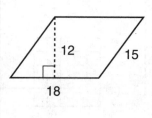

32

GAME MASTER 198 *Rugs and Fences* **Polygon Deck C**

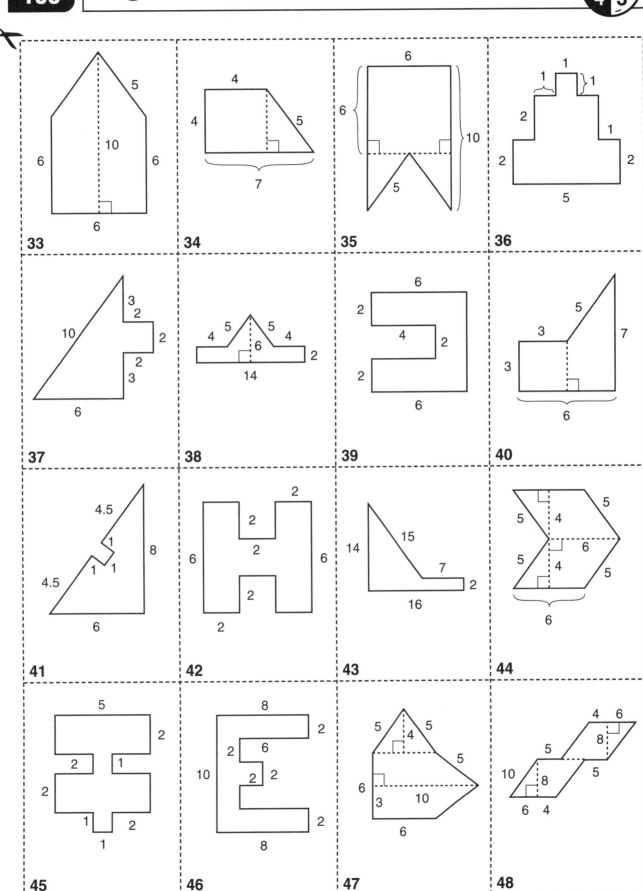

GAME MASTER 199

Rugs and Fences Area and Perimeter Cards

A Find the area of the polygon.	**A** Find the area of the polygon.	**A** Find the area of the polygon.	**A** Find the area of the polygon.
P Find the perimeter of the polygon.	**P** Find the perimeter of the polygon.	**P** Find the perimeter of the polygon.	**P** Find the perimeter of the polygon.
A or P Opponent's Choice	**A or P** Opponent's Choice	**A or P** Opponent's Choice	**A or P** Opponent's Choice
A or P Player's Choice	**A or P** Player's Choice	**A or P** Player's Choice	**A or P** Player's Choice

Scientific Notation Toss Record Sheets

Game 1

	Roll 1	Roll 2	Roll 3
Numbers Rolled			
Scientific Notation	☐ * 10☐	☐ * 10☐	☐ * 10☐
Standard Notation			
Order largest to smallest	_____ , _____ , _____ (largest) (smallest)		

Game 2

	Roll 1	Roll 2	Roll 3
Numbers Rolled			
Scientific Notation	☐ * 10☐	☐ * 10☐	☐ * 10☐
Standard Notation			
Order largest to smallest	_____ , _____ , _____ (largest) (smallest)		

Game 3

	Roll 1	Roll 2	Roll 3
Numbers Rolled			
Scientific Notation	☐ * 10☐	☐ * 10☐	☐ * 10☐
Standard Notation			
Order largest to smallest	_____ , _____ , _____ (largest) (smallest)		

Seega **Game Mat**

Player 1

Player 2

Shading Shapes

Materials   ☐   Reference Quadrangles (Game Master 203)

Players   2

Skill   Identifying quadrangles; exploring quadrangle properties

Object of the Game To claim more quadrangles.

Directions

1. Take turns shading one small triangle on the grid.

2. Continue shading one triangle per turn. Try to make one of the Reference Quadrangles shown on Game Master 203.

3. After you finish shading a quadrangle, claim it. Trace it with your finger and say its name to score a point.

4. Small triangles may be colored twice. Finished quadrangles may overlap, but the same quadrangle may not be claimed twice.

5. The game ends when time runs out or when all of the triangles are shaded. The player with more points wins.

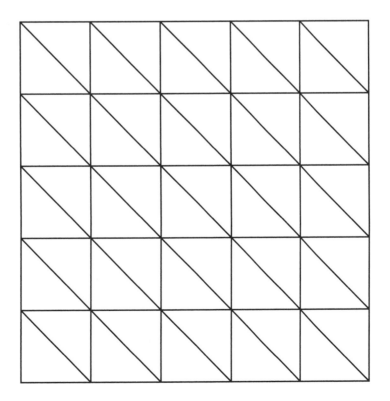

Shading Shapes Reference Quadrangles

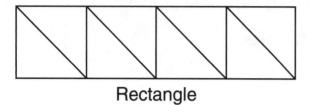
Rectangle

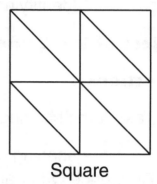
Square

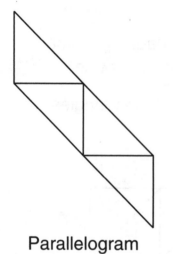
Parallelogram

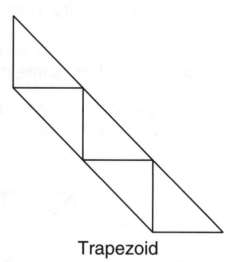
Trapezoid

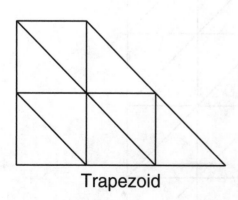
Trapezoid

GAME MASTER 204

Shaker Addition Top-It Record Sheet

Roll 2 dice. Add. Compare all players' sums. If you have the greatest sum, take a counter. The player with the most counters wins.

+   ☐ / ☐ = ☐   +   ☐ / ☐ = ☐   +   ☐ / ☐ = ☐   +   ☐ / ☐ = ☐   +   ☐ / ☐ = ☐

☐ = ☐ + ☐   ☐ = ☐ + ☐   ☐ = ☐ + ☐

☐ = ☐ + ☐   ☐ = ☐ + ☐   ☐ = ☐ + ☐

+   ☐ / ☐ = ☐   +   ☐ / ☐ = ☐   +   ☐ / ☐ = ☐   +   ☐ / ☐ = ☐   +   ☐ / ☐ = ☐

☐ = ☐ + ☐   ☐ = ☐ + ☐   ☐ = ☐ + ☐

☐ = ☐ + ☐   ☐ = ☐ + ☐   ☐ = ☐ + ☐

Triangle Cards

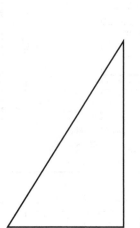

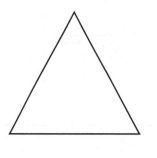

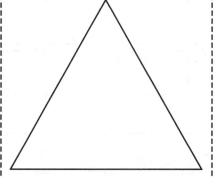

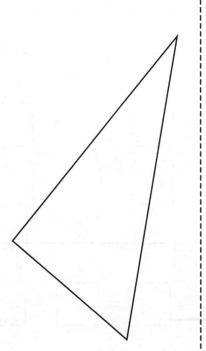

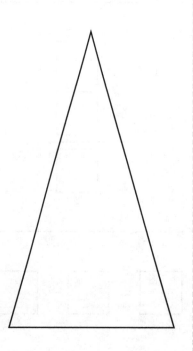

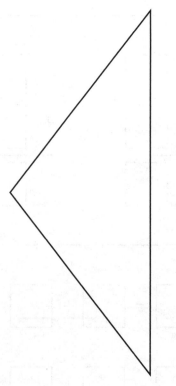

GAME MASTER 206

Rectangle Cards

Square and Circle Cards

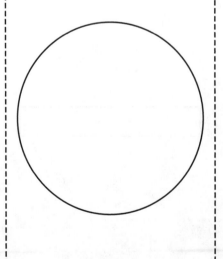

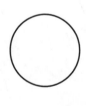

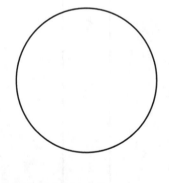

Soccer Spin Spinners

Soccer Spin **Game Mat**

Stripes Win!

Checks Win!

Soccer Spin

Solution Search Cards

$q * 2 > 20$	$m < 3.5$	$y^2 < 5$	$x > 9$
$b < 6$	$5 \neq s$	$100 / k > 25$	$(9 * z) + 2 > 65$
$49 \leq p^2$	$r / 2 \geq 5$	$w - 3 < 2$	$-2 + a \geq 5$
$\sqrt{25} \leq t$	$10 < 50 / d$	$c * 7 \leq 14$	$81 > f^2$

Spin a Number Game Mat

End

Start

Spinning for Money Spinner

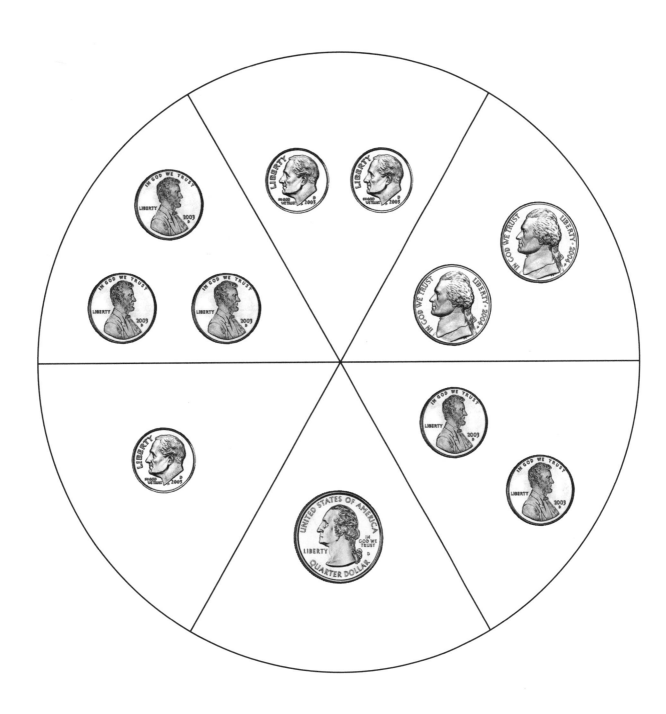

GAME MASTER 213 *Spinning to Win*

Materials ☐ 50 counters

☐ transparent spinner

Players 2–4

Skill Using chance data to develop a winning game strategy

Object of the Game To collect the most counters.

Directions

1. Put all of the counters in a pile between the players.

2. For each game, players will need a tally chart like this one:

Win 1	Win 2	Win 5	Win 10

3. Each player chooses one section of the spinner—1, 2, 5, or 10. Each player must choose a different section.

4. Take turns spinning the spinner. There are 12 spins per game.

5. When the spinner lands on your section, take the number of counters shown in the section. Then make a tally mark in the matching part of the table.

6. The player with the most counters after 12 spins wins.

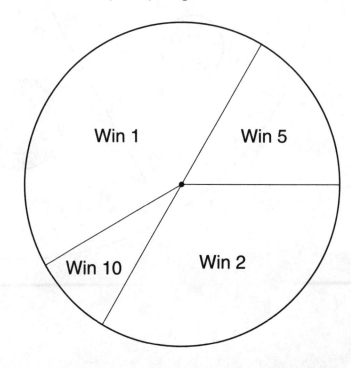

GAME MASTER 214 | ***Spoon Scramble* Card Deck A**

$\frac{1}{4}$ of 24	$\frac{3}{4} * 8$	50% of 12	$0.10 * 60$
$\frac{1}{3}$ of 21	$3\frac{1}{2} * 2$	25% of 28	$0.10 * 70$
$\frac{1}{5}$ of 40	$2 * \frac{16}{4}$	1% of 800	$0.10 * 80$
$\frac{3}{4}$ of 12	$4\frac{1}{2} * 2$	25% of 36	$0.10 * 90$

GAME MASTER 215 | *Spoon Scramble* **Card Deck B**

$\dfrac{1}{7}$ of 42	$\dfrac{24}{4} * \dfrac{5}{5}$	$\dfrac{54}{9}$	$2\dfrac{16}{4}$
$\dfrac{1}{5}$ of 35	$\dfrac{21}{3} * \dfrac{4}{4}$	$\dfrac{56}{8}$	$4\dfrac{36}{12}$
$\dfrac{1}{8}$ of 64	$\dfrac{48}{6} * \dfrac{3}{3}$	$\dfrac{32}{4}$	$3\dfrac{25}{5}$
$\dfrac{1}{4}$ of 36	$\dfrac{63}{7} * \dfrac{6}{6}$	$\dfrac{72}{8}$	$5\dfrac{32}{8}$

Spoon Scramble Card Deck C

$1 \div 2$	$\dfrac{35}{70}$	$\dfrac{1}{8} * 4$	0.5
$\dfrac{1}{3}$	$\dfrac{1}{6} * 2$	$33\dfrac{1}{3}\%$	$\dfrac{1}{2} - \dfrac{1}{6}$
$\dfrac{26}{13}$	$\left(\dfrac{6}{9} * \dfrac{9}{6}\right) * 2$	2	$4 * \dfrac{1}{2}$
$\dfrac{3}{4}$	$\dfrac{600}{800}$	0.75	$3 \div 4$

GAME MASTER 217

Spreadsheet Scramble Game Mats

	A	B	C	D	E	F
1						Total
2						
3						
4						
5	Total					

	A	B	C	D	E	F
1						Total
2						
3						
4						
5	Total					

	A	B	C	D	E	F
1						Total
2						
3						
4						
5	Total					

	A	B	C	D	E	F
1						Total
2						
3						
4						
5	Total					

	A	B	C	D	E	F
1						Total
2						
3						
4						
5	Total					

	A	B	C	D	E	F
1						Total
2						
3						
4						
5	Total					

	A	B	C	D	E	F
1						Total
2						
3						
4						
5	Total					

	A	B	C	D	E	F
1						Total
2						
3						
4						
5	Total					

Sz'kwa **Game Mat**

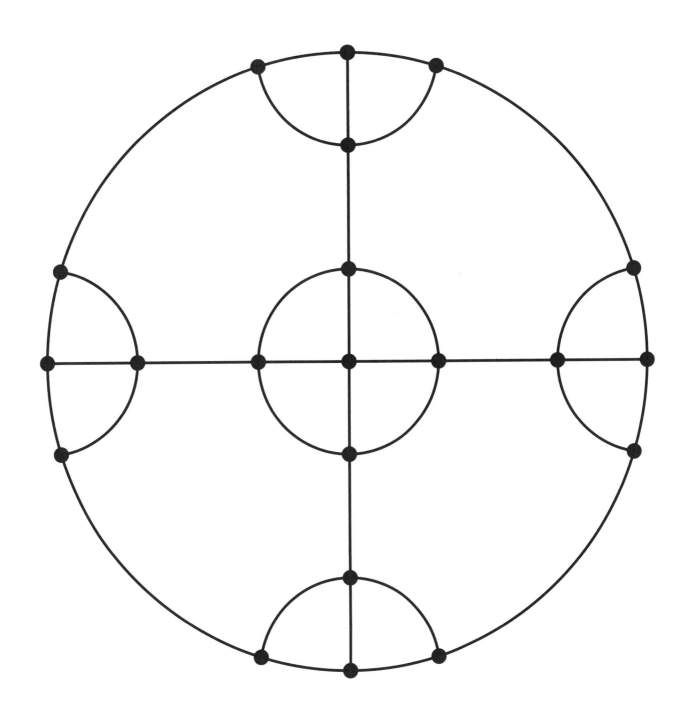

3-Digit Place-Value Mat

	Ones	Tens	Hundreds

Target 50

GAME MASTER 220 | *Target 50* **Record Sheet**

For each of your turns, record the number you made, whether you added or subtracted, and the final value of the base-10 blocks on your Place-Value Mat.

Number You Made	Add or Subtract?	Value on Place-Value Mat

GAME MASTER 221

Teen Frame Game Mats

Player 1

Player 2

222

Teen Frame (11–20) Spinner

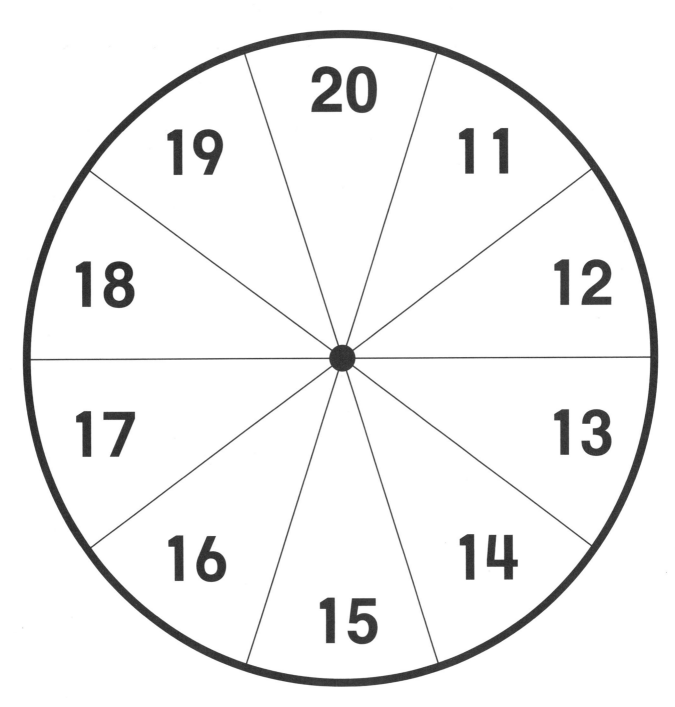

GAME MASTER 223

Teen Frame Ten Strips

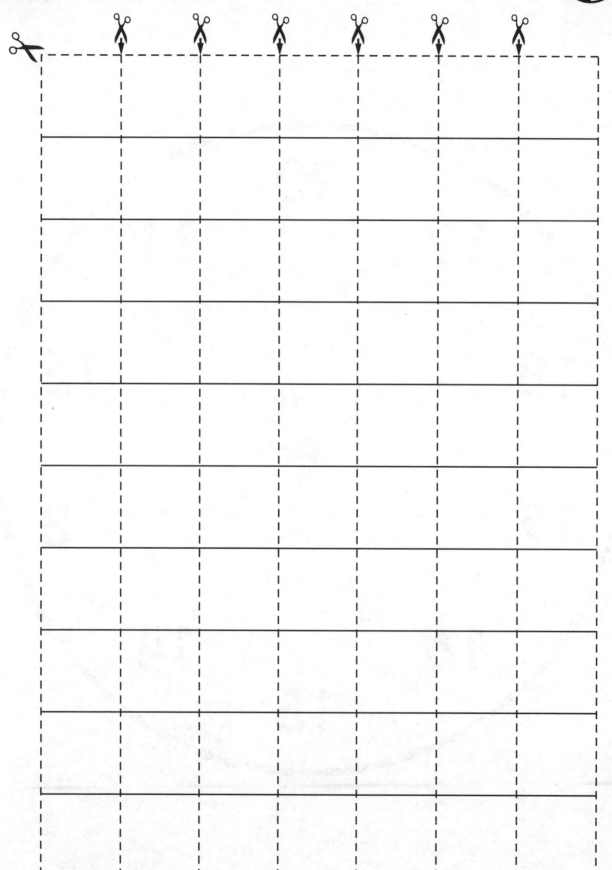

GAME MASTER 224

Three Addends Record Sheet

For each turn:

- Write the 3 numbers.

- Add the numbers.

- Write a number model to show how you added.

1. Numbers: _____, _____, _____

Number model:

_____ + _____ + _____ = _____

2. Numbers: _____, _____, _____

Number model:

_____ + _____ + _____ = _____

3. Numbers: _____, _____, _____

Number model:

_____ = _____ + _____ + _____

4. Numbers: _____, _____, _____

Number model:

_____ = _____ + _____ + _____

5. Numbers: _____, _____, _____

Number model:

_____ + _____ + _____ = _____

6. Numbers: _____, _____, _____

Number model:

_____ + _____ + _____ = _____

7. Numbers: _____, _____, _____

Number model:

_____ + _____ + _____ = _____

8. Numbers: _____, _____, _____

Number model:

_____ + _____ + _____ = _____

9. Numbers: _____, _____, _____

Number model:

_____ = _____ + _____ + _____

10. Numbers: _____, _____, _____

Number model:

_____ = _____ + _____ + _____

GAME MASTER 225

3-D Shape Sort Shape Cards

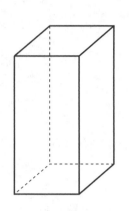

Rectangular
Prism

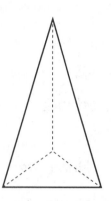

Triangular
Pyramid

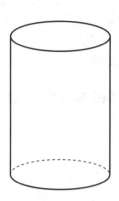

Cylinder

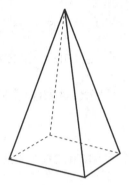

Rectangular
Pyramid

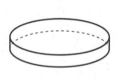

Cylinder

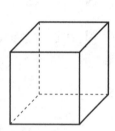

Cube

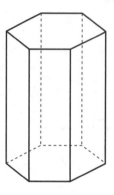

Hexagonal
Prism

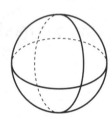

Sphere

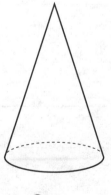

Cone

Truncated
Cone

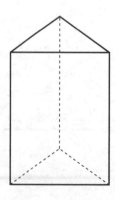

Triangular
Prism

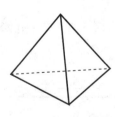

Tetrahedron

3-D Shape Sort Property Cards

I have an even number of vertices.	I have no vertices.	I have at least 2 edges that are parallel to each other.	I have an odd number of edges.
One of my vertices is formed by an even number of edges.	I have at least one curved edge.	I have fewer than 6 vertices.	I have at least 2 edges that are perpendicular to each other.
All of my surfaces are polygons.	I have at least one face (flat surface).	I have at least one curved surface.	All of my faces are triangles.
All of my faces are regular polygons.	At least one of my faces is a circle.	I have at least one pair of faces that are parallel to each other.	**Wild Card:** Pick your own surface property.

Time Match Cards (Analog)

GAME MASTER 228 | **Time Match Cards (Digital)**

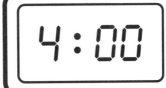

Tric-Trac **Game Mats**

Player 1

0 1 2 3 4 5 6 7 8 9

Player 2

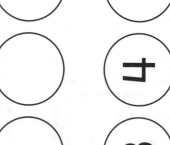
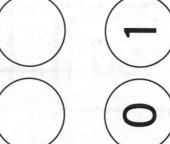

Tric-Trac

GAME MASTER 230 | ***Venn Diagram Challenge* Game Mat**

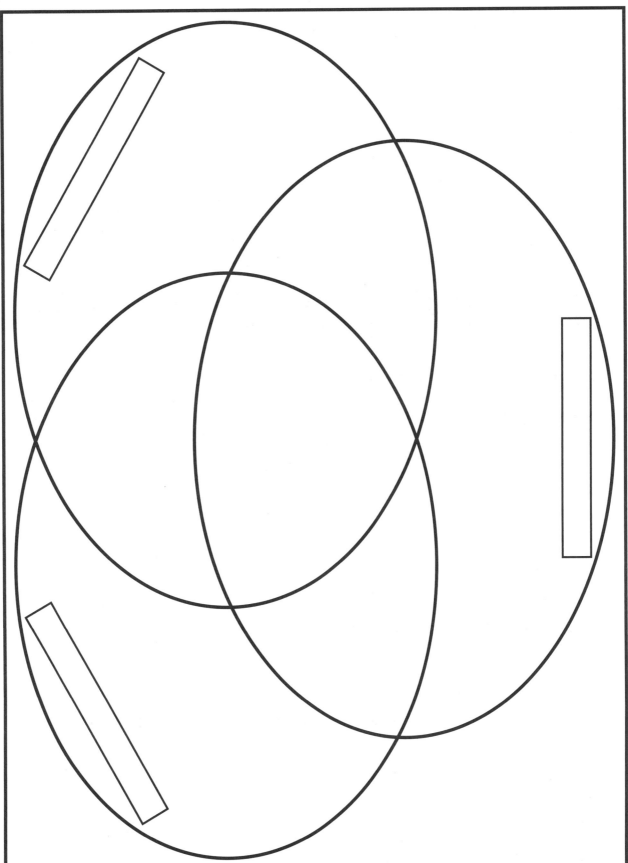

GAME MASTER 231

Venn Diagram Challenge Record Sheet

Round	Player 1's Points	Player 2's Points	Player 3's Points
1			
2			
3			
Total			

- -

Name   Date   Time

GAME MASTER 231

Venn Diagram Challenge Record Sheet

Round	Player 1's Points	Player 2's Points	Player 3's Points
1			
2			
3			
Total			

- -

Name   Date   Time

GAME MASTER 231

Venn Diagram Challenge Record Sheet

Round	Player 1's Points	Player 2's Points	Player 3's Points
1			
2			
3			
Total			

GAME MASTER
232 | **Paper Clock**

Attribute Rule Cards

small, blue shapes	large, red shapes	large shapes, but not triangles	circles, but not red
blue and yellow shapes, but not circles	red and yellow small shapes	not triangles or squares	large triangles, but not yellow
large circles, but not red	large circles or squares		

Coins

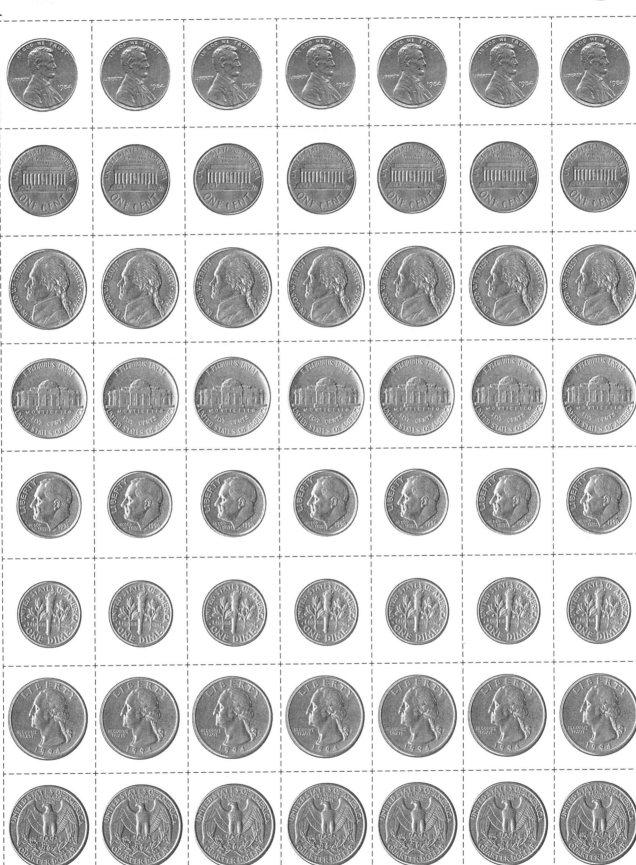

GAME MASTER 235 | **Dominoes (Double-6)**

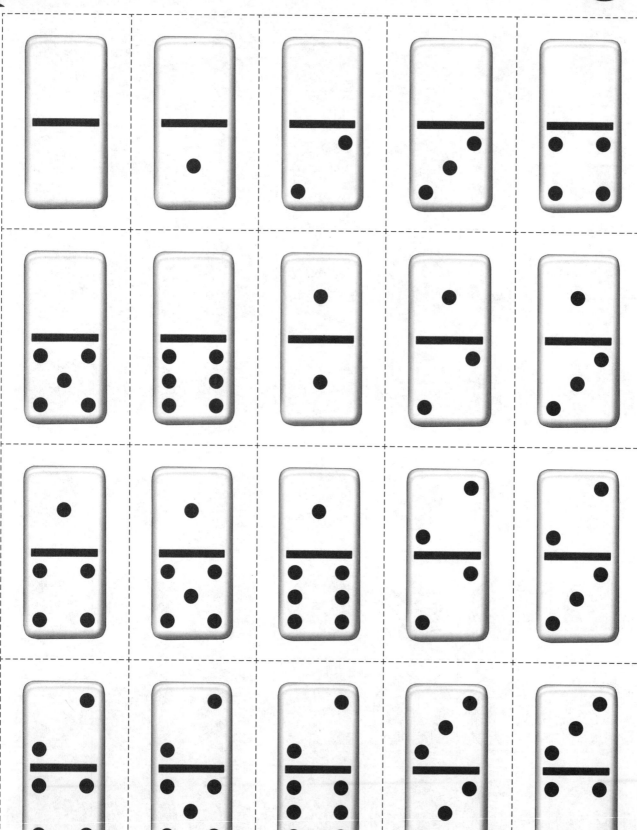

GAME MASTER 236

Dominoes (Double-6 and Double-9)

GAME MASTER 237

Dominoes (Double-9)

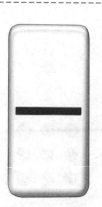

One-Inch Grid

6-Digit Place-Value Chart

Hundred-Thousands	Ten-Thousands	Thousands	Hundreds	Tens	Ones

Small Number Cards (1–10)

1

6

2

7

3

8

4

9

5

10

GAME MASTER 241   **Small Number Cards (11–20)**

11

16

12

17

13

18

14

19

15

20

GAME MASTER 242

Small Number Cards (21–30)

21 22 23 24 25

26 27 28 29 30

GAME MASTER 243 | **$1,000 Bank Drafts**

$1,000   **B A N K   D R A F T** $1,000
100,000 cents

Pay to _____

$1,000   One Thousand Dollars $1,000

$1,000   **B A N K   D R A F T** $1,000
100,000 cents

Pay to _____

$1,000   One Thousand Dollars $1,000

$1,000   **B A N K   D R A F T** $1,000
100,000 cents

Pay to _____

$1,000   One Thousand Dollars $1,000

$1,000   **B A N K   D R A F T** $1,000
100,000 cents

Pay to _____

$1,000   One Thousand Dollars $1,000

$1,000   **B A N K   D R A F T** $1,000
100,000 cents

Pay to _____

$1,000   One Thousand Dollars $1,000

$1,000   **B A N K   D R A F T** $1,000
100,000 cents

Pay to _____

$1,000   One Thousand Dollars $1,000

$1,000   **B A N K   D R A F T** $1,000
100,000 cents

Pay to _____

$1,000   One Thousand Dollars $1,000

$1,000   **B A N K   D R A F T** $1,000
100,000 cents

Pay to _____

$1,000   One Thousand Dollars $1,000

$1,000   **B A N K   D R A F T** $1,000
100,000 cents

Pay to _____

$1,000   One Thousand Dollars $1,000

$1,000   **B A N K   D R A F T** $1,000
100,000 cents

Pay to _____

$1,000   One Thousand Dollars $1,000

$1,000   **B A N K   D R A F T** $1,000
100,000 cents

Pay to _____

$1,000   One Thousand Dollars $1,000

$1,000   **B A N K   D R A F T** $1,000
100,000 cents

Pay to _____

$1,000   One Thousand Dollars $1,000

Family Letter: Games Response Form

Dear Family,

Games are an important part of *Everyday Mathematics*. They help your child memorize basic math facts, they provide practice that supports the lessons, and they give your child an opportunity to apply problem-solving strategies. You can help your child become a mathematical problem solver by playing *Everyday Mathematics* games together.

Included in this packet are all the materials needed to play this game:

_____

The materials are:

☐ _____

☐ _____

☐ _____

Please check that all of these items are in the packet before returning it to school with your child. If an item is missing, indicate that on the **Games Response Form** on the bottom part of this sheet.

I am eager to hear from you about your game-playing experience. Please include your comments on the **Games Response Form** below when you send the game to school with your child. Have your child return this packet to school by

_____

Thank you for your interest in your child's education. Together, we can help your child develop a love of learning and confidence as a mathematical problem solver.

Sincerely,

✂ -

Games Response Form

Child's Name _____   Parent / Guardian's Name _____

Are all checklist items in the packet? Yes _____   No _____ (If no, list missing items.)

Please comment on playing this game. Use the back of this sheet, if necessary.

Sign-Out Sheet for Take-Home Kits

NAME	KIT NUMBER	Date Out	Date In

Index